D0365407

Elementary Statistics

Elementary Statistics

second edition

PAUL G. HOEL

Professor of Mathematics
University of California
Los Angeles

John Wiley & Sons, Inc.
New York · London · Sydney

Preface

The changes that have been incorporated in this edition of *Elementary Statistics* are based largely on the suggestions and desires of those who have used the first edition in their classes. Unfortunately, it is difficult to strike a happy balance between the ideas of those who would like more mathematical sophistication and those who feel a more earthy approach is preferable. In carrying out some of the suggested changes, I have attempted to preserve the theoretical level of the first edition by placing the more sophisticated changes and additions in supplementary sections.

Among the more noticeable changes is an extensive revision of the chapter on probability. Many instructors felt that the exposition was much too brief and that a geometrical approach based on sample spaces would be more easily understood. The probability chapter was rewritten from this point of view. Some material on combinatorics and Bayes formula was also introduced in supplementary sections. Although it is possible to explain the basic notions of statistical theory with little formal discussion of probability, the importance of probability in this modern world suggests that all students should be exposed to some of the basic concepts of probability for cultural reasons alone, and therefore an instructor or student should not look upon the probability chapter as merely a necessary obstacle to be overcome in the study of statistical concepts.

Another obvious change is the increased discussion and emphasis on sampling distributions. The notion of random sampling is introduced in Chapter 2 and extended further in Chapter 5. I hope that the student will now acquire a clearer understanding of sampling variation and the distinction between empirical and theoretical distributions.

For the benefit of students who like to give themselves a review on the material of a chapter, a section of review exercises has been added to most chapters. A student should solve the problems of that section without first looking at the solutions, and then check his answers and methods with the solutions presented there. Additional review exercises of the same type have been included in the regular sets of exercises at the end of each chapter, so there should now be ample problem-solving material available.

A number of additional topics have been included as supplementary material in this revision. The chapter on regression, for example, has been expanded to include more material on regression of several variables and on nonlinear regression. These and similar additions were made for the benefit of those students who possess more than the minimum amount of high school algebra necessary for an understanding of the basic material. All such sections have been indicated by means of the ▶ label. Instructors should not assign such sections and the corresponding problems carrying this label unless time permits and their students possess more than the minimum mathematical background needed for the basic material. For students with a minimum background, I feel that it is more important to spend a considerable amount of time on basic concepts than it is to attempt to develop their breadth of knowledge and their problem-solving techniques; therefore the ▶ sections should not be considered essential for a good substantial course in elementary statistics.

I wish to express my gratitude to those instructors who were kind enough to offer suggestions for the improvement of this book. If it has been improved, they deserve much of the credit. Professor W. K. Smith was again kind enough to read the entire manuscript and help eliminate some of the errors.

PAUL G. HOEL

Los Angeles, California
January 1966

Preface to the First Edition

This book is designed for a one-semester course for the student whose background in mathematics is limited to high-school algebra. A number of mathematics departments offer a service course of this kind; however, in many schools a department with strong interests in the applications of statistics gives the course.

My interest in writing a book at this level arose from having taught such a service course and being somewhat dissatisfied with the available texts. I felt that a mathematical statistician could write a descriptive book just as well as someone primarily interested in the applications and at the same time present the theory in a more satisfactory manner. Blandishments on the part of the publisher of my *Introduction To Mathematical Statistics* were undoubtedly as influential in causing the book to be written as these less mundane reasons.

I have some rather positive views on how elementary statistics should be taught. In particular, I believe in teaching students the simple classical ideas of sampling very thoroughly rather than attempting to introduce them to some of the more sophisticated modern notions. As in mathematics, there is a considerable body of material that needs to be understood before one can proceed to the study of more recent material. In writing this book I have attempted to include what I consider to be basic material, and I have tried to write for the student's benefit rather than to impress my colleagues.

The material in the first nine chapters, exclusive of the sections marked by a boldface arrowhead (▶), should suffice for the ordinary one-semester course. The arrowhead sections of these chapters contain material for amplifying the basic course if time permits. The last four chapters have been included as additional optional material to enable the instructor with particular interests to include topics related to those interests. None of these chapters is strictly elementary, although the nonparametric methods are relatively easy to explain.

I feel compelled to justify the existence of the last chapter. Time series is not a subject that I include in my own course, but several referees urged me to include a brief introduction to the topic as an optional chapter. I feel that many of the statistical concepts involved are too advanced and too delicate for beginning undergraduates. My approach has been to select some of the more elementary topics that are both sound and useful. As a consequence, though the treatment may not satisfy some economists and statisticians, it should represent an honest and elementary introduction from the viewpoint of students.

A number of individuals whose names I do not know read an early version of the manuscript and made many helpful suggestions for its improvement. If the book is slightly more difficult than I first intended it to be, the blame is partly theirs because most of the suggestions involved the addition of somewhat more difficult material. The revised manuscript was given a final reading by Professor W. K. Smith, who was most helpful in improving its exposition by his exceptionally careful reading of it. One of my graduate students, Robert Jennrich, was very helpful in eliminating errors in the answers to the exercises. Answers to the even-numbered problems can be obtained in pamphlet form from the publisher.

PAUL G. HOEL

Los Angeles, California
January 1960

Contents

CHAPTER 1

The Nature
of Statistical Methods

1. INTRODUCTION

Statistical methods are often described as methods for treating numerical data. Such a definition, however, is much too broad in scope. It is necessary to restrict both the nature of the data and the reasons for studying them before such methods can rightfully be called statistical.

Statisticians are concerned with data that have been obtained from taking observations, in the form of measurements or counts, from a source of such observations. For example, in studying the quality of bricks in a certain brickyard, a number of bricks would be selected and tested for quality; or, in studying public opinion on a controversial measure being considered by a city council, a small percentage of the inhabitants of the city would be selected and asked whether they favored the measure.

Statisticians take observations of the type just described for the purpose of drawing conclusions about the source of the observations. Thus, bricks are selected and tested for quality for the purpose of trying to determine the quality of the entire supply of bricks in the brickyard. Similarly, the purpose of questioning only a small percentage of the inhabitants of a city concerning a controversial measure is to determine to a satisfactory approximation the opinions of all the inhabitants on this measure.

The set of observations that is taken from some source of observations for the purpose of obtaining information about the source is called a *sample*, whereas the source of those observations is called a *population*. In view of the preceding discussion, *statistical methods may be described as methods for drawing conclusions about populations by means of samples.* The single word "statistics" is often used in place of statistical methods. Thus a student who is taking a course in statistics is taking a course in statistical methods.

At first glance, the foregoing definition may seem to be rather technical and contrary to the popular notion about statistics. For example, many business people look upon statistical methods as methods for collecting and summarizing business facts. The Federal government employs a number of statisticians whose principal duty is to design efficient ways of collecting and summarizing various kinds of information. According to the preceding definition of statistical methods, these statisticians do not appear to be using statistical methods because they do not apply the information they have collected for drawing conclusions about the sources of the information. This viewpoint, however, does not take into account the fact that such information is gathered for the consumption of others who will use it to reach conclusions. Business concerns do not collect and summarize business facts just to admire the information obtained. They expect to use the information to make decisions, and whether or not they openly arrive at conclusions concerning the sources of the information the fact remains that they do make decisions on the basis of samples.

That part of statistical methods concerned with the collecting and summarizing of data is usually called *descriptive statistics.* The part concerned with drawing conclusions about the source of the data is called *statistical inference.* Since the ultimate objective is to make inferences, that is, draw conclusions, the descriptive part of statistics should be looked upon as a sort of preliminary to the main bout.

The use of statistical methods has increased remarkably in the last few decades, particularly in the biological and social sciences. Such methods have also proved very useful in various branches of the physical sciences and engineering. Because of this varied and strong interest, these methods have developed rapidly and have increased in complexity and diversity; nevertheless, many of the most important techniques are quite simple and are the same for all branches of application. Some of these universal methods are studied in this book. They should prove useful both to students who wish to understand how simple experimental data are handled and to students who need this type of background for more advanced work.

2. ILLUSTRATIONS

This section describes a few problems of the type that statistical methods were designed to solve. It does not begin to cover the broad class of problems capable of being solved by statistical methods but rather illustrates a few of the simpler ones that can be solved by using only the methods developed in this book. One problem is of academic interest, whereas the others are typical real-life problems.

(*a*) A television program sponsor wishes to know how popular his program is, compared to others at the same hour. In particular, he wishes to know what percentage of the television audience is viewing his program rather than some other. To satisfy him, an organization engaged in determining program popularity agrees to take a poll of the television audience at that hour to evaluate program preferences. By using statistical methods, such an organization can decide how large a poll will be necessary in order to estimate, within any desired degree of accuracy, the percentage of the audience viewing this program.

(*b*) A medical research team has developed a new serum it hopes will help to prevent a common children's disease. It wishes to test the serum. In order to assist the researchers in carrying out such a test, a school system in a large city has agreed to inoculate half of the children in certain grades with the serum. Records of all children in those grades are kept during the following year. On the basis of the percentages of those children who contract the disease during that year, both for the inoculated group and for the remaining half, it is possible by statistical methods to determine whether the serum is really beneficial.

(*c*) An industrial firm is concerned about the large number of accidents occurring in its plant. In the process of trying to discover the various causes of such accidents, an investigator considers factors related to the time of day. He collects information on the number of accidents occurring during the various working hours of the day, and by using statistical methods he is able to show that the accident rate increases during the morning and also during the afternoon. Further statistical studies then reveal some of the major contributing factors involved in these accidents.

One might be tempted to say that statistical methods are not needed in a problem such as this, and that all one needs to do is to calculate percentages and look at them to decide what is happening. If one has a large amount of properly selected data, such decisions will often be correct; however the high cost of collecting data usually forces one to work with only small amounts and it is precisely in such situations that statistical methods are needed to yield valid conclusions.

(*d*) A rabbit farmer, interested in experimenting with different rations for his rabbits, wishes to determine the effect on gain in weight of giving rabbits increased amounts of a certain food. In order to study the effect, he uses a standard ration and six new rations obtained by adding from one to six ounces, respectively, of this food to the standard ration. Seventy rabbits are divided into 7 groups of 10 each, with each group receiving one of the rations. After the rabbits have been on those rations for a certain period of time, their gains in weight are determined. By using statistical methods, it is then possible to estimate the increased gains due to the increased amounts of the supplementary food, together with the accuracy of those estimates.

(*e*) An instructor of an elementary statistics course is having difficulty convincing some of his students that the chances of winning from a slot machine are just as good immediately after someone has won some money as after a run of losses. For the purpose of convincing them, he, together with a few students of sterling character, performs the following experiment on a slot machine located in a private golf club. The machine is played for one hour, or until the combined resources of instructor and students are exhausted, whichever occurs first. A record is kept of the number of wins and losses that occur immediately after a win, together with the amounts won, and also of the number of wins and losses, and amounts won, immediately after a run of, say, five losses. With data of this type available, the instructor should be able to apply statistical methods to convince the skeptics of his wisdom in this matter. Since a run of bad luck might make it difficult to demonstrate this wisdom, unless the machine were played a long while, the instructor would be well advised to come amply supplied with cash. An experiment of this type should also convince the students that slot machines are designed to extract money from naïve individuals.

3. ESTIMATION AND HYPOTHESIS TESTING

An analysis of the preceding illustrations will show that they properly belong to the field of statistics because all are concerned with drawing conclusions about some population of objects or individuals and propose to do so on the basis of a sample from that population.

It may also be observed that these problems fall into two general categories. They are concerned either with estimating some property of the population or with testing some hypothesis about the population. The first illustration, for example, is concerned with estimating the percentage of the television audience that is watching a particular program at a certain hour. The second illustration is one of testing the hypothesis that the percentage of children contracting a disease is the same for inoculated children as for children receiving no inoculation. The third illustration considers the problem of testing the hypothesis that the accident rate for a population of workers is constant over the day. The fourth illustration is concerned with estimating the average gain in weight of rabbits as a function of increasing the amounts of a food supplementing a standard diet. The fifth illustration is one of testing the hypothesis that the average amount of money won from a slot machine after a run of losses is the same as after a win.

Most of the statistical methods to be explained in this book are those for treating problems of these two types, namely, estimating properties of or testing hypotheses about populations. Although there are other types of conclusions or decisions that can be related to populations on the basis of samples, the bulk of those made by statisticians falls into one of the two aforementioned categories, and therefore they alone are studied in this book.

4. PROBABILITY

In the problem of estimating the percentage of a certain kind of television audience the solution will consist of a percentage based on the sample and a statement of the accuracy of the estimate, usually in the form of "the probability is .95 that the estimate will be in error by less than 3 per cent." Similarly, in problems involving the testing of some hypothesis the decision to accept or reject the hypothesis will be based on certain probabilities.

It is necessary to use probability in such conclusions because a conclusion based on a sample involves incomplete information about the population, and therefore it cannot be made with certainty. The magnitude of the probability attached to a conclusion represents the degree of confidence one should have in the truth of the conclusion. The basic ideas and rules of probability are studied in a later chapter; meanwhile it should be treated from an intuitive point of view. Thus the statement that the probability is .95 that an estimate will be in error by less than 3 per cent should be interpreted as meaning that about 95 per cent of such statements made by a statistician are valid and about 5 per cent are not. In the process of studying statistical methods one will soon discover that probability is the basic tool of those methods.

Probability is an exceedingly interesting subject, even for those who have little liking for mathematics or quantitative methods. Many people enjoy some of the events associated with probability, if not the study itself; otherwise, how can one account for the large number of people who love to gamble at horse races, lotteries, cards, etc.? It may well be that it is their lack of probability sense that encourages them to gamble as they do. In any case, probability is used consciously or unconsciously by everyone in making all sorts of decisions based on uncertainty, and any student who wishes to be well educated, or to behave rationally, should have some knowledge of probability.

5. ORGANIZATION

The study of the statistical methods discussed in the preceding sections will proceed by first considering properties of samples and then properties of populations. As indicated in section 1, such studies constitute the descriptive part of statistics. It will then be possible to consider the two basic problems of statistical inference, namely the problems of estimation and hypothesis testing. This means that for any given type of problem the sample data will always be studied first before any attempt is made to introduce a theoretical population from which the sample might have come. In Chapter 2 a beginning is made in the study of properties of sample data, after which some basic theoretical populations are introduced. It is at this theoretical stage that probability will appear.

CHAPTER 2

The Description
of Sample Data

1. INTRODUCTION

Since the purpose of this chapter is to study properties of samples taken
from populations, it would seem necessary to agree first on how samples
are to be taken because the desired properties may well depend on the
method employed. Suppose, for example, that a student newspaper
reporter has been assigned the task of determining the percentage of
students having part-time jobs. He might attempt to estimate this percentage by polling the first 100 students he encountered in front of the
student union. This method of sampling, however, is not likely to give a
valid estimate of the population percentage because students found lolling
in front of the union are often the campus loafers and social butterflies,
and they are seldom the working type. The reporter would undoubtedly
do much better if he were to select 100 cards blindly from the student
enrollment card file and poll the selected students.

The problem of how to select a sample from a population so that valid
conclusions about the population can be drawn from the sample is quite
complicated. This problem is discussed rather extensively in Chapter 5.
In that discussion a method of sampling called random sampling is
advocated and justified. Anticipating that material somewhat, an introduction is given here to this type of sampling. In its simplest form, when
a single individual is to be selected from a population of individuals,
the sampling is said to be *random* if each member of the population has
the same chance of being chosen. Techniques used in games of chance
are often employed to obtain such a sample. For example, at a large

social affair at which a grand door prize is to be given away, it is customary to place all the numbered ticket stubs in a large container and then have a blindfolded individual select one ticket from the container, after the tickets have been thoroughly mixed. If, say, three individuals are to be selected from a population, the sampling will be random if every possible group of three individuals from the population has the same chance of being chosen. The preceding device that was employed to select one individual could also be used to select three individuals. Experience with such devices has shown that each individual, or group of individuals, is selected approximately the same number of times as every other individual, or group, when the experiment is repeated a large number of times, and therefore that they do conform to the requirement of showing no favoritism. In selecting a sample of 100 students from a student body, a selection of 100 cards from the enrollment files would undoubtedly be satisfactory as a practical method of random selection, provided the information desired about an individual is unrelated to his alphabetical position in the card file.

One reason for taking random samples is that samples selected in this manner correctly represent the population from which they are taken. This means, for example, that if the experiment of selecting 100 students from a student body were repeated a number of times and the percentage of students who worked part time was calculated for the entire sample, that percentage should tend to get increasingly close to the true percentage for the student body as the sampling continued. Other types of sampling in which personal judgment enters usually do not possess this desirable property.

As an illustration of this property of random samples correctly representing the population being sampled, a random sampling experiment was carried out for an artificially constructed population. Suppose a large population of individuals can be classified into three groups. For example, it might be on the basis of age, those less than 30 years of age, those between 30 and 50 inclusive, and those over 50. Suppose further that the proportions of individuals in those three groups are $\frac{3}{6}$, $\frac{2}{6}$, and $\frac{1}{6}$, respectively. Then random sampling from such a population can be simulated by sampling from a population of 6 playing cards consisting of, say, 3 aces, 2 twos, and 1 three, provided the sampling is done properly. After each drawing of a card, the number is recorded and the drawn card is returned to the set. The cards are then thoroughly mixed and another drawing is made. This repeated mixing and returning of the drawn card to the set insures that the population proportions remain the same and that no favoritism will occur. If the original population were very large the removal of some individuals from it by sampling would have no appreciable effect on the population proportions either. The preceding experiment was carried out 700 times in sets of 100 each. The accumulated results were reduced to percentages, calculated to the nearest decimal only, after each additional sample of 100 had been obtained. These random sample percentages, which are shown in Table 1, should be

TABLE 1

Sample Size	100	200	300	400	500	600	700
Aces	44	47	45.7	47.8	49.4	49.6	50.0
Twos	35	34	35.0	33.2	32.8	32.8	32.9
Threes	21	19	19.3	19.0	17.8	17.5	17.1

compared with the population percentages of 50, $33\frac{1}{3}$, and $16\frac{2}{3}$, respectively, to see how well the samples represent the population being sampled.

The sample percentages appear to conform well to the population percentages as the same size increases.

Hereafter, whenever a sample is to be taken it will be assumed that it will be obtained by a random sampling method, even though the word random is not used explicitly.

Now turn to the problem of studying properties of samples taken from populations. In this connection, although the word "population" would seem to refer to a group of human individuals, in statistics it refers to a group of individuals, human or not, or objects of any kind. In studying samples and populations it is often assumed that interest is centered on a single particular property of members of the population. Thus, one might be interested in the property of weight in a population of students at a university, or in the color of the eyes in a population of insects, or in the percentage of iron in a population of meteorites. Samples are taken of individuals in a population, but then the property of interest is measured or counted for those individuals. If the property is one that is measured it is often denoted by the letter x, largely because a graph of the sample is usually placed on the x-axis of a coordinate system.

As an illustration of how one proceeds in the study of samples consider the problem of what a physical education department at a university would do if it were interested in determining whether its male dormitory students were typical university students with respect to physical characteristics. In such a study it would undoubtedly wish to compare, as one source of information, the weight distribution of the dormitory students with that of nondormitory students. Now, weighing every male student on campus would certainly yield the desired information on weight distribution; however, this would become quite an undertaking in a large school at which such information is not required at registration time. The desired information, to sufficient accuracy, could be obtained much more easily by studying the weight distributions of samples of dormitory and nondormitory students.

Suppose then that a random sample of, say, 120 students has been obtained from the dormitory population. Since the only concern here is what to do with samples, the nondormitory sample can be ignored in this discussion—it would be treated in the same manner as the dormitory sample. Suppose, furthermore, that the weights of these 120 students have been recorded to the nearest pound and that they range from the lightest at 110 pounds to the heaviest at 218 pounds.

It is very difficult to look at 120 measurements and obtain any reasonably accurate idea of how those measurements are distributed. For the purpose of obtaining a better idea of the weight distribution of the 120 students, it is therefore convenient to condense the data somewhat by classifying the measurements into groups. It will then be possible to graph the modified distribution and learn more about the original set of 120 measurements. This condensation will also be useful for simplifying the computations of various averages that need to be evaluated, particularly if fast computing facilities are not available. These averages will supply additional information about the distribution. Thus the purpose of classifying data is to assist in the extraction of certain kinds of useful information from the data.

The weight measurements considered here comprise an example of observations made on what is called a *continuous variable*. This name is applied to variables, such as length, weight, temperature, and time, that can be thought of as capable of assuming any value in some interval of values. Thus the weight of a student in the 140–150 pound range can be deemed capable of assuming any value in this range. Variables such as the number of automobile accidents during a day, the number of beetles dying when they are sprayed with an insecticide, or the number of children in a family are examples of what is called a *discrete variable*. For the purposes of this book, discrete variables can be considered as variables whose possible values are integers; hence they involve counting rather than measuring.

Since any measuring device is of limited accuracy, measurements in real life are actually discrete in nature rather than continuous; however, this should not deter one from thinking about such variables as being continuous. Although the dormitory weights have been recorded to the nearest pound, they should be regarded as the values of a continuous variable, the values having been rounded off to the nearest integer. When a weight is recorded as, say, 152 pounds, it is assumed that the actual weight is somewhere between 151.5 and 152.5 pounds.

2. CLASSIFICATION OF DATA

The problem of classifying the data of a sample usually arises only for continuous variables because discrete variables by their very nature are naturally classified; therefore, consider the problem for the 120 dormitory weight measurements. What needs to be done is to place each weight in its proper weight class, for instance, between 130 and 140 pounds. Experience and theory indicate that for most types of data it is desirable to use from 10 to 20 classes, with the smaller number of classes for smaller quantities of data. With less than about 10 classes, too much sample detail is lost, whereas with more than about 20 classes computations become unnecessarily tedious. In order to determine boundaries between the various class intervals, it is necessary merely to know the smallest and largest measurements of the set. For the weight data, these are 110 and 218 pounds, respectively. Since the range of values, which is 108 pounds here, is to be divided into 10 to 20 equal intervals, the length of the class interval is first determined for those two extreme cases. If 10 intervals were chosen, the class-interval length would be $108/10 = 10.8$ pounds, whereas if 20 intervals were chosen, it would be $108/20 = 5.4$ pounds. Any convenient number between 5.4 and 10.8 may therefore be chosen. A class-interval length of 10 pounds will evidently be very convenient. Other class-interval lengths such as 6, 7, 8, or 9 would have been satisfactory also, although preference should be given to one of the larger intervals because 120 is not considered to be a large number of measurements. Since the first class interval should contain the smallest measurement of the set, it must begin at least as low as 110. Furthermore, in order to avoid having measurements fall on the boundary of two adjacent class intervals, it is customary to choose class boundaries to one-half unit beyond the accuracy of the measurements. Thus in this problem, with weights recorded to the nearest pound, it is satisfactory to choose the first class interval as 109.5–119.5, since 109.5 is one-half unit below the smallest measurement of 110, and it was agreed to use 10 pounds as the length of the class interval. This interval is certain to contain the smallest measurement, in view of the fact that a recorded weight of 110 pounds represents an actual weight between 109.5 and 110.5 pounds. The remaining class boundaries are determined by merely adding the class-interval length 10 repeatedly until the largest measurement, namely 218, is enclosed in the final interval. If 109.5–119.5 is chosen as the first class interval, there will be 11 class intervals, and the last class interval will turn out to be 209.5–219.5. When the class boundaries have been determined, it is a simple matter to list each measurement of the set in its proper class interval by merely recording a short vertical bar to represent it, as shown in Table 2(*a*). In doing this no attempt should be made to arrange the measurements in order of size; they are taken in their original order. When this listing has been completed and the number of bars for each class interval has been recorded, the data are said to have been classified in a *frequency table*.

It is assumed in such a classification that all measurements in a given class interval have been assigned the value at the midpoint of the interval. This midpoint value is called the *class mark* for that interval. Thus, for the first interval, 109.5–119.5, the class mark is 114.5, and any weight within this interval is assigned the value 114.5. The midpoint value of an interval is obtained by adding one-half the length of the interval to the number representing the left boundary of the interval. For example, the preceding first interval class mark of 114.5 was obtained by adding 5 to 109.5 because the length of the class interval is 10 and the left boundary of that interval is 109.5. Replacing all measurements in a given interval by the midpoint value of that interval replaces a set of measurements by a new more convenient set whose values are only approximately equal to the original values. The approximations are, however, usually very good.

Table 2 illustrates the tabulation (*a*) and resulting frequency table (*b*) for a set of 120 weights of the type under consideration. The class marks are usually listed in such a table because they are the new values assigned to the measurements. The letter x is used to denote a class mark, and the letter f to denote the corresponding frequency. Subscripts on x and f designate the class interval. Thus $x_1, x_2, x_3, \ldots, x_{11}$ denote the class marks for the 11 class intervals in Table 2, and $f_1, f_2, f_3, \ldots, f_{11}$ denote the corresponding frequencies. For example, $x_2 = 124.5$, and $f_2 = 4$. The

TABLE 2

(a)		(b)	
Class Boundaries	Frequencies	Class Marks: x	Frequencies: f
109.5–119.5	/	114.5	1
119.5–129.5	////	124.5	4
129.5–139.5	N̸ N̸ N̸ //	134.5	17
139.5–149.5	N̸ N̸ N̸ N̸ N̸ ///	144.5	28
149.5–159.5	N̸ N̸ N̸ N̸ N̸	154.5	25
159.5–169.5	N̸ N̸ N̸ ///	164.5	18
169.5–179.5	N̸ N̸ ///	174.5	13
179.5–189.5	N̸ /	184.5	6
189.5–199.5	N̸	194.5	5
199.5–209.5	//	204.5	2
209.5–219.5	/	214.5	1

letter n is used to denote the total number of measurements. Since the sum of the frequencies for the various intervals must equal the total number of measurements, it follows that

$$n = f_1 + f_2 + \cdots + f_h,$$

in which h denotes the number of class intervals in the frequency table.

As another illustration of how class boundaries and class marks are chosen, suppose a list of the hourly wages in 200 industrial plants yielded values in dollars of 1.90 to 2.74. These values possess a range of .84; hence if 10 classes were chosen, the length of the class interval would be .84/10 = .084. If 20 classes were chosen, the length would be .84/20 = .042. Since any convenient value between .042 and .084 may be selected, it follows that .05 is a natural choice for the length of the class interval. Wages are given to the nearest cent; therefore in order to include the lowest wage, $1.90, in the first class interval it will suffice to choose 1.895

as the left boundary of this interval. The right boundary is obtained by adding the class interval length to this value; hence it is given by the value 1.895 + .05 = 1.945. The class mark is obtained by adding one-half the class-interval length to this same first boundary value; hence it is given by the value 1.895 + .025 = 1.92. Successive boundaries and class marks can now be obtained by adding .05 to the preceding ones. If this is done repeatedly until the maximum wage, 2.74, is included in an interval, it will be found that there are 17 intervals and that the boundaries of the last interval are 2.695 and 2.745.

Magazines and newspapers often indicate class intervals in a slightly different manner from that suggested here. They do not record actual class interval boundaries but rather noncontiguous boundaries. Thus they would indicate the first three class intervals in the preceding problem by 110–119, 120–129, and 130–139. When intervals are so indicated, the boundaries, as defined earlier, are ordinarily half way between the upper and lower recorded boundaries of adjacent intervals. Thus, one would choose the half-way point between 119 and 120, namely 119.5, as the boundary between the first and second class intervals. Another method used by them employs common boundaries but agrees that an interval includes measurements up to but not including the upper boundary. With this method, the first three class intervals would be indicated by 110–120, 120–130, and 130–140. A measurement that falls on a boundary is placed in the higher of the two intervals. These alternative methods are undoubtedly used because the reading public finds them easier to follow. If one knows the accuracy of measurement of the variable involved, there will be little difficulty in determining the correct boundaries and class marks for those two methods of classification. It is important to use the correct class marks; otherwise a systematic error will be introduced in many of the computations to follow.

3. GRAPHICAL REPRESENTATION

Frequency distributions are easier to visualize if they are represented graphically. For a discrete type of variable this representation is usually made by means of a line chart. For example, the sample distributions obtained in the earlier experiment of Table 1 would employ such a chart. One can graph either the actual frequencies obtained, or the relative frequencies, or the percentages, whichever is desired. Figure 1

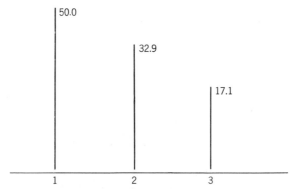

Fig. 1   Line chart for percentages in a sampling experiment.

shows such a line chart for the final percentages obtained in that experiment. In such charts one chooses any convenient units on the horizontal and vertical axis, but without necessarily showing the vertical axis and its units.

For continuous variables, a more useful type of graph is a graph called a *histogram*. The histogram for the frequency distribution of Table 2 is shown in Fig. 2. The class boundaries of Table 2 are marked off on the *x*-axis starting and finishing at any convenient points. The frequency

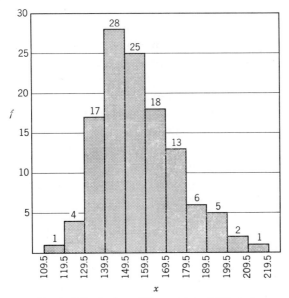

Fig. 2   Distribution of the weights of 120 students.

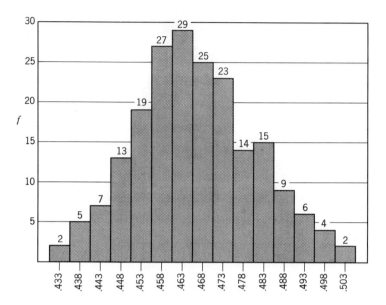

Fig. 3   Distribution of the diameters in inches of 200 steel rods.

corresponding to any class interval is represented by the height of the rectangle whose base is the interval in question. The vertical axis is therefore the frequency, or f, axis. Histograms are particularly useful graphs for later work when frequency distributions of populations are introduced.

The histogram of Fig. 2 is typical of many frequency distributions obtained from data found in nature and industry. They usually range from a rough bell-shaped distribution, such as that in Fig. 3, to something resembling the right half of a bell-shaped distribution, such as that in Fig. 5. A distribution of the latter type is said to be *skewed*. Skewness refers to lack of symmetry with respect to a vertical axis. If a histogram has a long right tail and a short left tail, it is said to be skewed to the right; it is skewed to the left if the situation is reversed. The greater the unbalance, the greater the degree of skewness. It will be found, for example, that the following variables have frequency distributions that possess shapes of the·type being discussed with approximately increasing degrees of skewness: stature, certain industrial measurements, various linear biological measurements, weight, age at marriage, mortality age for certain disease, and wealth. Figures 3, 2, 4, and 5 give the histograms for four typical distributions with increasing degrees of skewness. It

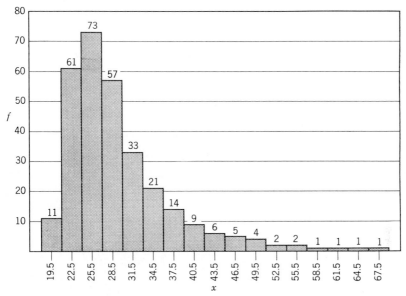

Fig. 4 Distribution of 302,000 marriages classified according to the age of the bridegroom. Frequencies are in units of 1000.

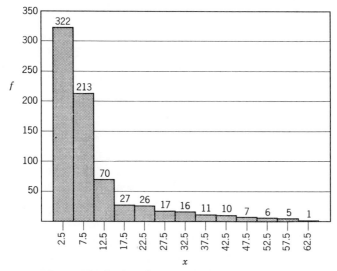

Fig. 5 Distribution of 727 deaths from scarlet fever classified according to age.

should be noted that in Figs. 3, 4, and 5 the class marks rather than the class boundaries are specified on the x-axis. This is advantageous if it yields numbers with fewer digits to list along the x-axis, as in Fig. 3. In Figs. 4 and 5 it would probably have been better if the class boundaries had been listed.

4. ARITHMETICAL DESCRIPTION

The principal reason for classifying data and drawing the histogram of the resulting frequency table is to determine the nature of the distribution. Some of the theory that is developed in later chapters requires that the distribution resemble the type of distribution displayed in Fig. 3; consequently, it is necessary to know whether one has this type of distribution before attempting to apply such theories to it.

Although a histogram yields a considerable amount of general information concerning the distribution of a set of sample measurements, more precise and useful information for studying a distribution can be obtained from an arithmetical description of the distribution. For example, if the histogram of weights for a sample of nondormitory students were available for comparison with the histogram of the dormitory sample, it might be difficult to state, except in very general terms, how the two distributions differ. Rather than compare the two weight distributions in their entirety, it might suffice to compare the average weights and the variation in weights of the two groups. Such descriptive quantities are called arithmetic because they yield numbers, as contrasted to a histogram which is geometric in nature.

The nature of a statistical problem largely determines whether a few simple arithmetical properties of the distribution will suffice to describe it satisfactorily. Most of the problems that are encountered in this book are of the type that requires only a few properties of the distribution for its solution. For more advanced problems such a condensation of the information supplied by a distribution may not suffice. The situation here is similar to that arising when one discusses problems related to women's clothes and female beauty contests. A dress salesman, for example, might be satisfied to be told that a girl is 5 feet 7 inches tall and has measurements of 36–24–36 inches; however, a beauty contest judge would hardly be satisfied with such an arithmetical description. He most certainly would want to see the entire distribution.

Now, there are many different kinds of quantities that can be used for an arithmetical description of a distribution. For simple frequency distributions, such as those whose graphs are given in Figs. 2, 3, 4, and 5, this description is accomplished satisfactorily by means of the low-order *moments* of the distribution. Moments are certain numerical quantities computed from a distribution that have proved particularly useful to statisticians. The more moments of a distribution known to him, the more information he has about the distribution. In many problems the statistician is concerned only with the first and second moments. These are the only moments that are discussed to any extent in this book. In a few problems he uses the first four moments, but seldom does he use more than four moments. One reason for this is that the higher moments are not very reliable unless one has a very large sample, so that little additional information is obtained from them in most problems.

The utility and importance of moments will become apparent when they are defined and applied in subsequent sections. Mention should be made here that a few measures other than moments are sometimes used; these will be discussed in a later section.

The next two sections are concerned with explaining what moments are, particularly the first two, and how they can be used to describe certain features of frequency distributions.

4.1 The First Moment

Suppose that a set of n sample values has been obtained from some population. These values are denoted by $X_1, X_2, \ldots, X_n$. This means that X_1 is the first sample value obtained, and X_n the last one. The familiar average of this set of numbers, which is denoted by $\overline{X}$, is given by the formula

$$(1) \qquad \overline{X} = \frac{X_1 + X_2 + \cdots + X_n}{n}.$$

These capital X's should not be confused with the small x's used earlier to denote class marks. A capital X refers to the original measurement, whereas a small x refers to the classified value. Since there are other averages also used in statistics, it is necessary to give $\overline{X}$ a special name. It is called the arithmetic mean, or, for brevity, the *mean*.

Now consider the problem of calculating the mean when the data have been classified into a frequency table, such as the weight measurements in Table 2. For such data, each of the original measurements has been replaced by the class mark corresponding to the class interval into which the measurement fell. Thus, for classified data, the only values that arise in calculating the mean are the class marks. Suppose there are h class intervals in the frequency table. As in the case of Table 2, the class marks are denoted by $x_1, x_2, \ldots, x_h$, and the frequencies corresponding to those classes by $f_1, f_2, \ldots, f_h$.

In order to calculate the mean of the classified data by means of formula (1), it is necessary to add each of the class marks as many times as it occurs. Since f_1 measurements have the class mark x_1, it follows that x_1 must be added f_1 times, which is equivalent to multiplying x_1 by f_1. The same reasoning applies to the other class marks. The sum of all the measurements in a classified table is therefore the sum of all the products like $x_1 f_1$. The mean for such a table, which is denoted by $\bar{x}$, therefore assumes the form

$$(2) \qquad \bar{x} = \frac{x_1 f_1 + x_2 f_2 + \cdots + x_h f_h}{n}.$$

The preceding formula can be written in much neater form if the summation symbol Σ (Greek sigma) is used. Since this symbol appears in other formulas also, it may be well to become acquainted with it now. As you probably realize, mathematicians will go to great lengths to create a language of symbols to save themselves the necessity of writing out lengthy expressions. The summation symbol Σ is certainly one of their better time and energy savers.

Let $z_1, z_2, \ldots, z_i, \ldots, z_n$ denote a set of n numbers. Here z_i denotes the ith number in the set, just as z_1 denotes the first number in the set. Thus, i represents any integer from 1 to n, inclusive. It is a symbol commonly employed to represent a typical integer in a set of integers. The Σ symbol specifies that all numbers like the one indicated must be added; therefore, by definition,

$$\sum_{i=1}^{n} z_i = z_1 + z_2 + \cdots + z_n.$$

The Σ symbol has n above it and $i = 1$ below it to indicate that all the numbers like z_i should be added, starting with $i = 1$ and finishing with $i = n$. As an illustration, if $z_1 = 6$, $z_2 = 4$, $z_3 = 8$, $z_4 = 2$, then

$$\sum_{i=1}^{4} z_i = 6 + 4 + 8 + 2 = 20.$$

Similarly, if k is any constant, it follows, by writing out what the summation symbol means, that

$$\sum_{i=1}^{n} kz_i = kz_1 + kz_2 + \cdots + kz_n = k \sum_{i=1}^{n} z_i,$$

and that

$$\sum_{i=1}^{n} (z_i + k) = (z_1 + k) + (z_2 + k) + \cdots + (z_n + k) = \sum_{i=1}^{n} z_i + nk.$$

In the preceding illustration, if $k = 10$, then

$$\sum_{i=1}^{4} 10z_i = 10 \sum_{i=1}^{4} z_i = 200$$

and

$$\sum_{i=1}^{4} (z_i + 10) = \sum_{i=1}^{4} z_i + 4(10) = 60.$$

A more general version of the last formula arises when one has a second set of n numbers, which is denoted by $z_1', z_2', \ldots, z_n'$. Then

$$\sum_{i=1}^{n} (z_i + z_i') = (z_1 + z_1') + (z_2 + z_2') + \cdots + (z_n + z_n')$$

$$= \sum_{i=1}^{n} z_i + \sum_{i=1}^{n} z_i'.$$

By the use of this summation symbol, formula (2) can be written in the compact form:

$$(3) \qquad \bar{x} = \frac{1}{n} \sum_{i=1}^{h} x_i f_i.$$

Replacing each measurement of a sample by its class mark will usually yield a value of the mean that differs slightly from the mean of the original measurements; however, the difference is usually so small that it can be ignored in most statistical problems.

The purpose of this chapter is to consider sample frequency distributions and to try to give a partial description of them by means of their first two moments. Thus far, however, the first moment has not even been defined. This sad state of affairs must be altered at once. Fortunately, the first moment of a sample frequency distribution is the same as the mean of the distribution; therefore, formula (3) actually defines the first moment. Since moments are usually denoted by the letter m, and the subscript on m designates which moment is meant, the first moment is defined by the formula

(4) $$m_1 = \frac{1}{n} \sum_{i=1}^{h} x_i f_i.$$

Now it can be shown that the numerical value of the first moment, or the mean, represents the point on the x-axis at which a sheet of metal in the shape of the histogram of the distribution would balance on a knife edge. Since this balancing point is usually somewhere near the middle of the base of the histogram, it follows that $\bar{x}$ usually gives a fairly good idea where the histogram is located or centered. Thus the first moment helps to describe a frequency distribution by telling where the histogram of the distribution is located along the x-axis. It is therefore often called a *measure of location*.

For the frequency distribution of Table 2, whose histogram is shown in Fig. 2, calculations will show that the mean is approximately equal to 156. An inspection of Fig. 2 certainly shows that the histogram there ought to balance on a knife edge somewhere in the vicinity of 156. Thus the value of $\bar{x}$ here gives one a good idea of where the histogram of the distribution is located, or centered, on the x axis.

4.2 Computation of the Mean by Coding

The computation of the mean, using formula (3), is easy for classified data, provided the x_i and f_i values are not large. If the x_i and f_i values are large, considerable time is saved by using a short method based on the introduction of a coding variable denoted by u, which is easier to work with than x. What one does is to replace the class marks by small positive and negative integers, with zero chosen near the middle of the distribution. This device, applied to Table 2, is shown in Table 3.

It is not particularly important that 0 be chosen near the middle of the distribution; however, the computations are somewhat easier if this is done. Placing 0 opposite 154.5, for example, would have been just as satisfactory. Having located the zero value of u, one then chooses the

TABLE 3

x	114.5	124.5	134.5	144.5	154.5	164.5	174.5	184.5	194.5	204.5	214.5
u	−5	−4	−3	−2	−1	0	1	2	3	4	5

positive and negative integer values of u, as shown, so that increasing values of u correspond to increasing values of x.

If x_0 is used to designate the class mark that corresponds to $u = 0$ and if c denotes the length of the class interval, then the relationship between the x's and the u's, when the foregoing technique is used, can be shown to be given by the formula

(5) $$x_i = cu_i + x_0.$$

Since the length of the class interval for Table 3 is 10, this formula for Table 3 would become

$$x_i = 10u_i + 164.5.$$

The correctness of this formula for Table 3 is easily verified by substituting each of the u values and observing that it produces the correct x value. It will be seen that any particular u value denotes the number of class intervals its corresponding x class mark is away from the class mark x_0, chosen to correspond to $u = 0$. The sign of u determines whether it is to the right or to the left of the zero value. Thus, the value $u = -3$ shows that the class mark 134.5 is three class intervals to the left of the class mark 164.5. The correctness of formula (5) in general is verified in the same manner by realizing that any class mark can be obtained from x_0 by adding or subtracting the proper number of class-interval lengths to it and that the u's give this proper number together with the proper sign.

The relationship between a u value and the corresponding x value in (5) is similar to the type of relationship that arises when one wishes to calculate the temperature in Fahrenheit degrees from that in Centigrade degrees. One employs the formula $F = \frac{9}{5}C + 32$, where F and C are the corresponding temperatures in degrees in those units and 32 represents the value of F corresponding to $C = 0$.

Now it is clear that the computation of the mean would be much easier if the x_i were replaced by the u_i. The resulting mean, of course, would have to be denoted by $\bar{u}$. Since there is a very simple way of obtaining the value of $\bar{x}$ from the value of $\bar{u}$, this device of introducing a coding variable results in the saving of considerable computing time. The relationship between $\bar{x}$ and $\bar{u}$, which enables one to obtain $\bar{x}$ from $\bar{u}$, is the same as that between the x_i and the u_i given by (5). This fact is demonstrated in a following paragraph. Thus, to compute $\bar{x}$, it suffices to compute $\bar{u}$ and then compute $\bar{x}$ by means of the formula

(6) $$\bar{x} = c\bar{u} + x_0.$$

The reasonableness of this formula should be apparent without a demonstration if one considers, for example, the problem of how one would calculate the mean monthly temperature of a city in Fahrenheit if the daily temperatures are given in Centigrade. One could either convert the daily temperatures to Fahrenheit and then calculate their mean or, what is simpler, first calculate the mean of the Centigrade values and then convert it to a Fahrenheit value. The latter method corresponds to using formula (6).

TABLE 4

x	f	u	uf
114.5	1	−5	−5
124.5	4	−4	−16
134.5	17	−3	−51
144.5	28	−2	−56
154.5	25	−1	−25
164.5	18	0	0
174.5	13	1	13
184.5	6	2	12
194.5	5	3	15
204.5	2	4	8
214.5	1	5	5
Totals	120		−100

The computation of $\bar{x}$ for the data of Table 2 by means of this formula is shown in Table 4. To compute $\bar{u}$, one uses formula (3) in the form

$$\bar{u} = \frac{1}{n} \sum_{i=1}^{h} u_i f_i.$$

Formula (6) then yields, correct to one decimal place,

$$\bar{x} = 10(-\tfrac{100}{120}) + 164.5 = -8.3 + 164.5 = 156.2.$$

For the purpose of displaying the advantage of coding, the value of $\bar{x}$ is computed directly by means of formula (3) for this same set of data. The computations are given in Table 5.

The application of formula (3) yields, correct to one decimal place,

$$\bar{x} = \frac{18,740.0}{120} = 156.2.$$

It should be noted that the method that employs coding is an exact method, and therefore the two answers will always agree if they are computed to the same degree of accuracy.

It should be of some interest to those who like algebra, or who know some algebra, to see how formula (6) is derived from formula (5). Those of you who do not fall into either category may ignore this derivation. If the value of x_i given by (5) is substituted into formula (3) and the

TABLE 5

x	f	xf
114.5	1	114.5
124.5	4	498.0
134.5	17	2,286.5
144.5	28	4,046.0
154.5	25	3,862.5
164.5	18	2,961.0
174.5	13	2,268.5
184.5	6	1,107.0
194.5	5	972.5
204.5	2	409.0
214.5	1	214.5
Totals	120	18,740.0

properties of the Σ symbol, which were discussed earlier in connection with formula (3), are used, it will follow step by step that

$$\bar{x} = \frac{1}{n} \sum_{i=1}^{h} (cu_i + x_0) f_i$$

$$= \frac{1}{n} \sum_{i=1}^{h} (cu_i f_i + x_0 f_i)$$

$$= \frac{1}{n} \sum_{i=1}^{h} cu_i f_i + \frac{1}{n} \sum_{i=1}^{h} x_0 f_i$$

$$= c \frac{1}{n} \sum_{i=1}^{h} u_i f_i + x_0 \frac{1}{n} \sum_{i=1}^{h} f_i$$

$$= c\bar{u} + x_0.$$

4.3 The Second Moment

The second moment of a sample distribution, which is denoted by m_2, is defined by the formula

(7) $$m_2 = \frac{1}{n} \sum_{i=1}^{h} x_i^2 f_i.$$

Thus it differs from the first moment, m_1, given by formula (4), in that it uses the square of the variable rather than the variable itself. Higher moments are defined in a similar manner. The third moment, m_3, for example, would use x_i^3 in place of x_i^2 in formula (7).

The purpose of this section is to explain how the second moment can be used to describe a sample frequency distribution further. But before doing so it is necessary to consider what effect the addition of a constant to a set of measurements will have upon the histogram and also upon the first two moments of a distribution.

Suppose all the weights of Table 2 had 10 pounds added to them. The only effect that this would have upon the histogram of the distribution would be to shift it 10 units to the right. The mean, of course, would be increased by 10 pounds. If, however, 10 pounds had been subtracted from all the weights of Table 2, then the histogram would have been shifted 10 units to the left. Suppose that the mean weight $\bar{x}$ is subtracted from all the weights. This will shift the histogram $\bar{x}$ units to the left. Now, if $\bar{x}$ is thought of as locating a histogram, then subtracting $\bar{x}$ from all the measurements will cause the histogram to be centered at the origin. This device of subtracting the mean of a set of measurements from the measurements themselves enables one to compare different histograms, regardless of their original location, since they will all then be located, or centered, at the origin. This means that all such histograms will balance on a knife-edge placed at the origin, even though they may differ in size and shape.

If the second moment were calculated for the weights of Table 2 with 10 pounds added to each of them, it is clear from formula (7) that its value would be larger than for the original set of weights. Thus the value of the second moment is affected by the location of the histogram. Since the first moment gives the desired location information, the information to be obtained from the second moment should be additional information and hence independent of the location of the histogram. This independence can be obtained by the device, just explained, of subtracting the mean from all the measurements and then calculating the second moment of the new measurements. This implies that x_i must be replaced by $x_i - \bar{x}$ in formula (7). The second moment of a distribution when the *deviations* $x_i - \bar{x}$ are used in place of the x_i is called the second moment about the mean. It is given by

$$(8) \qquad \frac{1}{n} \sum_{i=1}^{h} (x_i - \bar{x})^2 f_i.$$

The second moment as defined by (7) is sometimes called the second moment about the origin; however, it is usually assumed that a second moment is about the origin unless a contrary statement is made.

Formula (8) can be expressed in terms of the two moments m_1 and m_2 about the origin by performing the following algebraic steps and applying formulas (4) and (7):

$$\frac{1}{n}\sum_{i=1}^{h}(x_i - \bar{x})^2 f_i = \frac{1}{n}\sum_{i=1}^{h}(x_i^2 - 2\bar{x}x_i + \bar{x}^2)f_i$$

$$= \frac{1}{n}\sum_{i=1}^{h}(x_i^2 f_i - 2\bar{x}x_i f_i + \bar{x}^2 f_i)$$

$$= \frac{1}{n}\sum_{i=1}^{h}x_i^2 f_i - 2\bar{x}\frac{1}{n}\sum_{i=1}^{h}x_i f_i + \bar{x}^2\frac{1}{n}\sum_{i=1}^{h}f_i$$

$$= m_2 - 2\bar{x}m_1 + \bar{x}^2.$$

But since $\bar{x} = m_1$, this reduces to

(9) $$\frac{1}{n}\sum_{i=1}^{h}(x_i - \bar{x})^2 f_i = m_2 - m_1^2.$$

In the solutions of statistical-inference problems in later chapters a slight modification of this second moment is more useful than the second moment itself. This modification consists in using the divisor $n - 1$ in place of n. The resulting quantity is denoted by the special symbol s^2 and is called the *sample variance*. Thus, by definition,

(10) $$s^2 = \frac{1}{n - 1}\sum_{i=1}^{h}(x_i - \bar{x})^2 f_i.$$

Since the variance involves the squares of deviations, it is a number in squared units. Thus, if the x_i represent weights measured in pounds, s^2 is a number whose unit is pounds-squared. In some problems it is desirable that quantities describing a distribution possess the same units as the original set of measurements. The mean satisfies this requirement but the variance does not; however, by taking the positive square root of the variance, the desired effect can be achieved. The resulting quantity, which naturally is denoted by s, is called the standard deviation of the distribution. Thus, by definition, the *sample standard deviation* is

(11) $$s = \sqrt{\frac{1}{n - 1}\sum_{i=1}^{h}(x_i - \bar{x})^2 f_i}.$$

At the present stage of the development of statistical theory it is difficult to give a good intuitive explanation of why one divides by $n - 1$ rather than by n in the formula for s^2. The reasoning behind this choice runs roughly as follows. Suppose one calculates the mean and the second moment about the mean for an entire population, such as the population of weights of students. Now suppose that one takes a small sample, say $n = 5$, from this population and then calculates the sample mean and the sample second moment about the sample mean based on dividing by n, namely 5, rather than by $n - 1$, namely 4. If one performs this experiment repeatedly and averages the resulting second moments, he will discover that this average will tend to be slightly smaller than the corresponding second moment previously calculated for the entire population. As a matter of fact, it will usually be only about four-fifths as large as the population second moment. Since sample values are going to be used to draw inferences about the corresponding population values, it is therefore desirable to modify the sample second moment so that it will conform more to the corresponding population second moment. This is accomplished by dividing by $n - 1$ rather than by n. For example, if $n = 5$, dividing by 4 rather than by 5 will increase the sample second moment by a factor of 5/4, thus compensating for the fact that it tended to be only four-fifths as large as the corresponding population second moment. It can be demonstrated by mathematical methods that this correction is precisely what is needed in general to accomplish the objective, and that in the long run of experiments the average of the values obtained using (10) will approach the value of the population second moment about the mean.

Although the standard deviation has been defined only for classified data, formula (11) can also be used for the original unclassified data, provided that it is modified properly. It suffices to replace h by n and to delete f_i. This modification will yield the formula

$$(12) \qquad s = \sqrt{\frac{1}{n-1} \sum_{i=1}^{n} (x_i - \bar{x})^2}.$$

Here the values $x_1, x_2, \ldots, x_n$ denote the original measurements and not class marks. Ordinarily one uses capital letters, such as in formula (1), to denote original measurements and small letters for class marks; however, it is simpler to use small letters for both types of measurements, provided no misunderstanding arises from doing so. If fast-computing equipment is available, it is unnecessary and inadvisable to classify the data when calculating moments. Formulas (1) and (12) should then be used.

4.4 Interpretation of the Standard Deviation

It will now be shown that the standard deviation can usually be considered a measure of the variability of the data of a frequency distribution. Of course, if the standard deviation can be considered such a measure, the variance can too; however, the standard deviation is somewhat easier to describe in this connection.

Consider the two sets of measurements,

$$4, 5, 6, 7, 8 \quad \text{and} \quad 2, 4, 6, 8, 10.$$

The mean of each set is 6. Since the common difference between successive pairs of measurements in the second set is twice what it is in the first set (2 to 1) and since the range of values of the second set is twice the range of values of the first set (8 to 4), most people would agree that the second set of measurements varies twice as much as the first set. Calculations of the standard deviation for the two sets by means of formula (12) will yield the values

$$s_1 = \sqrt{\tfrac{1}{4}[4 + 1 + 0 + 1 + 4]} = \frac{\sqrt{10}}{2}$$

and

$$s_2 = \sqrt{\tfrac{1}{4}[16 + 4 + 0 + 4 + 16]} = \sqrt{10}.$$

The fact that the value of the standard deviation is twice as large for the second set as for the first set is certainly a satisfying property of the standard deviation if it is to be considered a measure of variation.

The preceding illustration, which indicates that the standard deviation increases in size as the variability of the data increases, does not give any clue to the meaning of the magnitude of the standard deviation. Thus, if the values of the standard deviation in this illustration had been $3\sqrt{10}$ and $6\sqrt{10}$, instead of $\sqrt{10}/2$ and $\sqrt{10}$, the interpretation would have been the same. This situation is similar to that occurring when two students compare scores on a test. One student may score twice as many points as the other, but this does not reveal how much absolute knowledge of the subject either student possesses.

In order to give some quantitative meaning to the size of the standard deviation, it is necessary to anticipate certain results of later work. For a set of data that has been obtained by sampling a particular type of population, called a normal population, it will be shown later that when the sample is large the interval from $\bar{x} - s$ to $\bar{x} + s$ usually includes about 68 per cent of the observations and that the interval from $\bar{x} - 2s$ to $\bar{x} + 2s$ usually includes about 95 per cent of the observations. A

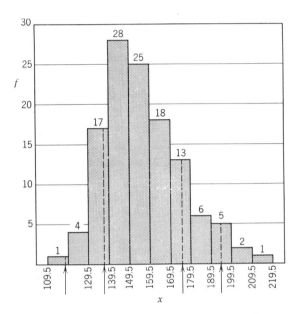

Fig. 6　Histogram for the distribution of 120 weights.

sample from a population of this type usually has a histogram that looks somewhat like the histogram of Fig. 3. As the sample increases in size, the histogram tends to approach the shape of a bell.

As an illustrative example of this property, consider the data of Table 2. Computations yielded the value of $s = 19.1$ for those data. Methods for computing the standard deviation are discussed in the next section; therefore, no thought need be given here as to how this value was obtained. Since it was found earlier that $\bar{x} = 156.2$, the two intervals $(\bar{x} - s, \bar{x} + s)$ and $(\bar{x} - 2s, \bar{x} + 2s)$ become (137.1, 175.3) and (118.0, 194.4), respectively. These values have been marked off with vertical lines on the x-axis of Fig. 6, which is the graph of the histogram for the frequency distribution of Table 2.

In computing the percentages of the data lying within each of these two intervals, it is necessary to approximate how many observations in an interval lie to the right, and to the left, of a point inside the interval. Toward this end, it is assumed that all the observations in an interval are spread uniformly along the interval. Thus, for the second interval, it is assumed that one of the four observations lies in the first quarter of the interval, another is in the second quarter of the interval, etc. With this understanding, the number of observations lying between 137.1 and 175.3 is approximately equal to $4 + 28 + 25 + 18 + 8 = 83$. The values of 4 and 8 are obtained by interpolating according to the preceding agreement on how observations are spread out. For example, 4 is obtained by realizing that the distance from 129.5 to 137.1 is 7.6 units, whereas the distance from 129.5 to 139.5 is 10 units; therefore 76 per cent of the 17 observations in this interval should be assumed to be to the left of 137.1 and 24 per cent to the right. Since 24 per cent of 17 is equal to 4, to the nearest integer, it follows that 4 of the 17 observations of this interval should be assumed to lie to the right of 137.1. The value of 8 in the preceding sum is obtained in a similar manner. Thus the distance from 169.5 to 175.3 is 5.8 units, whereas the distance from 169.5 to 179.5 is 10 units; hence 58 per cent of the 13 measurements in this interval should be treated as being to the left of the point 175.3. Since 58 per cent of 13 is 7.54, or 8 to the nearest integer, it follows that 8 of those 13 observations should be assumed to be to the left of 175.3. Now since the total number of observations is 120 and since $83/120 = .69$, it follows that approximately 69 per cent of the observations fall inside the interval $(\bar{x} - s, \bar{x} + s)$. Similar calculations will show that approximately 94 per cent of the observations fall inside the interval $(\bar{x} - 2s, \bar{x} + 2s)$. These results are certainly close to the theoretical percentages of 68 and 95 for normal distributions.

For a distribution whose histogram resembles the histogram in Fig. 4 or Fig. 5, one would not expect to find the percentages for the intervals discussed to be very close to the theoretical percentages for a normal distribution, yet the percentages are often fairly close to those theoretical values.

By using the foregoing geometrical interpretation of the standard deviation, it is possible to obtain a rough idea of the size of the standard deviation for familiar distributions. Consider, for example, the distribution of stature for adult males. One might guess that about 95 per cent of all adult males would have heights somewhere between 5 feet 2 inches and 6 feet 2 inches. Since this is a 12-inch interval, and since for a normal distribution 95 per cent of the observations would be expected to lie in the interval $(\bar{x} - 2s, \bar{x} + 2s)$ whose length is $4s$, one would guess that $4s = 12$ inches or that $s = 3$ inches. A crude estimate of the standard deviation of the frequency distribution of stature for adult males is therefore 3 inches. In a similar manner, one should be able to give a crude estimate of the size of the standard deviation for other familiar frequency distributions and thus acquire a feeling for the standard deviation as a measure of the variability of data.

4.5 Computation of the Standard Deviation by Coding

The computation of the standard deviation is considerably simplified for frequency tables with large x_i and f_i values by means of the same coding device used to simplify the computation of the mean. By using the coding formula given by (5) and using formula (6), one obtains

$$x_i - \bar{x} = c(u_i - \bar{u}).$$

If this value is substituted into (11), s will reduce to

$$s = \sqrt{\frac{1}{n-1} \sum_{i=1}^{h} c^2 (u_i - \bar{u})^2 f_i}.$$

This is equivalent to

(13)
$$s = c\sqrt{\frac{1}{n-1} \sum_{i=1}^{h} (u_i - \bar{u})^2 f_i}.$$

This formula shows that the standard deviation for x is equal to c times the standard deviation for u. A little additional algebra will show that the last formula can also be written in the form

(14)
$$s = c\sqrt{\frac{1}{n-1} \left[\sum_{i=1}^{h} u_i^2 f_i - \frac{1}{n} \left(\sum_{i=1}^{h} u_i f_i \right)^2 \right]}.$$

This formula is usually the best one for computing purposes.

To illustrate the use of this coding method for computing s, consider once more the data in Table 2. The computations are merely an extension of those in Table 4 and are displayed in Table 6. The application of formula (14) will yield the value

$$_,s = 10\sqrt{\tfrac{1}{119}[518 - \tfrac{1}{120}(-100)^2]}$$
$$= 10\sqrt{\tfrac{1}{119}[518 - 83.3]}$$
$$= 10\sqrt{3.65} = 19.1.$$

TABLE 6

x	f	u	uf	u^2f
114.5	1	−5	−5	25
124.5	4	−4	−16	64
134.5	17	−3	−51	153
144.5	28	−2	−56	112
154.5	25	−1	−25	25
164.5	18	0	0	0
174.5	13	1	13	13
184.5	6	2	12	24
194.5	5	3	15	45
204.5	2	4	8	32
214.5	1	5	5	25
Totals	120		−100	518

The value of the square root here was obtained from Table I in the appendix.

As stated earlier, the favorite quantities of most statisticians for describing frequency distributions are moments. This preference is based partly on tradition and partly on certain desirable theoretical properties possessed by moments. Only the first two moments have been discussed in detail because the solutions of the statistical inference problems that are studied in this book require a knowledge of the first two moments only, together with certain assumptions.

Although the first moment and a modification of the second moment are being chosen here as the preferred measures of location and variation, situations do arise in which other similar measures are more appropriate for describing a distribution. Some of these measures are discussed briefly in section 5; however, unless one has a particular need or interest in such measures, this section may be omitted or read very quickly.

▶5. OTHER DESCRIPTIVE MEASURES

It is interesting to observe in newspaper reports how different groups will employ different averages to describe the distribution of wages in their industry. Employers usually quote the mean wage to indicate the economic status of employees. Labor leaders, however, prefer to use the mode or the median as an indicator of the wage level.

The *mode* of a set of measurements is defined as the measurement with the maximum frequency, if there is one. Thus, for the set of measurements

3, 3, 4, 4, 4, 5, 5, 6, 6, 7, 8, 9, 9, the mode is 4. In certain industries there may be more laborers working at the lowest wage scale than at any of the other scales, and therefore labor leaders would naturally prefer to quote the mode in describing the distribution of wages. In most problems of this type one must know more than just a measure of location, and therefore the mode is likely to be of limited value here.

The *median* of a set of measurements is defined as the middle measurement, if there is one, after the measurements have been arranged in order of magnitude. For the set of measurements in the preceding paragraph, which is arranged in order of magnitude, the median is 5. If there is an even number of measurements, one chooses the median to be halfway between the two middle measurements. Thus, if one of the 5's were deleted from the preceding set, there would be no middle measurement and the median would become 5.5. The median is a more realistic measure to describe the wage level in certain industries than either the mode or the mean. Since the median wage is one such that half the employees receive at least this much and half receive at most this much, one usually obtains a fairly good picture of the wage level from the median. The mean has the disadvantage that if most of the wages are fairly low, but there is a small percentage of very high wages, the mean wage will indicate a deceptively high wage level. The median would seem to be better than the mean here as an indicator of what is popularly meant by the wage level.

The median has another rather attractive property. If the variable being studied is income and incomes are listed in intervals of 500 dollars, but with all over 20,000 dollars listed as 20,000 dollars or more, it is not possible to compute the mean income because of the uncertainty of the incomes in the last interval. The median income would be unaffected by this lack of information and therefore could substitute for the mean here.

For data that have been classified, the median is defined to be the value of x such that a vertical line through the corresponding point on the x-axis cuts the histogram into two parts having equal areas. This property is quite different from the balancing property of the mean. The calculations necessary to determine a median for classified data are based on this geometrical property. As an illustration of such calculations consider the problem for the data of Fig. 2. Since there are 120 measurements represented by that histogram, and areas are proportional to frequencies, the problem is equivalent to that of finding a point on the x-axis such that

60 of the measurements will be to the left of it and 60 to the right of it. If absolute frequencies are summed it will be found that the first four class intervals yield a total of 50 frequencies, whereas the first five intervals yield a total of 75 frequencies. The median must therefore be located in the fifth class interval, ideally halfway between the sixtieth and sixty-first measurement of the entire set. Since 10 of the 25 measurements in the fifth interval are needed to yield a total of 60 measurements, the median should be located at a point that is $\frac{10}{25}$ of the way along that interval. The interval is 10 units long and it begins at the point 149.5; therefore the median is the value

$$149.5 + \tfrac{10}{25}(10) = 153.5.$$

It is to be noted that the median is slightly smaller than the mean for this problem. This is usually true for distributions skewed to the right. From Fig. 2 it will be observed that there is a slight amount of this skewness here.

In view of the foregoing remarks about some of the attractive properties of the median, one might wonder why statisticians usually prefer the mean to the median. There are some computational advantages of the mean over the median; however, the principal reason for preferring the mean is that it is a much more useful and reliable measure to use in making statistical inferences. Since the ultimate objective is to solve statistical inference problems, the mean is usually preferred to the median when both measures can be found.

Several measures of variation, in addition to the standard deviation, are occasionally used. The simplest measure of the variation of a set of measurements is the range. The *range* has already been employed in the process of classifying data and is merely the difference between the largest and smallest measurements of the set. It is a popular measure in such fields as industrial quality control and meteorology. This popularity rests principally on its ease of computation and interpretation. It is a simple matter to find the largest and smallest measurements of a set, in contrast to calculating the standard deviation of the set. It is also a simple matter to explain how the range measures variation, in contrast to explaining how the standard deviation does so. However, an unfortunate property of the range is the tendency of its value to increase in size as the sample size increases. For example, one would expect the range in the weights of a sample of ten college students to be considerably smaller than the range in the weights of a sample of 100 students. It is possible to adjust the range for this growth by means of fancy formulas, but then the range loses its simplicity.

Another measure of variation that is encountered frequently is the *mean deviation*. It is defined by the formula

$$\text{M.D.} = \frac{1}{n} \sum_{i=1}^{n} |X_i - \bar{X}|.$$

The two vertical bars enclosing $X_i - \bar{X}$ are absolute value symbols. They indicate that one should calculate the difference $X_i - \bar{X}$ and then ignore the minus sign in case the difference is a negative number. Thus one calculates all the differences of this type, ignores the minus signs, sums the resulting numbers, and divides by n. The mean deviation differs from the second moment about the mean in using the absolute values rather than the squares of deviations. The preceding formula can be applied to classified data by rewriting it in the form

$$\text{M.D.} = \frac{1}{n} \sum_{i=1}^{h} |x_i - \bar{x}| f_i.$$

Here x_i denotes the ith class mark, whereas the preceding X_i denoted the ith measurement.

To illustrate the computation of the mean deviation, consider once more the data of Table 4. In section 4.2 the value of $\bar{x}$ was found to be 156.2. The computations follow, as shown in Table 7. These results yield, correct to one decimal place,

$$\text{M.D.} = \frac{1811}{120} = 15.1.$$

Since the mean deviation is quite different from the standard deviation, there is no reason to expect the values of these two measures to be similar for the same set of data. The value of the standard deviation for this problem was computed earlier to be 19.1.

There are shorter ways of computing the mean deviation than by using its definition; however, since the purpose of this entire section is to acquaint students with some of the other descriptive measures that may be encountered by them, these shorter methods are ignored here.

Measures of variation can also be constructed by methods similar to that used to define the median. Instead of merely finding a value of x that divides the histogram into a lower and upper half, one could also

TABLE 7

x	f	$x - \bar{x}$	$\|x - \bar{x}\| f$
114.5	1	−41.7	41.7
124.5	4	−31.7	126.8
134.5	17	−21.7	368.9
144.5	28	−11.7	327.6
154.5	25	−1.7	42.5
164.5	18	8.3	149.4
174.5	13	18.3	237.9
184.5	6	28.3	169.8
194.5	5	38.3	191.5
204.5	2	48.3	96.6
214.5	1	58.3	58.3
Totals	120		1811.0

find two other values of x, one dividing the histogram at a point such that one-fourth of the area is to the left of it and the other such that one-fourth of the area is to the right of it. These two measures, together with the median, constitute the three *quartiles* of the distribution. The smallest quartile is called the first quartile, the median is called the second quartile, and the largest quartile is called the third quartile. A simple measure of variation can be constructed from the quartiles by taking the difference between the third quartile and the first quartile. This measure, which is used in some fields, is called the *interquartile range*.

As an illustration of the computation of a quartile, consider the problem of finding the first quartile for the data of Fig. 4. The total number of recorded frequencies here is 302, in thousands; therefore the total area of the histogram is proportional to 302. Since $\frac{1}{4}(302) = 75.5$ and the first 2 intervals yield a total of 72 measurements, it is necessary to use 3.5 of the 73 measurements in the third interval. Thus the first quartile is located at a point inside the third interval that is 3.5/73 of the way along that interval. The interval is 3 units long and it begins at 24; therefore the first quartile is the value

$$24 + \frac{3.5}{73}(3) = 24.14.$$

One could construct other measures of variation in a similar manner by considering deciles rather than quartiles. Deciles are values of x that divide the histogram into tenths. Thus one might use the difference between the ninth decile and the first decile as a measure of variation.

Measures of this general type possess certain advantages over the standard deviation similar to those possessed by the median over the mean. However, the same kind of superiority of the standard deviation exists here as exists for the mean over the median when it comes to solving problems of statistical inference.

Deciles can be used for purposes other than constructing measures of variation. They often serve as satisfactory substitutes for moments in describing a distribution in more detail than that given by a measure of location and a measure of variation. Knowing all the deciles of a distribution would give a large amount of information concerning the nature of it.

These ideas can be extended further by introducing percentiles, which are values of x that divide the histogram into 100 equal area parts. Deciles and percentiles are calculated in the same manner as quartiles. Percentiles are used extensively in such fields as psychology and educational testing, for example in comparing students' results on standardized examinations with national averages. Undoubtedly some of you had the experience of being told at what percentile you rated on a scholastic aptitude test.

6. REVIEW EXERCISES

This section is designed to serve as a problem-solving review of some of the concepts discussed in this chapter. Unless the optional section 5 has been assigned, a student should ignore those parts that carry a ▶ symbol.

The following data represent the number of hours worked per week for 100 laborers. Using these data (a) classify them into a frequency table, (b) draw the histogram, (c) calculate the mean and standard deviation using coding techniques, (d) calculate the mean of the original data and compare with the result obtained in (c), (e) calculate the percentage of measurements lying in the two intervals $(\bar{x} - s, \bar{x} + s)$ and $(\bar{x} - 2s, \bar{x} + 2s)$, ▶(f) calculate the mean deviation, ▶(g) calculate the median and the interquartile range, ▶(h) calculate the ninety-fifth percentile.

36 | 36 | 32 | 35 | 41 | 32 | 41 | 30 | 22 | 32 | 27 | 35 | 35 | 10 | 29 | 41 | 45 | 45 | 30 | 39
45 | 33 | 23 | 28 | 27 | 43 | 44 | 31 | 34 | 33 | 36 | 28 | 31 | 39 | 29 | 42 | 43 | 31 | 28 | 39
33 | 18 | 25 | 36 | 45 | 45 | 24 | 37 | 52 | 26 | 23 | 23 | 38 | 37 | 38 | 42 | 40 | 42 | 40 | 40
42 | 40 | 34 | 37 | 34 | 36 | 40 | 33 | 40 | 20 | 10 | 23 | 15 | 28 | 28 | 32 | 28 | 37 | 37 | 44
25 | 36 | 26 | 40 | 40 | 39 | 39 | 41 | 33 | 39 | 40 | 38 | 39 | 16 | 39 | 38 | 41 | 41 | 28 | 27

(*a*) These numbers range from 10 to 52, which is a spread of 42. Dividing by 10 and 20 gives 4.2 and 2.1, respectively; hence choose a class interval of length 3. Starting the first interval at 9.5 will give 9.5–12.5 as the boundaries for the first interval. The tabulation for these 100 measurements then becomes:

		x	f
9.5–12.5	//.	11	2
12.5–15.5	/	14	1
15.5–18.5	//	17	2
18.5–21.5	/	20	1
21.5–24.5	ⅣⅣ /	23	6
24.5–27.5	ⅣⅣ //	26	7
27.5–30.5	ⅣⅣ ⅣⅣ /	29	11
30.5–33.5	ⅣⅣ ⅣⅣ //	32	12
33.5–36.5	ⅣⅣ ⅣⅣ //	35	12
36.5–39.5	ⅣⅣ ⅣⅣ ⅣⅣ //	38	17
39.5–42.5	ⅣⅣ ⅣⅣ ⅣⅣ ////	41	19
42.5–45.5	ⅣⅣ ////	44	9
45.5–48.5		47	0
48.5–51.5		50	0
51.5–54.5	/	53	1

(*b*)

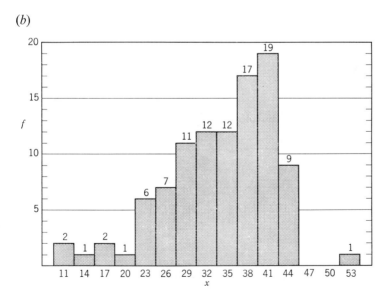

(c)

x	f	u	uf	u^2f
11	2	−7	−14	98
14	1	−6	−6	36
17	2	−5	−10	50
20	1	−4	−4	16
23	6	−3	−18	54
26	7	−2	−14	28
29	11	−1	−11	11
32	12	0		
35	12	1	12	12
38	17	2	34	68
41	19	3	57	171
44	9	4	36	144
47	0	5		
50	0	6		
53	1	7	7	49
	$\overline{100}$		$\overline{69}$	$\overline{737}$

$$\bar{x} = 3\bar{u} + 32$$
$$= 3(\tfrac{69}{100}) + 32$$
$$= 34.07 = 34.1$$

$$s = 3\sqrt{\frac{1}{99}\left[737 - \frac{(69)^2}{100}\right]}$$
$$= 3\sqrt{\tfrac{1}{99}[689.39]}$$
$$= 3(2.64)$$
$$= 7.9.$$

(d) 34.07; hence the classification caused no error in $\bar{x}$, but this was mostly luck.

(e) $(\bar{x} - s, \bar{x} + s) = (26.2, 42.0)$
$(\bar{x} - 2s, \bar{x} + 2s) = (18.3, 49.9)$

Measurements inside the first interval total

$$\frac{1.3}{3}(7) + 11 + 12 + 12 + 17 + \frac{2.5}{3}(19) = 71; \text{ hence 71 per cent.}$$

Measurements outside the second interval total

$$2 + 1 + \frac{2.8}{3}(2) + 1 = 6; \text{ hence 94 per cent inside.}$$

(f) Using $\bar{x} = 34.1$ gives

x	f	$\|x - \bar{x}\|$	$\|x - \bar{x}\| f$
11	2	23.1	46.2
14	1	20.1	20.1
17	2	17.1	34.2
20	1	14.1	14.1
23	6	11.1	66.6
26	7	8.1	56.7
29	11	5.1	56.1
32	12	2.1	25.2
35	12	.9	10.8
38	17	3.9	66.3
41	19	6.9	131.1
44	9	9.9	89.1
47	0	12.9	
50	0	15.9	
53	1	18.9	18.9
	100		635.4

$$\text{M.D.} = \frac{635.4}{100} = 6.354.$$

(g) Median $= 33.5 + \frac{8}{12}(3) = 35.5$

First quartile $= 27.5 + \frac{6}{11}(3) = 29.1$

Third quartile $= 39.5 + \frac{4}{19}(3) = 40.1$

Interquartile range $= 40.1 - 29.1 = 11$

(h) Ninety-fifth percentile $= 42.5 + \frac{5}{9}(3) = 44.2$

EXERCISES

1. Toss a coin 500 times, recording the number of heads obtained in sets of 50. Calculate the cumulative proportion of heads obtained in decimal form and observe whether the resulting set of 10 proportions appears to approach $\frac{1}{2}$.

2. Roll a die 500 times, recording only the number of times that a 1 or a 6 appears in sets of 50 rolls. Calculate the cumulative proportion of such results and observe whether the proportions seem to approach $\frac{1}{3}$.

3. Weights of 300 babies ranged from 82 ounces to 176 ounces, correct to the nearest ounce. Determine class boundaries and class marks for the first and last class intervals.

4. The thicknesses of 400 washers ranged from 0.421 to 0.563 centimeter. Determine class boundaries and class marks for the first and last class intervals.

5. Given the following frequency table of the diameters in feet of 56 shrubs from a common species, draw its histogram showing the class marks.

x	1	2	3	4	5	6	7	8	9	10	11	12
f	1	7	11	16	8	4	5	2	1	0	0	1

6. Given the following frequency table of the heights in centimeters of 1,000 students, draw its histogram showing the class marks.

x	155–157	158–160	etc.											
f	4	8	26	53	89	146	188	181	125	92	60	22	4	1	1

7. The following data are for the traveling time to and from work in hours per day for a group of aircraft workers. Draw the histogram, assuming continuous time.

Under 1 hour	80
1 up to 2	42
2 up to 3	7
3 up to 4	4
4 up to 5	3
5 up to 6	2

8. Given the following frequency distribution of the number of children born to wives aged 40–44 during their married lives, draw its histogram.

x	0	1	2	3	4	5	6	7	8	9	10 or more
f	1230	1520	1545	962	537	301	174	108	69	51	73

9. What type of distribution would you expect grade-point averages of college students to possess? Sketch your idea of the nature of this distribution with the proper units on the x-axis.

10. If you were to study the age distribution of college students, would you consider age to be a discrete or continuous variable? What would you choose for class boundaries?

11. Draw a sample of 100 one-digit random numbers from Table II in the appendix by taking consecutive digits from as many columns as needed. Classify these numbers into a frequency table and draw the histogram, even though the variable here is discrete. These numbers, which are discussed in Chapter 5, possess a "rectangular" distribution; hence your histogram should resemble a rectangle.

12. Given the values $z_1 = 1$, $z_2 = 2$, $z_3 = 3$, $z_4 = 4$, find the values of

$$(a) \sum_{i=1}^{4} z_i, \qquad (b) \sum_{i=1}^{4} 2z_i, \qquad (c) \sum_{i=1}^{4} (z_i + 2),$$

$$(d) \sum_{i=1}^{4} z_i^2, \qquad (e) \sum_{i=1}^{4} 2z_i^2, \qquad (f) \sum_{i=1}^{4} (z_i + 2)^2.$$

13. Show that (a) $\dfrac{1}{n} \sum_{i=1}^{n} (x_i + c) = \bar{x} + c$, (b) $\sum_{i=1}^{n} (x_i - \bar{x}) = 0$.

14. For the histogram of problem 5, guess the value of $\bar{x}$. Do the same for the histograms of problems 6 and 7.

15. Write down a coding formula that would express an individual's height in feet (x) in terms of his height in inches above 5 feet (u).

16. For the data of problem 5, calculate $\bar{x}$ by (a) definition, (b) the short method.

17. For the data of problem 6, calculate $\bar{x}$ by the short method.

18. Without classifying the data, calculate (a) the mean, (b) the standard deviation for the following set of weights of 11 children: 38, 50, 37, 44, 46, 53, 48, 38, 42, 46, 42.

19. Without classifying the data, calculate (a) the mean, (b) the standard deviation for the following set of grade-point averages of 20 students: 2.4, 1.2, 1.4, 2.4, 1.0, 1.8, 1.8, 1.4, 1.8, 3.2, 2.4, 2.2, 2.4, 1.8, 3.6, 1.8, 1.2, 2.4, 1.8, 3.4.

20. For the data of problem 5, calculate s by (a) definition, (b) the short method.

21. For the data of problem 6, calculate s by the short method.

22. For the histogram of problem 5, using the results in problems 16 and 20, calculate the approximate percentages of the data that lie within the intervals $\bar{x} \pm s$ and $\bar{x} \pm 2s$.

23. For the histogram of problem 6, using the results of problems 17 and 21, calculate the approximate percentages of the data that lie within the intervals $\bar{x} \pm s$ and $\bar{x} \pm 2s$.

24. Suppose you found that 5 per cent of the shots on a target were a radial distance of more than three standard deviations of such distances from the center. What might you conclude about the distribution of the shots?

25. If shoe sizes of college male (or female) students were assumed to possess a normal distribution, what would you guess the standard deviation of shoe size to be if, by your knowledge of shoe sizes, you estimated a two standard deviation interval about the mean?

26. What can be said about a distribution if $s = 0$?

27. If the scores on a set of examination papers are changed by (a) adding 10 points to all scores, (b) increasing all scores by 10 per cent, what effect will these changes have on the mean and on the standard deviation?

28. Cite some type of data for which you feel the standard deviation would tend to exaggerate the amount of variation present in the data.

29. Calculate the standard deviation for the discrete distribution consisting of the two points $x = -1$ and $x = 1$ with frequencies of 50 each and comment about the 68 per cent and 95 per cent interpretation of s here.

30. As a review exercise, use your results from problem 11 to work the problems that were solved in the review exercise of section 6.

31. As a review exercise, work the problems that were solved in the review exercise of section 6 for the following set of weekly wages of certain laborers. Choose a class interval of length 2 units and begin the first class interval $\frac{1}{2}$ unit below the smallest measurement.

49 47 51 48 50 46 53 46 45 50 49 50 50 47 56 51 46 47 54 53 48 50 51 50 60

51 46 48 52 52 46 61 52 49 50 45 57 54 51 60 50 56 52 44 49 45 51 50 40 46

54 47 50 55 55 47 48 53 50 49 45 50 50 51 47 54 43 53 55 50 53 52 52 51 47

51 48 45 44 50 52 49 51 51 47 53 49 46 61 49 52 48 39 46 52 51 57 49 45 50

▶32. Cite some type of data for which you feel the median would be a more appropriate measure of location than the mean.

▶33. For the data of problem 18, calculate the mode, median, range, and mean deviation.

▶34. For the data of problem 5, calculate the median, range, and mean deviation.

▶35. For the data of problem 5, calculate the interquartile range, the ninth decile, and the twelfth percentile.

CHAPTER 3

Probability

1. INTRODUCTION

As indicated in Chapter 1, the solutions to the statistical problems posed there are given in terms of probability statements. Although probability is applied to a variety of practical situations, an understanding of the subject is made much simpler if it is applied to nonpractical situations, such as those that arise in certain games of chance. For this reason, the definition and the rules of probability are presented in terms of idealized problems, but it is assumed that the same rules may later be applied to practical statistical problems.

Before discussing probability, it is necessary to discuss experiments that can be repeated or that can be conceived of as being repeatable. Tossing a coin, reading the daily temperature on a thermometer, or counting the number of bad eggs in a carton are examples of a simple repetitive experiment. An experiment in which several rabbits are fed different rations in an attempt to determine the relative growth properties of the rations may be performed only once with those same animals; nevertheless, the experiment may be thought of as the first in an unlimited number of similar experiments, and therefore it may be considered repetitive. Selecting a sample from a population is a repetitive experiment and is, of course, the type of experiment that is of particular interest in solving statistical problems.

Consider a simple repetitive experiment such as tossing a coin twice or, what is equivalent, tossing two distinct coins simultaneously. In this experiment there are four possible outcomes of interest; they are denoted by

HH, HT, TH, TT.

The symbol HT, for example, means that a head is obtained on the first toss and a tail on the second toss. If the experiment had consisted of tossing the coin three times, there would have been eight possible outcomes of the experiment, which would be denoted by

HHH, HHT, HTH, THH, HTT, THT, TTH, TTT.

The three letters in a group here express the outcomes of the three tosses in the given order. An experiment such as reading the temperature on a thermometer, however, has an infinite number of possible outcomes, since the temperature is a continuous type of variable. In this discussion of probability only experiments with a finite number of possible outcomes are considered. Other types are discussed in Chapter 4.

For any experiment to which probability is to be applied, it is first necessary to decide what possible outcomes of the experiment are of interest, and to make a list of all such outcomes. This list must be such that when the experiment is performed, exactly one of the outcomes will occur. In the experiment of tossing a coin three times, interest was centered on whether the coin showed a head or a tail on each of the tosses; therefore all the possible outcomes are those that were listed previously. In selecting a digit from the table of random digits in Table II in the appendix one might be interested in knowing which digit was obtained, in which case there are ten possible outcomes corresponding to the digits 0, 1, . . . , 9. However, one might be interested only in knowing whether the digit was less than 3 in magnitude. Then there would be only two possible outcomes of the experiment, namely obtaining a digit that is less than 3 or obtaining a digit that is at least as large as 3. A game of chance experiment that will be used frequently for illustrative purposes is the experiment of drawing one ball from a box of balls of different colors. Thus, suppose a box contains three red, two black, and one green ball. Then interest will be centered only on what color a drawn ball is and not on which particular ball is obtained. Here there are three possible outcomes of the experiment corresponding to the three colors. Another interesting game of chance experiment is the experiment of rolling two dice. If it is assumed that one can distinguish between the two dice and interest centers on what number of points shows on each of the dice, then there are 36 possible outcomes, because each die has six possible outcomes and these outcomes can be paired in all possible ways. Table 1 gives a list of the possible outcomes.

TABLE 1

11	21	31	41	51	61
12	22	32	42	52	62
13	23	33	43	53	63
14	24	34	44	54	64
15	25	35	45	55	65
16	26	36	46	56	66

The first number of each pair denotes the number that came up on one of the dice, and the second number denotes the number that came up on the other. If the two dice are not distinguishable, it is necessary to roll them in order rather than simultaneously.

It is convenient, in developing the theory of probability, to visualize things geometrically and to represent each of the possible outcomes of an

HHH	HHT	HTH	THH	HTT	THT	TTH	TTT
•	•	•	•	•	•	•	•
e_1	e_2	e_3	e_4	e_5	e_6	e_7	e_8

Fig. 1   A sample space for a coin-tossing experiment.

experiment by means of a point. Thus, in the experiment of tossing a coin three times one would use eight points. It makes no difference what points are chosen as long as one knows which point corresponds to which possible outcome. Each point is labeled with a letter or symbol to indicate the outcome that it represents. Since possible outcomes are often called simple events, the letter e with a subscript corresponding to the number of the outcome in the list of possible outcomes is customarily used in labeling a point. In the coin tossing experiment, for example, one could label the eight points by means of $e_1, e_2, \ldots, e_8$. Thus e_1 would represent the event of obtaining HHH and e_2 that of obtaining HHT. Since a label such as HHT is self explanatory there seems little point to introducing additional labels here. However, it is easier to write e_2 than HHT; consequently the e symbol does possess an advantage. The set of points representing the possible outcomes of an experiment is called the *sample space* for the experiment. A sample space for the coin tossing experiment is shown in Fig. 1, in which the numbering of the points is shown by the symbols directly above the points.

A natural sample space to choose for the experiment of selecting a digit from the table of random digits consists of the 10 points on the x-axis corresponding to the integers $0, 1, \ldots, 9$. This is shown in Fig. 2. The letter e was not used in Fig. 2 because the labeling of a point by means of its x-coordinate is about as simple as one could desire.

Fig. 2   A sample space for a random-digit experiment.

For the experiment of choosing a colored ball from the box of balls, the sample space consists of three points, which have been labeled in the order of the colors given and which are shown in Fig. 3.

$$e_1 \text{ (red)} \qquad e_2 \text{ (black)} \qquad e_3 \text{ (green)}$$

Fig. 3   Sample space for colored-ball experiment.

A convenient sample space for the experiment of rolling two dice is a double array of 36 points, with six rows and six columns, attached to the elements of Table 1. This sample space will not be illustrated because Table 1 and your imagination should suffice. The symbols of Table 1 are highly descriptive of the experimental outcomes and are also very simple; there is no point in introducing a new set of symbols here.

Thus far there has been no apparent reason for introducing a geometrical representation of the outcomes of an experiment; however, later in the development of the theory the advantage of this approach will become apparent.

The next step in the construction of a mathematical model for an experiment is to attach numbers to the points in the sample space that will represent the relative frequencies with which those outcomes are expected to occur. If the experiment of tossing a coin three times were repeated a large number of times and a cumulative record kept of the proportion of those experiments that produced, say, three heads, one would expect that proportion to approach $\frac{1}{8}$ because each of the eight possible outcomes would be expected to occur about equally often. Actual experiments of this kind usually show that such expectations are justified, provided the coin is well balanced and is tossed vigorously. In view of such considerations, the number $\frac{1}{8}$ would be attached to each of the points in the sample space shown in Fig. 1. The number assigned to the point labeled e_i in a sample space is called the probability of the event e_i and is denoted by the symbol $P\{e_i\}$. Thus, in the coin-tossing experiment each of the events $e_1, e_2, \ldots, e_8$ possesses the probability $\frac{1}{8}$.

If the experiment of selecting a digit from the table of random digits is carried out a large number of times, it will be found that each of the ten digits $0, 1, \ldots, 9$ will be obtained with approximately the same relative frequency, and therefore that the experimental relative frequency for each of the digits will be close to $\frac{1}{10}$. On the basis of such experience each of the sample points in the sample space shown in Fig. 2 would be assigned the probability $\frac{1}{10}$.

The situation for the experiment corresponding to the sample space shown in Fig. 3 is somewhat different from the preceding ones. It is no longer true that each of the possible outcomes would be expected to occur with the same relative frequency. If the balls are well mixed in the box before each drawing and the drawn ball is always returned to the box so that the composition of the box is unchanged, one would expect to obtain a black ball twice as often as a green ball and a red ball three times as often as a green ball. This implies that in repeated sampling experiments one would expect the relative frequencies for the three colors red, black, and green to be close to $\frac{3}{6}$, $\frac{2}{6}$, and $\frac{1}{6}$, respectively. Thus, the three points e_1, e_2, and e_3 in Fig. 3 would be assigned the probabilities $\frac{3}{6}$, $\frac{2}{6}$, and $\frac{1}{6}$, respectively.

The experiment of rolling two dice is treated in much the same manner as the coin-tossing experiment. Symmetry and experience suggest that each point in the sample space corresponding to Table 1 should be assigned the probability $\frac{1}{36}$.

The preceding experiments illustrate how one proceeds in general to assign probabilities to the points of a sample space. If the experiment is one for which symmetry and similar considerations suggest what relative frequencies are to be expected for the various outcomes, then those expected relative frequencies are chosen as the probabilities for the corresponding points. This was the basis for the assignment of probabilities in the coin-tossing experiment, the colored-ball experiment, and the die-rolling experiment. If no such symmetry considerations are available but experience with the given experiment is available, then the relative frequencies obtained from such experience can be used for the probabilities to be assigned. The assignment of probabilities for the sample space of Fig. 2 was based partly on experience and partly on faith in the individuals who constructed Table II. There are various methods for constructing tables of random digits, some of them being very complicated. In all such tables it is to be expected that each digit will occur about the same number of times and that there will be no discernible patterns in sequences of digits. For example, the pair 12 should not occur more frequently than any other pair, say the pair 74. However, since such sets of digits are often based on physical devices that are assumed to produce digits possessing such properties, it is unreasonable to expect a set of such digits to behave in this ideal manner. A good approximation is all that can be hoped for.

Since the probabilities assigned to the points of a sample space are either the expected relative frequencies based on symmetry considerations or the long run experimental relative frequencies, probabilities must be numbers between 0 and 1 and their sum must be 1, because the sum of a complete set of relative frequencies is always 1. In the experiments related to coin tossing, colored balls, and dice rolling, the probabilities obviously sum to 1 because they were constructed that way. If the probabilities for the random-digit experiment had been based entirely on the relative frequencies obtained in a long run of experiments, then those probabilities would obviously sum to 1 because the sum of all the relative frequencies must be 1.

Now, in any given experimental situation, whether academic or real, it is the privilege of the statistician to assign any probabilities he desires to the possible outcomes of the experiment, provided they are numbers between 0 and 1 and provided they sum to 1. Of course if he is sensible he will try to assign numbers that will represent what he believes or knows to be the long-run relative frequencies for those outcomes, otherwise his mathematical model is not likely to represent the actual experiment satisfactorily and therefore his conclusions derived on the basis of the model are likely to be erroneous.

It is usually quite easy to assign satisfactory probabilities to the possible outcomes of games of chance; however, this is not the case for most real-life experiments. For example, if the experiment consists of selecting an individual at random from the population of a city and interest is centered on whether the individual will die during the ensuing year, then there is no satisfactory way of assigning a probability here other than by using the experience of insurance companies. If one were interested in determining proper insurance premiums, it would be necessary to assign probabilities of death at the various ages. These are usually chosen to be the values obtained from extensive experience of insurance companies over the years. Since mortality rates have been decreasing over the years for most age groups, any mortality table based on past experience is likely to be out of date for predicting the future. Thus the probabilities assigned on the basis of past experience may not be very close to the actual relative frequencies existing today, and therefore the premiums calculated from them will not be very accurate. Fortunately for the insurance companies, premiums calculated on the basis of past experience are larger than they would be if they had been based on more up-to-date experience.

In view of the foregoing discussion, it follows that the probability of a simple event is to be interpreted as a theoretical, or idealized, relative frequency of the event. This does not imply that the observed relative frequency of the event will necessarily approach the probability of the event for an increasingly large number of experiments because one may have chosen an incorrect model; however, one hopes that it will. Thus, if one has a supposedly honest die, one would hope that the observed relative frequency of, say, a 4 showing would approach the probability $\frac{1}{6}$ as an increasingly large number of rolls is made; but one would not be too upset if it did not approach $\frac{1}{6}$ because of the imperfections in any manufactured article and because of the difficulty of simulating an ideal experiment. In this connection, it should be noted that the operators of gambling houses have done well financially by assuming that dice do behave as expected. They have certainly rolled dice enough to check on such assumptions. Of course, if experience shows that a die is not behaving as expected, they will replace it very quickly with a new die.

Constructing theoretical models to explain nature is the chief function of scientists. If the models are realistic, the conclusions derived from them are likely to be realistic. A probability model is such a model designed to enable one to draw conclusions about relative frequencies of experimental outcomes.

2. PROBABILITY OF AN EVENT

Now that a geometrical model has been constructed for an experiment, consisting of a set of points with labels $e_1, e_2, \ldots$ to represent all the possible outcomes and a corresponding associated set of probabilities $P\{e_1\}, P\{e_2\}, \ldots$, the time has come to discuss the probability of composite events. The possible outcomes $e_1, e_2, \ldots$ of a sample space are called *simple events*. A *composite event* is defined as a collection of simple events. For example, the event of obtaining exactly two heads in the coin-tossing experiment of Fig. 1 is a composite event that consists of the three simple events e_2, e_3, and e_4. Similarly, the event of obtaining a random digit smaller than 4 in the random-digit experiment of Fig. 2 is a composite event consisting of the four simple events $x = 0, 1, 2, 3$. Composite events are usually denoted by capital letters such as A, or B, or C.

Now since the probabilities assigned to the simple events of Fig. 1, namely $\frac{1}{8}$, represent expected relative frequencies for their occurrence, one would expect the composite event consisting of the simple events e_2, e_3, and e_4 to occur in about three-eighths of such experiments in the long run of such experiments. Similarly, for the experiment represented by Fig. 2, one would expect the composite event consisting of the simple events $x = 0, 1, 2, 3$ to occur in the long run in about four-tenths of such experiments. In view of such expectations, and because probability has been introduced as an idealization of relative frequency, the following definition of probability for a composite event should seem very reasonable.

(1)   **Definition.** *The probability that a composite event A will occur is the sum of the probabilities of the simple events of which it is composed.*

As an illustration, if A is the event of obtaining two heads in tossing a coin three times, it follows from this definition and the sample space in Fig. 1 that
$$P\{A\} = P\{e_2\} + P\{e_3\} + P\{e_4\} = \tfrac{3}{8}.$$
Similarly, if B is the event of getting a digit smaller than 4 in selecting a random digit, it follows from this definition and Fig. 2 that
$$P\{B\} = P\{0\} + P\{1\} + P\{2\} + P\{3\} = \tfrac{4}{10}.$$
As another illustration, let C be the event of getting a red or a green ball in the experiment for which Fig. 3 is the sample space. Since C is composed of the events e_1 and e_3, it follows that
$$P\{C\} = P\{e_1\} + P\{e_3\} = \tfrac{4}{6}.$$

As a final illustration for which the composite events are not quite so obvious, consider once more the experiment of rolling two dice. Table 1, with points associated with each outcome and with the probability $\frac{1}{36}$ attached to each point, can serve as the sample space here. First, let E be the event of getting a total of 7 points on the two dice. The simple events that yield a total of 7 points are the following: 16, 25, 34, 43, 52, 61.

The sum of the corresponding six probabilities of $\frac{1}{36}$ each therefore gives $P\{E\} = \frac{6}{36} = \frac{1}{6}$. Next, let F be the event of getting a total number of points that is an even number. Simple events such as 11, 13, 22, etc. satisfy the requirement of yielding an even numbered total. The sum of two even digits, or the sum of two odd digits, will yield an even number. From Table 1 it will be observed that there are 18 points of this type; hence it follows that $P\{F\} = \frac{18}{36} = \frac{1}{2}$. Finally, let G be the event that both dice will show at least 4 points. Here the simple events such as 44, 45, 56, etc. will satisfy. Table 1 shows that there are 9 such; therefore $P\{G\} = \frac{9}{36} = \frac{1}{4}$.

In many games-of-chance experiments the various possible outcomes are expected to occur with the same relative frequency; therefore all the points of the sample space for such experiments are assigned the same probability, namely $1/n$, where n denotes the total number of points in the sample space. This was true, for example, in the experiments of coin tossing, random digit selection, and dice rolling. It was not true, however, for the colored ball experiment. When the experiment is of this simple type, that is when all the simple-event probabilities are equal, the calculation of the probability of a composite event is very easy. It consists of merely adding the probability $1/n$ as many times as there are simple events comprising the composite event. Thus, if the composite event A consists of a total of $n(A)$ simple events, the value of $P\{A\}$ can be expressed by the simple formula

(2) $$P\{A\} = \frac{n(A)}{n}.$$

In the experiment of rolling two dice, for example, the probability of obtaining a total of 7 points is obtained by counting the number of points in the sample space given in Table 1 that produce a 7 total, of which there are 6, and dividing this number by the total number of points, namely 36.

Although it is not often possible in real-life problems to use formula (2), it is easier to work with than is the general definition (1) involving the addition of probabilities; therefore, it alone is used in the next few sections to derive basic formulas. The formulas obtained in this manner can be shown to hold equally well for the general definition and therefore are applicable to all types of problems. Since only the formulas are needed in applied problems, there will be no appreciable loss in the understanding of how to solve practical problems by following this procedure.

3. ADDITION RULE

Applications of probability are often concerned with a number of related events rather than with just one event. For simplicity, consider two such events, A_1 and A_2, associated with an experiment. One may be interested in knowing whether both A_1 and A_2 will occur when the experiment is performed. This joint event is denoted by the symbol $(A_1$ and $A_2)$ and its probability by $P\{A_1$ and $A_2\}$. On the other hand, one may be interested in knowing whether at least one of the events A_1 and A_2 will occur when the experiment is performed. This event is denoted

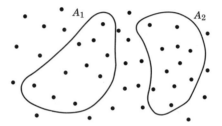

Fig. 4   Sample space with two mutually exclusive events.

by the symbol $(A_1$ or $A_2)$ and its probability by $P\{A_1$ or $A_2\}$. At least one of the two events will occur if A_1 occurs but A_2 does not, if A_2 occurs but A_1 does not, or if both A_1 and A_2 occur. Thus, the word "or" here means "or" in the sense of either one, the other, or both. The purpose of this section is to obtain a formula for $P\{A_1$ or $A_2\}$.

If two events A_1 and A_2 possess the property that the occurrence of one prevents the occurrence of the other, they are called *mutually exclusive* events. For example, let A_1 be the event of getting a total of 7 in rolling two dice, and A_2 the event of getting a total of 11: then A_1 and A_2 are mutually exclusive events. For mutually exclusive events there are no outcomes that correspond to the occurrence of both A_1 and A_2; therefore the two events do not possess any points in common in the sample space. This is shown schematically in Fig. 4. In this diagram the points lying inside the two closed curves labeled A_1 and A_2 represent the simple events that yield the composite events A_1 and A_2, respectively. If $n(A_1)$ denotes the number of points lying inside the curve labeled A_1 and $n(A_2)$ the number lying inside the curve labeled A_2, then the total number of points associated with the occurrence of either A_1 or A_2 is the sum of those two numbers; consequently, if n denotes the total number of sample points, it follows from formula (2) that

$$P\{A_1 \text{ or } A_2\} = \frac{n(A_1) + n(A_2)}{n}$$

$$= \frac{n(A_1)}{n} + \frac{n(A_2)}{n}.$$

Since the last two fractions are precisely those defining $P\{A_1\}$ and $P\{A_2\}$, this result yields the desired addition formula, which may be expressed as follows:

(3)   **Addition Rule.** *When A_1 and A_2 are mutually exclusive events,*

$$P\{A_1 \text{ or } A_2\} = P\{A_1\} + P\{A_2\}.$$

For more than two mutually exclusive events, it is merely necessary to apply this formula as many times as required. A slightly more complicated formula can be derived for events that are not mutually exclusive; however there will be no occasion to use such a formula in later sections and so it is omitted here.

In the preceding illustration of rolling two dice, in which A_1 and A_2 denoted the events of getting a total of 7 and 11 points, respectively, the probability of getting either a total of 7 or a total of 11 can be obtained by means of formula (3). From Table 1 it is clear that A_1 and A_2 contain no points in common and, from counting points, that $P\{A_1\} = \frac{6}{36}$ and $P\{A_2\} = \frac{2}{36}$; therefore

$$P\{A_1 \text{ or } A_2\} = \frac{6}{36} + \frac{2}{36} = \frac{8}{36}.$$

This result is, of course, the same as that obtained by counting the total number of points, namely 8, that yield the composite event (A_1 or A_2) and applying formula (2) directly.

As another illustration, what is the probability of getting a total of at least 10 points in rolling two dice? Let A_1, A_2, and A_3 be the events of getting a total of exactly 10 points, 11 points, and 12 points, respectively. From Table 1 it is clear that these events have no points in common and that their probabilities are given by $P\{A_1\} = \frac{3}{36}$, $P\{A_2\} = \frac{2}{36}$, and $P\{A_3\} = \frac{1}{36}$. Therefore, by formula (3), the probability that at least one of those mutually exclusive events will occur is given by

$$P\{A_1 \text{ or } A_2 \text{ or } A_3\} = \frac{3}{36} + \frac{2}{36} + \frac{1}{36} = \frac{1}{6}.$$

This result also could have been obtained directly from Table 1 by counting favorable and total outcomes. Although the formula does not seem to possess any advantage here over direct counting for problems related to Table 1, it is a very useful formula for problems in which probabilities of events are available but for which tables of possible outcomes are not.

4. MULTIPLICATION RULE

The purpose of this section is to obtain a formula for $P\{A_1$ and $A_2\}$ in terms of probabilities of single events. In order to do so, it is necessary

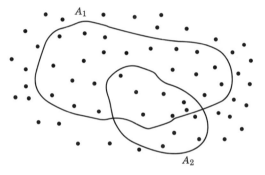

Fig. 5　A sample space for conditional probability.

to introduce the notion of conditional probability. Suppose one is interested in knowing whether A_2 will occur subject to the condition that A_1 is known to have occurred or else is certain to occur. The geometry of this problem is shown in Fig. 5. It is assumed here that A_1 and A_2 are not mutually exclusive events.

Since A_1 must occur, the only experimental outcomes that need be considered are those corresponding to the occurrence of A_1. The sample space for this problem is therefore reduced to the simple events that comprise A_1. They are represented in Fig. 5 by the points lying inside the curve labeled A_1. Among those points, the ones that also lie inside the curve labeled A_2 correspond to the occurrence of both A_1 and A_2. They are the points that lie in the overlapping parts of A_1 and A_2. Let $n(A_1)$ denote the number of points lying inside A_1 and let $n(A_1$ and $A_2)$ denote the number that lie inside both A_1 and A_2. Then, from formula (2), the probability that A_2 will occur if the sample space is restricted to be the set of points inside A_1 is given by the ratio $n(A_1$ and $A_2)/n(A_1)$. But this probability is what is meant by the probability that A_2 will occur subject to the restriction that A_1 must occur. If this latter probability is denoted by the new symbol $P\{A_2 \mid A_1\}$, then

(4) $$P\{A_2 \mid A_1\} = \frac{n(A_1 \text{ and } A_2)}{n(A_1)}.$$

As an illustration of the application of this formula, a calculation will be made of the probability that the sum of the points obtained in rolling

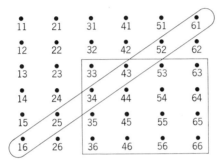

Fig. 6   Sample space for a conditional probability problem.

two dice is 7, if it is known that the dice showed at least 3 points each. Let A_1 denote the event that two dice will show at least 3 points each and let A_2 denote the event that two dice will show a total of 7 points. The sample space for this problem is shown in Fig. 6; it was obtained directly from Table 1.

The points that comprise the event A_1 are all the points except those in the first two rows and the first two columns of Fig. 6. They are shown inside the rectangle of Fig. 6. Here $n(A_1) = 16$. The points that comprise the event A_2 are the diagonal points shown in Fig. 6. The number of points that lie inside A_2 which also lie inside A_1 is seen to be $n(A_1$ and $A_2) = 2$. As a result, formula (4) gives the result

$$P\{A_2 \mid A_1\} = \frac{2}{16} = \frac{1}{8}.$$

What this means in an experimental sense is that in the repeated rolling of two dice one discards all those experimental outcomes in which either die showed a number of points less than 3. Then among the experimental outcomes that are retained one calculates the proportion of them that yielded a total of 7 points. This proportion in the long run of experiments should approach $\frac{1}{8}$. It is interesting to note that the chances of getting a total of 7 points is less when one knows that both dice show at least 3 points than under ordinary rolls.

Now consider formula (4) in general terms once more. From Fig. 5 and formula (2) it is clear that

$$P\{A_1\} = \frac{n(A_1)}{n}$$

and that

$$P\{A_1 \text{ and } A_2\} = \frac{n(A_1 \text{ and } A_2)}{n}.$$

Dividing the second of these two expressions by the first and canceling n will give

$$\frac{P\{A_1 \text{ and } A_2\}}{P\{A_1\}} = \frac{n(A_1 \text{ and } A_2)}{n(A_1)}.$$

This result in conjunction with (4) will yield the formula

(5) $$P\{A_2 \mid A_1\} = \frac{P\{A_1 \text{ and } A_2\}}{P\{A_1\}}.$$

This formula, when written in product form, yields the fundamental multiplication formula for probabilities, which may be expressed as follows:

(6)   *Multiplication Rule.* $P\{A_1 \text{ and } A_2\} = P\{A_1\}P\{A_2 \mid A_1\}.$

In words, this formula states that the probability that both of two events will occur is equal to the probability that the first event will occur, multiplied by the conditional probability that the second event will occur when it is known that the first event is certain to occur. Either one of the two events may be called the first event, since this is merely convenient language for discussing them, and there is no time order implied in the way they occur. Even though there is no time order implied for the two events A_1 and A_2 in the symbol $P\{A_2 \mid A_1\}$, it is customary to call this conditional probability "the probability that A_2 will occur when it is known that A_1 has occurred." Thus, if you are being dealt a five-card poker hand, someone might ask, "what is the probability that your hand will contain the ace of spades if it is known that you have received the ace of hearts?" This is merely convenient language for discussing probabilities of a poker hand that must contain the ace of hearts, and there is no implication that if the ace of spades is in the hand it was obtained after obtaining the ace of hearts. For many pairs of events, however, there is a definite time-order relationship. For example, if A_1 is the event that a high-school graduate will go to college and A_2 is the event that he will graduate from college, then A_1 must precede A_2 in time.

As an illustration of the multiplication rule, a calculation will be made of the probability of getting two red balls in drawing two balls from a box containing three red, two black, and one green ball. It will be assumed here that the first ball drawn is not returned to the box before the second drawing is made. This experiment differs from the one that was considered in Fig. 3, since there repetitions of the experiment involved returning the drawn ball each time.

Let A_1 denote the event of getting a red ball on the first drawing and A_2 that of getting a red ball on the second drawing. In order to be able to continue using formula (2) rather than the more general definition (1), it is necessary to give each ball a number and use six points in the sample space. The first three will represent red balls, the next two the black balls, and the last one the green ball. Then, by formula (2),

$$P\{A_1\} = \frac{3}{6}.$$

For the purpose of calculating $P\{A_2 \mid A_1\}$ it suffices to consider only those experimental outcomes for which A_1 has occurred. Since the first ball drawn is not returned to the box, this means considering only those experiments in which the first ball drawn was one of the three red balls. Thus, the second part of the experiment can be treated as a new single experiment in which one ball is to be drawn from a box containing two red, two black, and one green ball. As a result, $P\{A_2 \mid A_1\}$ represents the probability of getting a red ball in drawing one ball from this new box of balls. Here there are five points in the sample space, the first two representing red balls, the next two black balls, and the last one a green ball. Hence, by formula (2),

$$P\{A_2 \mid A_1\} = \frac{2}{5}.$$

Application of formula (6) to these two results then gives

$$P\{A_1 \text{ and } A_2\} = \frac{3}{6} \cdot \frac{2}{5} = \frac{1}{5}.$$

The advantage of using formula (6) on this problem will become apparent if one tries to solve this problem by applying formula (2) directly to the sample space that corresponds to this two-stage experiment. That sample space will consist of thirty points and will resemble the sample space shown in Fig. 6, except that the main diagonal points will be missing because they correspond to getting the same numbered colored ball on both drawings. The advantage of formula (6) is most pronounced in two-stage and multiple-stage experiments, which usually possess complicated sample spaces with a large number of points, because it reduces the calculation of probabilities to calculations for one-stage experiments only. The sample spaces for one-stage experiments are usually quite simple and much easier to visualize than those for multiple-stage experiments. Hereafter, in calculating probabilities, the techniques based on formula (6) and single-stage experiments will be used almost exclusively in order to avoid the time-consuming method based on applying formula (2) directly to the sample space of the entire experiment. It should be understood, however, that it is always possible to calculate any type of probability that may arise by working exclusively with the original sample space. A student should occasionally work a problem in this manner to test his understanding of basic concepts. It would be well for him, for example, to solve the preceding illustrative problem by constructing the sample space for that two-stage experiment.

As another illustration of the multiplication rule, calculate the probability of getting 2 prizes in taking 2 punches on a punch board which contains 5 prizes and 20 blanks. If A_1 denotes the event of getting a prize on the first punch and A_2 the event of getting a prize on the second punch, then formula (6) gives

$$P\{A_1 \text{ and } A_2\} = \frac{5}{25} \cdot \frac{4}{24} = \frac{1}{30}.$$

The value of $P\{A_2 \mid A_1\} = \frac{4}{24}$ arises from the fact that since the first punch yielded a prize there are only 4 prizes left and only 24 punches left.

As a final illustration, consider the problem of calculating the probability of getting three red balls from the box of colored balls used in the first illustration if three balls are drawn from the box without any replacements being made. Here there are three events A_1, A_2, and A_3, corresponding to a red ball on each of the three drawings. Formula (6) can be generalized to treat three events; however, without complicating the problem further by additional notation it will be solved by taking each single stage of the experiment in order and multiplying the appropriate probabilities together. The calculations would proceed as follows:

$$P\{A_1 \text{ and } A_2 \text{ and } A_3\} = \frac{3}{6} \cdot \frac{2}{5} \cdot \frac{1}{4} = \frac{1}{20}.$$

If the events A_1 and A_2 are such that the probability that A_2 will occur does not depend upon whether or not A_1 occurs, then A_2 is said to be independent of A_1, and one can write

$$P\{A_2 \mid A_1\} = P\{A_2\}.$$

For this case, the multiplication rule reduces to

$$P\{A_1 \text{ and } A_2\} = P\{A_1\}P\{A_2\}.$$

Since the event (A_1 and A_2) is the same as the event (A_2 and A_1), A_1 and A_2 may be interchanged in (6) to give

$$P\{A_1 \text{ and } A_2\} = P\{A_2\}P\{A_1 \mid A_2\}.$$

Comparing the right sides of these two formulas shows that $P\{A_1 \mid A_2\} = P\{A_1\}$. This demonstrates that A_1 is independent of A_2 when A_2 is independent of A_1. Because of this mutual independence, it is proper to say that A_1 and A_2 are independent, without specifying which is independent of the other. As a result,

When A_1 and A_2 are independent,

(7) $$P\{A_1 \text{ and } A_2\} = P\{A_1\}P\{A_2\}.$$

In view of this result, one can state that two events are independent if, and only if, the probability of their joint occurrence is equal to the product of their individual probabilities. Although it is easy to state the condition that must be satisfied if two events are to be independent, it is not always so easy in real life to decide whether two events are independent. As a rather far-fetched example, suppose the two events are A_1: the stock market will rise next week, and A_2: a stockholder will catch a cold next week. It would seem obvious that the probability that one of these events will occur would be the same whether or not the other event occurred, hence that these are independent events. However, if it should happen that stocks rose considerably in value, the chances are that many stockholders might go out to celebrate their good fortune and thereby increase their chances of catching a cold during that week, in which case these events would not be independent in a probability sense.

In games of chance, such as roulette, it is always assumed that consecutive plays are independent events. If one were not willing to accept this assumption, then one would be forced to assume that the roulette wheel possessed a memory or that the operator of the wheel was secretly manipulating it.

As illustrations of the application of the preceding rules of probability, consider a few simple card problems.

Two cards are drawn from an ordinary deck of 52 cards, the first card drawn being replaced before the second card is drawn.

1. What is the probability that both cards will be spades? Let A_1 denote the event of getting a spade on the first draw, and A_2 the event of getting a spade on the second draw. Since the first card drawn is replaced, the probability of getting a spade on the second draw should not depend upon whether or not a spade was obtained on the first draw; hence A_2 may be assumed to be independent of A_1. Formula (7) will then give

$$P\{A_1 \text{ and } A_2\} = \frac{13}{52} \cdot \frac{13}{52} = \frac{1}{16}.$$

2. What is the probability that the cards will be either two spades or two hearts? Let B_1 be the event of getting two spades, and B_2 the event of getting two hearts. Then, from the preceding result, it follows that

$$P\{B_1\} = P\{B_2\} = \frac{1}{16}.$$

Since the events B_1 and B_2 are mutually exclusive and the problem is to calculate the probability that either B_1 or B_2 will occur, formula (3) applies; hence

$$P\{B_1 \text{ or } B_2\} = \frac{1}{16} + \frac{1}{16} = \frac{1}{8}.$$

As before, let two cards be drawn from a deck, but this time the first card drawn will not be replaced.

3. What is the probability that both cards will be spades? Now A_2 is not independent of A_1 because if a spade is obtained on the first draw

the chances of getting a spade on the second draw will be smaller than if a nonspade had been obtained on the first draw. For this problem formula (6) must be used. Here

$$P\{A_1 \text{ and } A_2\} = \frac{13}{52} \cdot \frac{12}{51} = \frac{1}{17}.$$

The second factor is $\frac{12}{51}$ because there are only 51 cards after the first drawing, all of which are assumed to possess the same chance of being drawn, and there are only 12 spades left.

Although the preceding rules of probability were derived on the assumption that all the possible outcomes of the experiment in question were expected to occur with the same relative frequency, the rules hold for more general experiments. They can even be applied to events related to experiments involving an infinite number of possible outcomes. These more general experiments are considered in Chapter 4.

▶5. BAYES FORMULA

There is a certain class of important problems based on the application of formula (5) that lead to rather involved computations; therefore it is convenient to have a formula for solving such problems in a systematic manner. These problems may be illustrated by the following academic one. Suppose a box contains 2 red balls and 1 white ball and a second box contains 2 red balls and 2 white balls. One of the boxes is selected by chance and a ball drawn from it. If the drawn ball is red, what is the probability that it came from the first box? Let A_1 denote the event of choosing the first box and let A_2 denote the event of drawing a red ball. Then the problem is to calculate the conditional probability $P\{A_1 \mid A_2\}$. This will be done by the use of formula (5) with A_1 and A_2 interchanged in that formula. Since the phrase by chance is understood to mean that each box has the same probability of being chosen, it follows that the probability of drawing the first box is $\frac{1}{2}$, and that of drawing the second box is the same. The calculation of the numerator term in (5) can be accomplished by using formula (6) in the order of events listed there. Thus

$$P\{A_2 \text{ and } A_1\} = P\{A_1 \text{ and } A_2\} = \frac{1}{2} \cdot \frac{2}{3} = \frac{1}{3}.$$

The denominator, $P\{A_2\}$, can be calculated by considering the two mutually exclusive ways in which A_2 can occur, namely, getting the first box and then a red ball or getting the second box and then a red ball. By formula (3), $P\{A_2\}$ will be given by the sum of the probabilities of those two mutually exclusive possibilities; hence

$$P\{A_2\} = \frac{1}{2} \cdot \frac{2}{3} + \frac{1}{2} \cdot \frac{2}{4} = \frac{7}{12}.$$

Application of the modified version of formula (5) then yields the desired result, namely,

$$P\{A_1 \mid A_2\} = \frac{1/3}{7/12} = \frac{4}{7}.$$

This problem could have been worked very easily by looking at the sample space for the experiment; however, the objective here is to work with formula (5) and attempt to obtain a formula for treating more complicated problems of the type of the present one.

The foregoing problem is a special case of problems of the following type. One is given a two-stage experiment. The first stage can be described by stating that exactly one of, say, k possible outcomes must occur when the complete experiment is performed. Those possible outcomes will be denoted by $e_1, e_2, \ldots, e_k$. In the second stage there are, say, m possible outcomes, exactly one of which must occur. These will be denoted by $o_1, o_2, \ldots, o_m$. The values of the probabilities for each of the possible outcomes $e_1, e_2, \ldots, e_k$ are given. As before, they will be denoted by $P\{e_1\}, P\{e_2\}, \ldots, P\{e_k\}$. The values of all the conditional probabilities of the type $P\{o_j \mid e_i\}$, which represents the probability that the second stage event o_j will occur when it is known that the first-stage event e_i occurred, are also given. The problem is to calculate the probability that the first-stage event e_i occurred when it is known that the second-stage event o_j occurred. This conditional probability would be written $P\{e_i \mid o_j\}$. For simplicity of notation, the calculations will be carried out for $P\{e_1 \mid o_1\}$; the calculations for any other pair would be the same.

In terms of the present notation, formula (5) assumes the form

(8) $$P\{e_1 \mid o_1\} = \frac{P\{e_1 \text{ and } o_1\}}{P\{o_1\}}.$$

Formula (6) gives

(9) $$P\{e_1 \text{ and } o_1\} = P\{e_1\}P\{o_1 \mid e_1\}.$$

From the information given in this problem it will be observed that the two probabilities on the right side of (9) are known; therefore the numerator in (8) can be obtained from (9). The value of $P\{o_1\}$ in (8) can be computed by considering all the mutually exclusive ways in which o_1 can occur in conjunction with the first stage of the experiment. The second-stage event o_1 will occur if the first-stage event e_1 occurs and then o_1 occurs, or if the first-stage event e_2 occurs and then o_1 occurs, ..., or if the first-stage event e_k occurs and then o_1 occurs. If e_1 is replaced by e with the appropriate subscript in (9), that formula can be used to calculate the probability for each of these mutually exclusive possibilities. Application of formula (3) then yields the formula

$$P\{o_1\} = P\{e_1\}P\{o_1 \mid e_1\} + P\{e_2\}P\{o_1 \mid e_2\} + \cdots + P\{e_k\}P\{o_1 \mid e_k\}.$$

This result together with (9) when applied to (8) will give the desired formula which is known as Bayes formula. If a summation symbol is used, it becomes

(10)   ***Bayes Formula.*** $$P\{e_1 \mid o_1\} = \frac{P\{e_1\}P\{o_1 \mid e_1\}}{\displaystyle\sum_{i=1}^{k} P\{e_i\}P\{o_1 \mid e_i\}}.$$

Returning to the problem that was solved earlier without this formula, one will observe that there were two events e_1 and e_2 in the first stage corresponding to choosing the first or the second box and that $P\{e_1\} = P\{e_2\} = \frac{1}{2}$. The second stage also consisted of two events o_1 and o_2 corresponding to obtaining a red or a white ball. The conditional probabilities of obtaining a red ball based on what transpired at the first stage were given by $P\{o_1 \mid e_1\} = \frac{2}{3}$ and $P\{o_1 \mid e_2\} = \frac{2}{4}$. It will be observed that the substitution of these values in (10) yields the result that was obtained before.

Consider now a more practical application of this formula. Suppose a test for detecting a certain rare disease has been perfected that is capable of discovering the disease in 97 per cent of all afflicted individuals. Suppose further that when it is tried on healthy individuals, 5 per cent of them are incorrectly diagnosed as having the disease. Finally, suppose that when it is tried on individuals who have certain other milder diseases, 10 per cent of them are incorrectly diagnosed. It is known that the percentages of individuals of the three types being considered here in the population at large are 1 per cent, 96 per cent, and 3 per cent, respectively. The problem is to calculate the probability that an individual, selected at random from the population at large and tested for the rare disease, actually has the disease if the test indicates he is so afflicted.

Here there are three events e_1, e_2, and e_3 in the first stage corresponding to the three types of individuals in the population. Their corresponding probabilities are $P\{e_1\} = .01$, $P\{e_2\} = .96$, and $P\{e_3\} = .03$. There are two events o_1 and o_2 in the second stage corresponding to whether the test claims that the individual has the disease or not. The conditional probabilities are given by $P\{o_1 \mid e_1\} = .97$, $P\{o_1 \mid e_2\} = .05$, and $P\{o_1 \mid e_3\} = .10$. In terms of the present notation, the problem is to calculate $P\{e_1 \mid o_1\}$. A direct application of formula (10) based on the preceding probabilities will supply the answer, namely,

$$P\{e_1 \mid o_1\} = \frac{(.01)(.97)}{(.01)(.97) + (.96)(.05) + (.03)(.10)} = .16.$$

This result may seem rather surprising because it shows that only 16 per cent of the individuals whom the test would indicate have the disease actually do have it when the test is applied to the population at large. The 84 per cent who were falsely diagnosed might resent the temporary mental anguish caused by their belief that they had the disease before further tests revealed the falsity of the diagnosis. They might also resent the necessity of having been required to undergo further tests when it turned out that those tests were really unnecessary. A calculation such as the preceding one might therefore cause authorities to ponder a bit before advocating mass testing.

▶6. COUNTING FORMULAS

It is convenient in solving some of the more difficult probability problems of games of chance to have some formulas to assist in counting the number of points in a sample space that make up an event A. This section derives two such formulas.

Consider the set of letters a, b, c, and d. Suppose one wishes to write down all the two-letter words that can possibly be formed from them, where a word merely indicates a pair of letters without regard to any meaning. It is assumed that a letter can occur only once in a given word. Thus, the letters are treated as letters printed on blocks, and one chooses two blocks at a time. It is clear that the problem can be treated as a two-stage experiment, and that the number of possible outcomes is given by a square array of points with four rows and four columns but with the main diagonal terms missing because the same block cannot be obtained twice. Thus, there are twelve such words that can be formed. Another way of looking at the problem that is considerably easier is to consider the various ways of forming a word. First one chooses the first letter, for which there are four choices. Then one chooses the second letter, for which there are only three choices because one letter has already been chosen. Since each choice of the first letter can be paired with each choice of the second letter to give distinct two-letter words, the number of words is given by the product of these two choice possibilities; hence the number of possible words is $4 \cdot 3 = 12$. They are the following: ab, ba, ac, ca, ad, da, bc, cb, bd, db, cd, dc.

This problem and technique can be generalized as follows. Suppose one is given n distinct objects, say n distinct letters a, b, c, ... , and one wishes to choose r of those objects and arrange them in a line. How many such arrangements are possible? The answer will be represented by the symbol $_nP_r$. Just as for the particular problem that was just solved, the answer is obtained by multiplying together the numbers that give the choices available for filling positions in the arrangement. Thus, there are n choices of objects for the first position, then $n - 1$ choices available for the second position, and continuing in this manner, there are $n - r + 1$ choices available for the rth position. The product of these numbers gives the formula

(11) $$_nP_r = n(n - 1)(n - 2) \cdots (n - r + 1).$$

A particular arrangement along a line of a set of objects is called a *permutation* of those objects. The symbol $_nP_r$ is usually called the number of permutations of n objects taken r at a time.

Next, consider the problem of counting the number of ways of choosing r objects from a set of n distinct objects if one is not interested in arranging them in a line, but is only concerned with what particular objects are chosen. For example, in choosing a poker hand of five cards from a deck of 52 cards, one is interested only in the composition of the hand and not in the order in which the cards are obtained. First consider the problem as it applies to the earlier problem of choosing two letters from the set of letters a, b, c, and d. If one analyzes how two-letter words are formed, he will realize that one first chooses two of the four letters and then arranges those two letters to form a word. Now it is clear that for each choice of two letters, say b and c, there are only two ways of arranging them to make distinct two-letter words, namely bc and cb. Thus, if there is no interest in the order in which the two letters are placed, there will be only half as many selections as arrangements; consequently there must be only six ways of choosing two letters from four letters when the arrangement of those letters is ignored. A selection of this type is called a *combination*, as contrasted to a permutation which involves arrangement also. The combinations in this problem are the following: ab, ac, ad, bc, bd, cd.

This problem can be generalized to the situation in which r objects are to be selected from a set of n distinct objects. As before, if one considers how permutations are formed, he will realize that one first chooses r of the objects and then arranges them to form a permutation. Now it is clear that all possible permutations are obtained by considering all possible selections of r different letters and then arranging each of those r selections in all possible ways. The symbol $\binom{n}{r}$ will be used to denote the total number of combinations possible, that is, selections of r objects from n objects. Each one of these selections can have its r letters arranged in a line in $_rP_r$ different ways. But from (11), $_rP_r = r(r-1)(r-2)\cdots 1$. The total number of permutations that can be formed is therefore equal to the number of combinations, $\binom{n}{r}$, multiplied by the number of permutations possible for each such combination, namely $r(r-1)(r-2)\cdots 1$. Thus it follows that

$$_nP_r = r(r-1)(r-2)\cdots 1 \cdot \binom{n}{r}.$$

Solving for $\binom{n}{r}$ and using formula (11) then gives the desired formula, namely,

$$(12) \qquad \binom{n}{r} = \frac{n(n-1)\cdots(n-r+1)}{r(r-1)\cdots 1}.$$

The symbol $\binom{n}{r}$ is usually called the number of combinations of n things taken r at a time.

Another convenient symbol to use in connection with formula (12) is the *factorial* symbol, which consists of an exclamation mark after an integer, indicating that the number concerned should be multiplied by all the positive integers smaller than it. Thus $4! = 4 \cdot 3 \cdot 2 \cdot 1$ and $r! = r(r-1)(r-2) \cdots 1$. Formula (12) can therefore be written in the form

$$\binom{n}{r} = \frac{n(n-1) \cdots (n-r+1)}{r!}.$$

The numerator of this expression can also be expressed in terms of factorial notation by observing that

$$\frac{n!}{(n-r)!} = \frac{n(n-1) \cdots (n-r+1)(n-r)(n-r-1) \cdots 1}{(n-r)(n-r-1) \cdots 1}$$

$$= n(n-1) \cdots (n-r+1).$$

By using factorial symbols in this manner, formula (12) can be written in the compact form

(13) $$\binom{n}{r} = \frac{n!}{r!\,(n-r)!}.$$

The usefulness of formula (12), or (13), for counting purposes will be illustrated in the calculation of the probability of getting five spades in a hand of five cards drawn from a deck of 52 playing cards. Here the total number of possible outcomes corresponds to the total number of five-card hands that can be formed from a deck of 52 distinct cards. Since arrangement is of no interest here, this is a combination counting problem. The total number of possible hands is, according to formula (12), given by

$$\binom{52}{5} = \frac{52 \cdot 51 \cdot 50 \cdot 49 \cdot 48}{5 \cdot 4 \cdot 3 \cdot 2 \cdot 1}.$$

The number of outcomes that correspond to the occurrence of the desired event is equal to the number of ways of selecting five spades from thirteen spades. This is given by

$$\binom{13}{5} = \frac{13 \cdot 12 \cdot 11 \cdot 10 \cdot 9}{5 \cdot 4 \cdot 3 \cdot 2 \cdot 1}.$$

The desired probability is given by the ratio of these two numbers; hence it is equal to

$$\frac{13 \cdot 12 \cdot 11 \cdot 10 \cdot 9}{52 \cdot 51 \cdot 50 \cdot 49 \cdot 48} = \frac{33}{66640} = .0005.$$

The moral seems to be that one should not expect to obtain a five-card poker hand containing only spades. Even if one settles for a hand containing five cards of the same suit, the probability is only four times as large, namely .002, which is still hopelessly small.

7. REVIEW EXERCISES

This section considers and solves some problems that review many of the concepts and techniques introduced in this chapter. The parts carrying a ▶ symbol should be ignored unless sections 5 and 6 were assigned for study.

1. Each of two dice has been altered by having its one-spot changed to a two-spot. As a result, each die will contain two two's but no one's. The two dice are then rolled once. Assuming that the two dice can be distinguished, solve the following problems: (a) Construct a sample space for the experiment. (b) Assign probabilities to the points of the sample space. (c) Using definition (1) calculate the probability i) of getting a total of 6 points on the two dice, ii) that at least one of the dice will show a 2, iii) that at least one of the dice will show a 2 if it is known that no number larger than 4 was obtained on either die. The solutions follow.

(a) The sample space is conveniently represented by the following 25 points which have been labeled by indicating the outcome on each die.

	.	.	.	.	.
	22	32	42	52	62
	.	.	.	.	.
	23	33	43	53	63
	.	.	.	.	.
	24	34	44	54	64
	.	.	.	.	.
	25	35	45	55	65
	.	.	.	.	.
	26	36	46	56	66

(b) Since the two dice are assumed to behave in the same manner as two normal dice for which the sample space is given in Table 1 and for which each point was assigned the probability $\frac{1}{36}$, the probabilities to be assigned here should be in agreement with those probabilities. Hence, since the event 22 here corresponds to the composite event consisting of the simple events 11, 12, 21, and 22 for Table 1, the probability $\frac{4}{36}$ should be assigned to the point labeled 22 of the present sample space. Each of the remaining points of this space that has a 2 in its label should be assigned the probability $\frac{2}{36}$ because there are two simple events of Table 1 that produced it. All other points should be assigned the probability $\frac{1}{36}$ because they do not differ from the corresponding ones in Table 1.

(c) i) If A denotes this event, it is seen by inspecting the sample space in (a) that the three points 24, 33, and 42 constitute the composite event A; hence applying definition (1) and using the probabilities assigned to those points in (b), it follows that

$$P\{A\} = \tfrac{2}{36} + \tfrac{1}{36} + \tfrac{2}{36} = \tfrac{5}{36}.$$

ii) If B denotes this event, it is seen that B consists of the simple events 22, 23, 24, 25, 26, 32, 42, 52, and 62. From (b), the point 22 was assigned the probability $\tfrac{4}{36}$ and the remaining points the probability $\tfrac{2}{36}$; consequently, since there are eight of the latter,

$$P\{B\} = \tfrac{4}{36} + 8(\tfrac{2}{36}) = \tfrac{5}{9}.$$

iii) If C denotes the event of getting at least one 2, and D denotes the event that no number larger than a 4 shows, it is seen that D consists of the simple events 22, 23, 24, 32, 33, 34, 42, 43, and 44. Of these points, only 22, 23, 24, 32, and 42 also lie in C; hence it follows from the assignment of probabilities in (b) that

$$P\{D\} = \tfrac{4}{36} + 4(\tfrac{2}{36}) + 4(\tfrac{1}{36}) = \tfrac{4}{9}$$
$$P\{C \text{ and } D\} = \tfrac{4}{36} + 4(\tfrac{2}{36}) = \tfrac{1}{3}$$
$$P\{C \mid D\} = \tfrac{1}{3}/\tfrac{4}{9} = \tfrac{3}{4}.$$

2. A box contains the following five cards: the ace of spades, the ace of clubs, the two of hearts, the two of diamonds, and the three of spades. An ace is considered as a one. Spades and clubs are black cards, whereas hearts and diamonds are red cards. Two cards are to be drawn from this box without replacing the first card drawn before the second drawing. Using the addition and multiplication formulas, calculate the probability that (a) both cards will be red, (b) the first card will be an ace and the second card will be a two, (c) both cards will be the same color, (d) one card will be a spade and the other will be a club, (e) a total of 4 on the two cards will be obtained,▶(f) exactly one ace will be obtained if it is known that both cards are black, ▶(g) the first card drawn was a spade if the second card drawn turned out to be the ace of spades. Work this part of the problem by employing formula (10). The solutions follow.

(a) Applying formula (6) and considering the experiment in two stages, $P\{RR\} = \tfrac{2}{5} \cdot \tfrac{1}{4} = \tfrac{1}{10}.$

(b) Applying formula (6), $P\{A_2\} = \tfrac{2}{5} \cdot \tfrac{2}{4} = \tfrac{1}{5}.$

(c) The two events RR and BB constitute the two mutually exclusive ways in which the desired event can occur; hence applying formula (3), the desired probability is given by

$$P\{RR \text{ or } BB\} = P\{RR\} + P\{BB\} = \tfrac{2}{5} \cdot \tfrac{1}{4} + \tfrac{3}{5} \cdot \tfrac{2}{4} = \tfrac{2}{5}$$

(d) The two events SC and CS will satisfy; hence

$$P\{SC \text{ or } CS\} = P\{SC\} + P\{CS\} = \tfrac{2}{5} \cdot \tfrac{1}{4} + \tfrac{1}{5} \cdot \tfrac{2}{4} = \tfrac{1}{5}.$$

(e) A total of 4 will be obtained if both cards are two's, or if one card is a three and the other is a one. If a subscript is used to denote the number on a card, the events that will satisfy are the following ones: H_2D_2, D_2H_2, S_3S_1, S_1S_3, S_3C_1, C_1S_2. Since these constitute the mutually exclusive ways in which the desired event can occur and since each of these possesses the same probability, namely $\tfrac{1}{5} \cdot \tfrac{1}{4} = \tfrac{1}{20}$, it follows that

$$P\{4 \text{ total}\} = \tfrac{6}{20} = \tfrac{3}{10}.$$

(f) Let A_1 denote the event that both cards will be black and A_2 the event that exactly one ace will be obtained. Then $P\{A_2 \mid A_1\}$ is the probability needed to solve the problem. From formula (5), this requires the computation of $P\{A_1\}$ and $P\{A_1 \text{ and } A_2\}$. First $P\{A_1\} = \tfrac{3}{5} \cdot \tfrac{2}{4} = \tfrac{3}{10}$. Next, both A_1 and A_2 will occur if one of the following mutually exclusive events occurs: S_1S_3, S_3S_1, C_1S_3, S_3C_1. Since each of these events has the probability $\tfrac{1}{5} \cdot \tfrac{1}{4} = \tfrac{1}{20}$ and there are four of them, it follows that $P\{A_1 \text{ and } A_2\} = \tfrac{4}{20} = \tfrac{1}{5}$. Hence,

$$P\{A_2 \mid A_1\} = \tfrac{1}{5}/\tfrac{3}{10} = \tfrac{2}{3}.$$

(g) Let A_1 denote the event of getting a spade on the first draw and let A_2 denote the event of getting the ace of spades on the second draw. The problem is to calculate $P\{A_1 \mid A_2\}$. Here one can consider five events, e_1, e_2, e_3, e_4, and e_5, to represent the possible outcomes of the first stage of the experiment where these symbols denote the events of getting S_1, C_1, H_2, D_2, and S_2 respectively. Since all these events have the same probability of occurring $P\{e_1\} = \cdots = P\{e_5\} = \tfrac{1}{5}$. Next, one can consider two events, o_1 and o_2, to represent the possible outcomes of the second stage of the experiment, where o_1 denotes the event of getting the ace of spades and o_2 the event of not getting the ace of spades on the second draw. Here

$$P\{o_1 \mid e_1\} = 0, P\{o_1 \mid e_2\} = P\{o_1 \mid e_3\} = P\{o_1 \mid e_4\} = P\{o_1 \mid e_5\} = \tfrac{1}{4}.$$

Now the event A_1 will occur if either of the two mutually exclusive events e_1 or e_5 occurs; hence

$$P\{A_1 \mid A_2\} = P\{e_1 \mid A_2\} + P\{e_5 \mid A_2\}.$$

In the present notation $A_2 = o_1$; therefore

$$P\{A_1 \mid A_2\} = P\{e_1 \mid o_1\} + P\{e_5 \mid o_1\}.$$

Each of these probabilities will be calculated by means of formula (10). Since they have the same denominator, the result can be written in the form

$$P\{A_1 \mid A_2\} = \frac{\frac{1}{5} \cdot 0 + \frac{1}{5} \cdot \frac{1}{4}}{\frac{1}{5}(0 + \frac{1}{4} + \frac{1}{4} + \frac{1}{4} + \frac{1}{4})} = \frac{1}{4}.$$

This problem and its solution calls for a few comments. No attempt was made in the solution to use what might be called common sense because the problem was treated as an exercise in the application of formula (10). Thus, the fact that e_1 could not have occurred if o_1 occurs would eliminate the necessity of considering the probability $P\{e_1 \mid o_1\}$. Furthermore, if one looks at the implication of the restriction that o_1 must occur, which means that the second card must be the ace of spades, it would suggest that this is equivalent to considering experiments in which the ace of spades is removed and saved for the second drawing, in which case the probability of getting a black card on the first draw is $\frac{1}{4}$. Thus, one can often arrive at correct answers very quickly by visualizing simpler experiments which are expected to yield equivalent results. This is not the same as solving the original problem by means of formulas, however, which was required here.

EXERCISES

1. List all the possible outcomes if a coin is tossed 4 times.

2. A box contains one red, one black, and one green ball. Two balls are to be drawn from this box without replacing the first ball drawn before the second drawing. Construct a sample space for this experiment similar to Table 1.

3. What probabilities should be assigned to the points of the sample space corresponding to the experiment of problem 1?

4. What probabilities would you assign to the points of the sample space of problem 2? What assignment would you have made if the first ball was returned to the box before the second drawing?

5. A box contains 2 black and 1 white ball. Two balls are to be drawn from this box. Construct a sample space for this experiment (a) using 6 points, (b) using 3 points.

6. What probabilities would you assign to the points of the two sample spaces constructed in problem 5?

7. Let e_1, e_2, and e_3 denote the events of getting a digit less than 4, getting a digit between 4 and 6 inclusive, and getting a digit larger than 6, respectively, when selecting a digit from the table of random digits. (a) Construct a sample space for this experiment and assign probabilities to the points. (b) Perform the experiment 200 times and calculate the experimental relative frequencies for the three events to see whether your model seems to be a realistic one.

8. A box contains 4 red, 3 black, 2 green, and 1 white ball. A ball is drawn from the box and then returned to the box. What is the probability that the ball will be (a) red, (b) red or black? Now simulate this experiment by means of random numbers by calling the digits 0, 1, 2, 3 red, the digits 4, 5, 6 black, the digits 7, 8 green, and the digit 9 white, and perform the experiment of selecting a digit from the table of random digits 400 times. Let A_1 and A_2 denote the events in parts (a) and (b), respectively, and keep a tabulation of the number of times A_1 and A_2 occurred. Observe whether the mathematical model assumed to hold here seems to be realistic.

9. An honest die is rolled twice. Using Table 1, calculate the probability of getting (a) a total of 4, (b) a total of less than 4, (c) a total that is an even number.

10. An honest coin is tossed 4 times. Using the model of problems 1 and 3, calculate the probability of getting (a) 4 heads, (b) 3 heads and 1 tail, (c) at least 2 heads.

11. For the experiment of rolling two honest dice, calculate the probability that (a) the sum of the numbers will not be 11, (b) neither 1 nor 2 will appear, (c) each die will show 3 or more points, (d) the numbers on the two dice will not be the same, (e) exactly one die will show fewer than 3 points.

12. What expected relative frequencies would you guess should be assigned to the possible outcomes of an experiment consisting of selecting a female student at random and noting whether she would be rated as a blonde, redhead, or brunette? How would you go about improving on your guess?

13. If you were interested in studying the fluctuations of the stock market over a period of time, would you expect the relative frequency of rises to be about the same as the relative frequency of declines? Would it be possible for this to be true and yet have the stock market rise in value regularly over a period of a year?

14. Two balls are to be drawn from an urn containing 2 white and 3 black balls. (a) What is the probability that the first ball will be white and the second black? (b) What is this probability if the first ball is replaced before the second drawing?

15. Two balls are to be drawn from an urn containing 2 white, 3 black, and 4 green balls. (*a*) What is the probability that both balls will be green? (*b*) What is this probability if the first ball is replaced before the second drawing? (*c*) What is the probability that both balls will be the same color?

16. A box contains 4 coins, 3 of which are honest coins but the fourth of which has heads on both sides. If a coin is selected from the box and then is tossed 2 times, what is the probability that 2 heads will be obtained?

17. The following numbers were obtained from a mortality table based on 100,000 individuals:

Age	Number Alive	Deaths per 1000 During That Year
17	94,818	7.688
18	94,089	7.727
19	93,362	7.765
20	92,637	7.805
21	91,914	7.855

If these numbers are used to define probabilities of death for the corresponding age group and if A, B, and C denote individuals of ages 17, 19, and 21, respectively, calculate the probability that during the year (*a*) A will die and B will live, (*b*) A and B will both die, (*c*) A and B will both live, (*d*) at least one of A and B will die, (*e*) at least one of A, B, and C will die.

18. Assume that there are equal numbers of male and female students in a high school and that the probability is $\frac{1}{5}$ that a male student and $\frac{1}{20}$ that a female student will be a science major. What is the probability that (*a*) a student selected at random will be a male science student, (*b*) a student selected at random will be a science student, (*c*) a science student selected at random will be a male student?

19. A testing organization wishes to rate a particular brand of table radios. Five radios are selected at random from the stock of radios and the brand is judged to be satisfactory if nothing is found wrong with any of the 5 radios. (*a*) What is the probability that the brand will be rated as satisfactory if 10 per cent of the radios actually are defective? (*b*) What is this probability if 20 per cent are defective?

20. Three cards are to be drawn from an ordinary deck of 52 cards. (*a*) What is the probability that all 3 cards will be spades? (*b*) What is the probability that all 3 cards will be of the same suit? (*c*) What is the probability that none of the 3 cards will be spades?

21. Assuming that the ratio of male children is $\frac{1}{2}$, find the probability that in a family of 6 children (*a*) all children will be of the same sex, (*b*) the 4 oldest children will be boys and the 2 youngest will be girls, (*c*) 5 of the children will be boys and 1 will be a girl.

22. If a poker hand of 5 cards is drawn from a deck, what is the probability that it will contain exactly 1 ace?

23. For the experiment of rolling the 2 altered dice of exercise 1 of section 7, calculate the probability that (a) the sum of the numbers will be less than 6, (b) the number 2 will occur, (c) exactly 1 die will show fewer than 3 points.

24. For the second of the two review exercises of section 7 work the following problems by means of the addition and multiplication formulas. Here, however, assume that the first card is returned before the second drawing. What is the probability that (a) both cards will be aces, (b) the ace of spades is certain to be obtained, (c) at least one card will be an ace, (d) at most one card will be an ace, (e) a red ace will not be obtained, (f) the sum of the numbers on the two cards will be less than 4, ▶(g) at least one ace will be obtained if it is known that neither card is a three, ▶(h) the first card was an ace if it is known that the second card is not an ace?

25. Work the review exercises of problem 24 under the assumption that the first card drawn is not returned before the second drawing.

▶26. Suppose a college aptitude test designed to separate high school students into promising and not-promising groups for college entrance has had the following experience. Among the students who made satisfactory grades in their first year at college 80 per cent passed the aptitude test. Among the students who did unsatisfactory work their first year 40 per cent passed the test. It is assumed that the test was not used for admission to college. If it is known that only 70 per cent of first year college students do satisfactory work, what is the probability that a student who passed the test will be a satisfactory student?

▶27. Find the probability that a poker hand of 5 cards will contain only black cards if it is known to contain at least 3 black cards.

▶28. If a box contains 40 good and 10 defective fuses and 10 fuses are selected, what is the probability that they will all be good? Use combination symbols here.

▶29. A bridge hand of 13 cards is drawn from a deck of 52 cards. Use combination symbols to calculate the probability that the hand (a) will contain exactly one ace, (b) will contain at least one ace, (c) will contain at least 6 spades, (d) will contain only spades.

CHAPTER 4

Theoretical
Frequency Distributions

1. INTRODUCTION

Chapter 2 was concerned with sample frequency distributions and their description. This chapter is concerned with population frequency distributions and their properties. A sample frequency distribution is an estimate of the population frequency distribution corresponding to it. If the size of the sample is large, one would expect the sample frequency distribution to be a good approximation of the population frequency distribution. For example, if in a study of dormitory weights one had taken a sample of 400 students and there were only 800 dormitory students on campus, one would have expected the sample and population frequency distributions to be very similar.

In most statistical problems the sample is not large enough to determine the population distribution with much precision. However, there is usually enough information in the sample, together with information obtained from other sources, to suggest the general type of population distribution involved. Experience with various kinds of biological weight distributions, for example, shows that they tend to possess a distribution very much like that shown in Fig. 2 of Chapter 2. Similarly, experience with distributions of various linear measurements, such as stature, foot length, and piston diameters shows that these variables possess distributions very much like that shown in Fig. 3 of Chapter 2. Thus, by combining experience and the information provided by the sample, one can usually postulate the general nature of the population distribution. This postulation leads to what is known as theoretical frequency distributions.

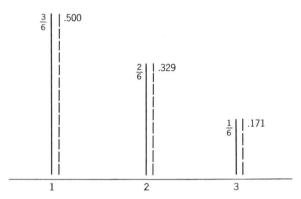

Fig. 1   A theoretical distribution and its empirical approximation.

A theoretical frequency distribution is a mathematical model for the actual frequency distribution. The probability models encountered in Chapter 3 in connection with games of chance are examples of theoretical frequency distributions for certain discrete variables. Thus the postulation that each of the 36 possible outcomes in rolling two dice will occur equally often in the long run yields a theoretical distribution for the two dice. For the experiment of weighing 120 dormitory students, the model might be a continuous frequency distribution, such as the bell-shaped distribution discussed in Chapter 2 in connection with the interpretation of the standard deviation. Models for continuous variables are more difficult to explain than those for discrete variables; therefore, discrete variables are considered first.

In discussing sample distributions and their theoretical counterparts, it is customary to call a sample distribution an *empirical* distribution. The relationship between an empirical distribution and its corresponding theoretical distribution has already been considered for a discrete variable in the illustration that produced Fig. 1 of Chapter 2. A sample of 700 was obtained by taking 700 drawings, with the drawn card replaced each time, from a set of cards consisting of 3 aces, 2 twos, and 1 three. From the results of the sampling, the relative frequencies for each type of outcome were calculated and, when expressed in decimal form, were found to be .500, .329, and .171, correct to three decimals. The corresponding theoretical distribution here is given by the three probabilities $\frac{3}{6}$, $\frac{2}{6}$, and $\frac{1}{6}$. A comparison of this theoretical distribution and its empirical approximation is shown in Fig. 1 as a pair of line charts, with the solid line representing theory and the broken line representing the sample.

2. RANDOM VARIABLES

In most experiments of the repetitive type, and this is particularly true of real-life experiments, one is usually not interested in all the possible outcomes of the experiment but only in certain properties of it. Thus in the experiment of tossing a coin three times, interest is usually centered on the total number of heads that will be obtained. Similarly, in rolling two dice, interest is centered only on the total number of points showing, because that is all that matters in the game of "craps."

This reduction of interest from all possible outcomes of an experiment to only a certain feature of it can often be accomplished by introducing what is known as a *random variable* to measure this feature of the experiment. The letter x will ordinarily be chosen to denote the random variable. In the experiment of tossing a coin three times the letter x will represent the total number of heads obtained. In the experiment of rolling two dice, the letter x will represent the total number of points showing. In that experiment much interest centers on whether x will assume the value of 7 or 11.

For the purpose of seeing how a random variable is introduced when interest is centered on a certain feature of an experiment, return once more to the sample space for the coin-tossing experiment which is given in Fig. 1 of Chapter 3. If x is used to denote the total number of heads obtained, then each point of that sample space will possess the value of x shown directly above the corresponding point in Fig. 2. It will be observed that the random variable x can assume any one of the values 0, 1, 2, or 3, but no other values.

As another illustration, let x denote the total number of points obtained in rolling two honest dice. The sample space for this experiment is given

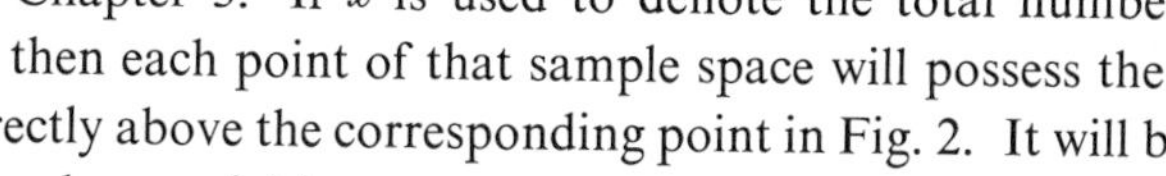

3	2	2	2	1	1	1	0
•	•	•	•	•	•	•	•
HHH	HHT	HTH	THH	HTT	THT	TTH	TTT

Fig. 2   The values of a random variable for a coin experiment.

2	3	4	5	6	7
•	•	•	•	•	•
3	4	5	6	7	8
•	•	•	•	•	•
4	5	6	7	8	9
•	•	•	•	•	•
5	6	7	8	9	10
•	•	•	•	•	•
6	7	8	9	10	11
•	•	•	•	•	•
7	8	9	10	11	12
•	•	•	•	•	•

Fig. 3 The values of a random variable for a dice experiment.

by Table 1 of Chapter 3. This sample space has been duplicated in Fig. 3 but with the omission of the labels attached to the points. The numbers attached to the points are the values of the random variable x for this experiment. It will be observed that this random variable x can assume any one of the values 2, 3, . . . , 12.

Now that interest is being centered on the values of a random variable for an experiment rather than on all the possible outcomes, a new simpler sample space can be constructed for the experiment, which can be substituted for the original sample space. Thus, in the coin-tossing experiment the only events of interest are the composite events given by $x = 0$, 1, 2, and 3. Now it follows from Fig. 2 and definition (1) of Chapter 3 that the probabilities for these composite events are given by $P\{0\} = \frac{1}{8}$, $P\{1\} = \frac{3}{8}$, $P\{2\} = \frac{3}{8}$, and $P\{3\} = \frac{1}{8}$, respectively. These composite events can now be treated as simple events in a new sample space of four points with each point associated with a value of the random variable x. The probabilities just calculated for those composite events are then assigned to the four points of the new sample space. Figure 4 shows this new sample space with its associated probabilities.

In a similar manner, a new sample space for the random variable representing the total number of points showing on two dice can be constructed by means of Fig. 3 and definition (1) of Chapter 3. Here the composite events are those corresponding to the random variable x assuming the values 2, 3, . . . , 12. The probabilities for those composite

Fig. 4   Sample space for a coin-tossing random variable.

Fig. 5   Sample space for a dice-rolling random variable.

events are readily calculated by means of definition (1) of Chapter 3 to be $\frac{1}{36}$, $\frac{2}{36}$, $\frac{3}{36}$, $\frac{4}{36}$, $\frac{5}{36}$, $\frac{6}{36}$, $\frac{5}{36}$, $\frac{4}{36}$, $\frac{3}{36}$, $\frac{2}{36}$, and $\frac{1}{36}$, respectively. As a result a new sample space consisting of eleven points based on the values of the random variable x can be constructed as shown in Fig. 5.

After the introduction of a random variable and its corresponding sample space has been completed for an experiment, one is in a position to discuss the distribution of the random variable. Both empirical and theoretical distributions have already been discussed with respect to the sample space of possible outcomes. Since a random variable merely introduces a new sample space of possible outcomes determined by possible values of the random variable, there is really nothing new to discuss. One slight difference is that the points of the new sample space will seldom be assigned equal probabilities as was often the case with earlier sample spaces of possible outcomes. A second difference is that the points of the new sample space can always be labeled by specifying the values of x that correspond to them. The distribution of a random variable x is always understood to be its theoretical distribution and not its empirical distribution. Such a distribution consists of the values that x can assume and the probabilities associated with them. Graphs of the distributions for the random variables of Figs. 4 and 5 are given in Figs. 6 and 7.

There are many experiments in which one is interested only in whether a particular outcome will occur. For such experiments it suffices to use only two points in the sample space. If the experiment is repeated a number of times interest will be centered only on the total number of those experiments that produced the desired outcome. The natural random variable to introduce for such situations is the random variable x that represents the

Fig. 6   Distribution for a coin-tossing random variable.

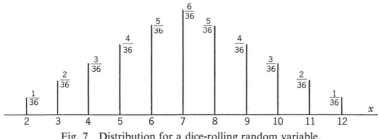

Fig. 7   Distribution for a dice-rolling random variable.

total number of desired outcomes. Because of the importance of such problems in real-life situations, a section of this chapter will be devoted to this type of random variable.   Such random variables give rise to what is known as the binomial distribution.

3. BINOMIAL DISTRIBUTION

Consider an experiment in which each of the possible outcomes can be classified as resulting or not resulting in the occurrence of an event A. If it resulted in the occurrence of A it will be classified as a success, otherwise as a failure.   The word success is used here as a convenient way of describing the occurrence of an event but it does not imply that the occurrence of the event is necessarily desired.   The experiment will be repeated a number of times, this number being denoted by the letter n.   A random variable x will be introduced which represents the total number of successes, that is, occurrences of A, that were obtained in the n repetitions of the experiment.   A random variable of this type is called a *binomial variable*.

The coin-tossing experiment that has been used so frequently can also be used here to give an example of a binomial variable.   Let that experiment be changed to consist of tossing the coin once instead of three times. Success will be defined as getting a head.   The experiment will be repeated three times; hence $n = 3$ here.   The random variable x will then represent the number of heads obtained in the three tosses, just as it did in section 2. The distribution of this binomial random variable is therefore given by Fig. 6.

The experiment of rolling two dice with x defined as the sum of the points on the two dice does not produce a binomial variable because one cannot classify each roll of a die as producing either a success or a failure and then have x represent the sum of the successes.

The experiment of drawing a ball from a box consisting of three red, two black, and one green ball is also not an experiment that leads to a binomial variable in its present form because there are three possible outcomes here rather than two. However, if one were interested only in knowing whether a red ball will be obtained, then the problem becomes a binomial distribution problem. The variable x would then represent the number of red balls obtained in performing the experiment n times. It is always understood in binomial-variable problems that replacements are made before the next experiment is made when it consists of drawing objects from containers. The repetitions of the experiment must be repetitions of the original experiment in every sense.

Now look at a slightly more complicated example of a binomial random variable and how its distribution is obtained. The basic experiment will consist of rolling a die once and success will be defined as getting an ace (one-spot). The experiment will be performed three times, so that $n = 3$, and the random variable x will represent the number of aces obtained in the three rolls. To obtain the distribution of this random variable one can proceed in the same manner as for the coin-tossing experiment of section 2. This consists of looking at the original sample space for the complete experiment and then reducing it to a new sample space for the random variable x by applying the definition of probability of events to the original sample space. Now for each roll of the die it is merely necessary to record whether a success or a failure occurred, where success corresponds to an ace showing. If S and F are used to represent success and failure, then there are eight points in the sample space, just as there were for three tosses of a coin in which either an H or a T must occur at each toss. These points have been represented in Table 1 by means of the letters S and F to indicate the various possible outcomes. The corresponding values of the random variable x have also been displayed in Table 1.

It will be observed that this table is precisely the same as for the problem of tossing a coin three times and which is shown in Fig. 2. However, the calculation of the probabilities for the various values of x is considerably different. The probabilities for these eight possible outcomes are not equal

TABLE 1

Outcome	SSS	SSF	SFS	FSS	SFF	FSF	FFS	FFF
Value of x	3	2	2	2	1	1	1	0

TABLE 2

Outcome	SSS	SSF	SFS	FSS	SFF	FSF	FFS	FFF
Probability	$(\frac{1}{6})^3$	$(\frac{1}{6})^2(\frac{5}{6})$	$(\frac{1}{6})^2(\frac{5}{6})$	$(\frac{1}{6})^2(\frac{5}{6})$	$(\frac{1}{6})(\frac{5}{6})^2$	$(\frac{1}{6})(\frac{5}{6})^2$	$(\frac{1}{6})(\frac{5}{6})^2$	$(\frac{5}{6})^3$

as was the case for the coin problem. The probabilities here will be calculated by using the multiplication rule of probability. Because of the independence of the three rolls of the die, it follows, for example, that

$$P\{SFS\} = \frac{1}{6} \cdot \frac{5}{6} \cdot \frac{1}{6} = \left(\frac{1}{6}\right)^2\left(\frac{5}{6}\right).$$

Calculations similar to this will yield probabilities for each of the eight possible outcomes. The results of such calculations are shown in Table 2.

This sample space of eight points with its assigned probabilities can now be reduced to the sample space for the random variable x by calculating the probabilities of the composite events corresponding to the various values of the random variable. Thus, the event $x = 2$ comprises the simple events SSF, SFS, FSS; therefore its probability is obtained by adding the probabilities associated with those three points. The results of such calculations are shown in Table 3. This table gives the distribution of the desired random variable. Its graph is shown in Fig. 8, in which the probabilities have been expressed in decimal form to two decimals.

In view of these results, it is clear that one should not expect to get three aces when rolling three dice. Such a result will occur in the long run about once in $6^3 = 216$ experiments. It is also clear that one should not accept a wager based on even money that one will get at least one ace in rolling three dice. Such a result will occur about 42 per cent of the time. If you wish to get the better of your naïve friends, give, say, 9 to 1 odds that they will not get at least two aces when rolling three dice. A fair wager would require you to give about 13 to 1 odds.

The technique employed in the two preceding illustrations can be used on any particular binomial problem that arises. One first constructs the

TABLE 3

x	0	1	2	3
$P\{x\}$	$(\frac{5}{6})^3$	$3(\frac{1}{6})(\frac{5}{6})^2$	$3(\frac{1}{6})^2(\frac{5}{6})$	$(\frac{1}{6})^3$

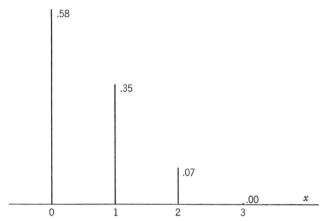

Fig. 8 Distribution for the number of aces in rolling a die three times.

sample space for the complete experiment. If there are, say, five repetitions of the basic success or failure experiment, there will be $2^5 = 32$ points in the sample space. The probability for each point is then calculated. Next, the proper value of the random variable x is associated with each point of the sample space. Then by summing the probabilities of those points that correspond to a particular value of x, the probabilities for the various values of x are obtained. These probabilities give the desired probability distribution of the binomial random variable x.

Because of the difficulty of carrying through the preceding computations each time a binomial problem arises it is convenient to have a formula that is applicable to all such problems. For this purpose consider a general binomial problem. An experiment is to be performed for which the outcome can always be classified as either a success or a failure. The probability that it will produce a success is assumed given and is denoted by the letter p. The corresponding probability of a failure is denoted by q; hence $p + q = 1$. The experiment is to be performed n times. The number of successes that will be obtained in the n repetitions of the experiment is denoted by the letter x. The problem then is to calculate the probabilities for the various possible values of the random variable x. As stated before, these computations can be carried out systematically for any given problem and they can also be done here for this general problem if the knowledge of optional section 6 of Chapter 3 is available. This is done in section 6 of this chapter for the benefit of those who have had time to study that earlier material; therefore only the results of those computations will be given here. The symbol $P\{x\}$ will be used to denote the probability for a typical value of this general binomial variable. These probabilities, which define what is known as the binomial distribution, are given by the following formula.

(1)   ***Binomial Distribution.*** $P\{x\} = \dfrac{n!}{x!\,(n-x)!}\,p^x q^{n-x}.$

As explained in section 6 of Chapter 3, the symbol $n!$ is read "n factorial." It denotes the product of all the positive integers from 1 through n. Thus, $5! = 1 \cdot 2 \cdot 3 \cdot 4 \cdot 5$. The value of $0!$ is defined to be 1 rather than 0, as might have been assumed. For large values of n and x the computations involved in evaluating the quantity $n!/x!\,(n-x)!$ become rather heavy; consequently a table of values of this quantity for various values of n and x has been made available in the appendix as Table III. This table handles values of n from 2 through 20, and for x from 2 through $n/2$ or more. It is not necessary to list the values for larger values of x because if x is replaced by $n - x$ in this quantity the same value will result; consequently one uses this device to handle values of x larger than $n/2$. Although this table enables one to write down binomial probabilities rather quickly it will not be used in the illustrative problems that follow because it seems desirable for the student to become acquainted with formula (1) by carrying out the required computations when n is fairly small.

It is customary to speak of the n experiments as n independent trials of an experiment for which p is the probability of success in a single trial. In this language $P\{x\}$ is the probability of obtaining x successes in n independent trials of an experiment for which p is the probability of success in a single trial.

The two frequency distributions displayed in Figs. 6 and 8 are special cases of the general binomial distribution given by (1). For the coin problem, $n = 3$ and $p = q = \frac{1}{2}$. For the die problem, $n = 3$, $p = \frac{1}{6}$ and $q = \frac{5}{6}$. The values of $P\{x\}$ given in Fig. 6 and Fig. 8 should be checked by means of formula (1) for the purpose of becoming familiar with its use. As an illustration of such a check, if the value of $P\{3\}$ is desired for the die problem, substitution of the proper values into (1) will yield

$$P\{3\} = \frac{3!}{3!\,0!}\left(\frac{1}{6}\right)^3\left(\frac{5}{6}\right)^0.$$

Since $0! = 1$ and since by algebra any number to the 0 power equals 1 it follows that $(\frac{5}{6})^0 = 1$, and hence that

$$P\{3\} = \left(\frac{1}{6}\right)^3.$$

Although the problems used to introduce the binomial distribution were related to games of chance, the binomial distribution is very useful for solving certain types of practical problems. Such problems are solved in the next few chapters; meanwhile, a few simple problems, which require only easy computations with formula (1), will be discussed.

The probability that parents with a certain type of blue-brown eyes will have a child with blue eyes is $\frac{1}{4}$. If there are six children in the family, what is the probability that at least half of them will have blue eyes? To solve this problem the six children in the family will be treated as six independent trials of an experiment for which the probability of success in a single trial is $\frac{1}{4}$. Thus $n = 6$ and $p = \frac{1}{4}$ here. It is necessary to calculate $P\{3\}$, $P\{4\}$, $P\{5\}$, and $P\{6\}$ and sum because these probabilities correspond to the mutually exclusive ways in which the desired event can occur. By formula (1),

$$P\{3\} = \frac{6!}{3!\,3!}\left(\frac{1}{4}\right)^3\left(\frac{3}{4}\right)^3 = \frac{540}{4096},$$

$$P\{4\} = \frac{6!}{4!\,2!}\left(\frac{1}{4}\right)^4\left(\frac{3}{4}\right)^2 = \frac{135}{4096},$$

$$P\{5\} = \frac{6!}{5!\,1!}\left(\frac{1}{4}\right)^5\left(\frac{3}{4}\right)^1 = \frac{18}{4096},$$

$$P\{6\} = \frac{6!}{6!\,0!}\left(\frac{1}{4}\right)^6\left(\frac{3}{4}\right)^0 = \frac{1}{4096}.$$

The probability of getting at least three successes is obtained by adding these probabilities; consequently, writing $x \geq 3$ to represent at least three successes, one obtains

$$P\{x \geq 3\} = \frac{694}{4096} = .169.$$

This result shows that there is a very small chance that a family such as this will have so many blue-eyed children. In only about 17 of 100 such families will at least half the children be blue-eyed.

A manufacturer of certain parts for automobiles guarantees that a box of his parts will contain at most two defective items. If the box holds 20 parts and experience has shown that his manufacturing process produces 2 per cent defective items, what is the probability that a box of his parts will satisfy the guarantee? This problem can be considered as a binomial-distribution problem for which $n = 20$ and $p = .02$. A box will satisfy the guarantee if the number of defective parts is 0, 1, or 2. By means of formula (1) the probabilities of these three events are given by

$$P\{0\} = \frac{20!}{0!\,20!}\,(.02)^0(.98)^{20} = (.98)^{20} = .668,$$

$$P\{1\} = \frac{20!}{1!\,19!}\,(.02)^1(.98)^{19} = 20(.02)(.98)^{19} = .273,$$

$$P\{2\} = \frac{20!}{2!\,18!}\,(.02)^2(.98)^{18} = 190(.02)^2(.98)^{18} = .053.$$

Since these are mutually exclusive events, the probability that there will be at most two defective parts, written $x \leq 2$, is the sum of these probabilities; hence the desired answer is

$$P\{x \leq 2\} = .994.$$

This result shows that the manufacturer's guarantee will almost always be satisfied.

4. BINOMIAL MOMENTS

The discussion of empirical distributions in Chapter 2 began with a geometrical representation by means of line charts and histograms, and then it proceeded to a partial arithmetic representation by means of the first two moments of the distribution, which in turn led to the mean and the standard deviation of the distribution. The same procedure will be followed for the theoretical distributions that are to be used as mathematical models for empirical distributions. Toward this objective, the calculation of the mean and the standard deviation for a binomial distribution will be discussed next. The only essential difference in the calculations for a theoretical distribution as compared to those for an empirical distribution is that one uses probabilities in place of observed relative frequencies. Now the formula for the first moment, given by formula (4) of Chapter 2, which is

$$m_1 = \frac{1}{n}\sum_{i=1}^{h} x_i f_i$$

can be written in the form

$$m_1 = \sum_{i=1}^{h} x_i \frac{f_i}{n}.$$

The corresponding theoretical first moment, which is denoted by the Greek letter μ_1, is obtained by replacing the sample relative frequency f_i/n for the value x_i by the probability $P\{x_i\}$; hence

(2)
$$\mu_1 = \sum_{i=1}^{h} x_i P\{x_i\}.$$

In a similar manner, the formula for the second moment of an empirical distribution, given by formula (7) of Chapter 2 and which can be written in the form

$$m_2 = \sum_{i=1}^{h} x_i^2 \frac{f_i}{n}$$

will give rise to the corresponding theoretical second moment in the form

(3)
$$\mu_2 = \sum_{i=1}^{h} x_i^2 P\{x_i\}.$$

The theoretical second moment about the mean, which is denoted by σ^2 and which corresponds to formula (8) of Chapter 2, then becomes

(4)
$$\sigma^2 = \sum_{i=1}^{h} (x_i - \mu_1)^2 P\{x_i\}.$$

The theoretical counterpart of formula (9) of Chapter 2 is therefore the formula

(5)
$$\sigma^2 = \mu_2 - \mu_1^2.$$

The theoretical standard deviation, σ, is the positive square root of σ^2. There is no problem here, as there was in defining s^2 about whether to divide by n or $n - 1$, because n is not involved in theoretical definitions. The foregoing theoretical values should be thought of as the values that would be approached by the corresponding sample values as the sample becomes increasingly large.

Since only the mean and the standard deviation will be used in this book, it is usually unnecessary to carry the subscript 1 on the label for the theoretical mean; therefore it will be denoted simply by μ.

Formulas (2), (3), and (5) will now be employed to calculate the mean and standard deviation of the binomial distribution given in Fig. 6. When

TABLE 4

x	$8P\{x\}$	$8xP\{x\}$	$8x^2P\{x\}$
0	1	0	0
1	3	3	3
2	3	6	12
3	1	3	9
		12	24

the probabilities $P\{x_i\}$ are given as fractions, it is advisable to omit the common denominator of those fractions in the calculations and then divide the results by this denominator. The calculations for this problem are shown in Table 4.

After the division of these numbers by the denominator 8 has been made, formula (2) will give

$$\mu = \frac{12}{8} = \frac{3}{2}.$$

Similarly, formulas (3) and (5) give

$$\mu_2 = \frac{24}{8} = 3,$$

and

$$\sigma^2 = 3 - \left(\frac{3}{2}\right)^2 = \frac{3}{4}.$$

Hence $\sigma = \sqrt{3/4}$. An inspection of Fig. 6 will show that $\mu = 1.5$ is certainly correct; however, it is difficult to check on the reasonableness of the value $\sigma = \sqrt{3/4} = .87$ on the basis of Fig. 6.

The calculations for the binomial distribution given by Table 3 and shown in Fig. 8 will also be carried out. Here it is convenient to ignore the common denominator $6^3 = 216$ and then divide by it at the end. The calculations for this problem are shown in Table 5.

TABLE 5

x	$216P\{x\}$	$216xP\{x\}$	$216x^2P\{x\}$
0	125	0	0
1	75	75	75
2	15	30	60
3	1	3	9
		108	144

After the division by 216, formulas (2), (3), and (5) give

$$\mu = \frac{108}{216} = \frac{1}{2}$$

and

$$\sigma^2 = \frac{144}{216} - \left(\frac{1}{2}\right)^2 = \frac{5}{12}.$$

As a result, $\sigma = \sqrt{5/12}$.

It is possible to employ some algebraic tricks to carry out similar calculations for the general binomial distribution given by (1). Such calculations yield formulas for the mean and standard deviation that can be used for all binomial problems. Since such calculations are rather complicated, they will not be carried out here; however, the resulting formulas will be given and used for solving binomial problems. These formulas, which are very simple, are

(6)
$$\mu = np$$
$$\sigma = \sqrt{npq}.$$

The advantage of having such neat formulas becomes apparent when one applies them to the two computational problems that were just completed. For the distribution of Table 4, $n = 3$, and $p = \frac{1}{2}$; therefore formulas (6) give

$$\mu = 3 \cdot \tfrac{1}{2} = \tfrac{3}{2}$$
$$\sigma = \sqrt{3 \cdot \tfrac{1}{2} \cdot \tfrac{1}{2}} = \sqrt{\tfrac{3}{4}}.$$

Similarly, for the distribution of Table 5, $n = 3$ and $p = \frac{1}{6}$; therefore formulas (6) give

$$\mu = 3 \cdot \tfrac{1}{6} = \tfrac{1}{2}$$
$$\sigma = \sqrt{3 \cdot \tfrac{1}{6} \cdot \tfrac{5}{6}} = \sqrt{\tfrac{5}{12}}.$$

5. CONTINUOUS VARIABLES

This section is concerned with a discussion of continuous random variables and their distribution. Such variables have already been studied in Chapter 2. The essential distinction between a continuous variable and a discrete variable is that the former involves measuring, whereas the latter involves counting. The variables of Chapter 2 for which the techniques of classification of data were explained were continuous variables, whereas the variables of Chapter 3 for which the rules of probability were derived were discrete variables. The distributions for the discrete variables of Chapter 3 were represented by line charts to distinguish them from the continuous-variable distributions of Chapter 2, for which histograms were introduced and employed. For discrete variables line charts are used for both empirical and theoretical distributions. This is illustrated in Fig. 1. For continuous variables the situation is not so simple because the nature of a histogram to represent an empirical distribution depends upon the length of the class interval that is selected. Since a theoretical distribution is supposed to represent the distribution that an empirical distribution will approach as the sample becomes increasingly large, it is clear that the choice of class interval will play an important role in determining a theoretical distribution.

For the purpose of discussion, consider a particular continuous variable, x, that represents the diameter of a steel rod obtained from the production line of a manufacturer. If the next 200 rods coming off the production line were measured, there would be 200 values of x with which to study the diameter variation of the production system. Classifying these 200 values of x and graphing the histogram would help to describe the distribution of diameters. Figure 3, Chapter 2, illustrates the results of one experiment. If 400 rods had been measured, the resulting histogram would have been about twice as tall as that in Fig. 3. This growth in the height of a histogram as the sample size increases makes it difficult to compare histograms based on different size samples. The difficulty can be overcome by requiring that the area of the histogram always be equal to 1. This in turn requires that the area of any rectangle of the histogram, say the ith, be equal to the relative frequency, f_i/n, for the corresponding class interval because the sum of these relative frequencies is also equal to 1. Since the area of the ith rectangle must be equal to f_i/n, the height of the ith rectangle must be equal to f_i/nc, in which c is the length of the class interval. Graphing a histogram with these heights for the rectangles will yield the desired unit area. This is illustrated in Fig. 9.

As an illustration, inspect Fig. 10 which is a reproduction of Fig. 3 of Chapter 2. Since the class interval here is .005 and $n = 200$, the preceding formula which is shown in Fig. 9 requires that the absolute frequencies, f_i displayed in Fig. 10 be divided by $nc = 200 \, (.005) = 1$ in order that the area of the histogram be equal to 1. Fortunately, no modification is needed here; the area is already equal to 1. For the histogram of Fig. 2 of Chapter 2 the class interval is 10 and $n = 120$; therefore the listed

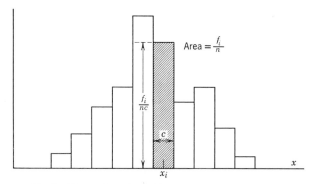

Fig. 9   Dimensions for a histogram possessing unit area.

absolute frequencies would need to be divided by $nc = 120(10) = 1200$ before the area would become equal to 1. In order to obtain a decent looking histogram one would need to rescale at least one of the axes drastically here.

The advantage of using a histogram whose area is equal to 1 becomes apparent when one calculates the relative frequencies for different sets of x values. Thus, from Fig. 10 the proportion of steel rods in the sample of 200 that had a diameter in inches between .4705 and .4755 is given by

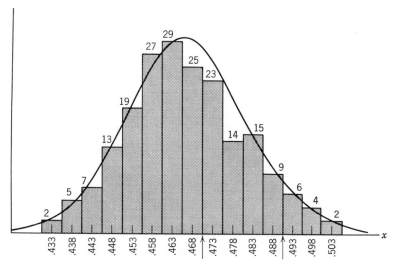

Fig. 10   Distribution of the diameters of 200 steel rods, with a fitted normal curve.

the area of the rectangle for which those numbers are the boundaries. This area is, of course, $23/200 = .115$ units. Similarly, the proportion of steel rods in the sample that had a diameter in inches between .4705 and .4905 is given by the sum of the areas of the rectangles that begin at .4705 and end with .4905 and which are between the two arrows shown in Fig. 10. This area is given by $(23 + 14 + 15 + 9)/200 = .305$. Although it is not customary to use areas to calculate such relative frequencies, since they are readily obtained from the observed frequencies, it is important to realize that such relative frequencies can be represented by areas of parts of the histogram because theoretical relative frequencies will be calculated by means of areas of theoretical distributions.

With the foregoing choice of heights of rectangles to produce an area of 1, a histogram would be expected to approach a fixed histogram as the sample size is increased. For example, if a sample of 1,000 steel rods were taken from the production line and the resulting histogram with area equal to 1 were graphed, one would not expect the histogram to change its shape much if additional samples were taken, because the histogram would already be an accurate estimate of the distribution of diameters for the production process. Now, if it is assumed that x can be measured as accurately as desired, so that the class interval can be made as small as desired, then the upper boundary of the histogram would be expected to settle down and approximate a smooth curve as the sample size is increased, provided the class interval is chosen very small. Such a curve is an idealization, or model, of the relative frequency with which different values of x would be expected to be obtained for runs of the actual experiment. The frequency distribution given by such a curve is a theoretical frequency distribution for the continuous variable x.

Figure 10 shows a curve that experience has indicated should conform closely to the kind of frequency distribution expected here and which therefore represents a theoretical frequency distribution for that variable.

Since a curve that represents a theoretical frequency distribution is thought of as the limiting form of the histogram under continuous sampling, it must possess the essential frequency properties of the histogram. Thus the area under a theoretical frequency-distribution curve must be equal to 1 because the area under the histogram is always kept equal to 1. Further, since the area of any rectangle of a histogram is equal to the relative frequency with which x occurred between the boundaries of the corresponding class interval, the area under the theoretical frequency-distribution curve between those same boundaries should represent the expected relative frequency of x occurring in that interval. In Fig. 9, for example, the area of the rectangle whose base extends from $x_i - c/2$ to $x_i + c/2$ is the observed relative frequency f_i/n; therefore the area from $x_i - c/2$ to $x_i + c/2$ under a proposed theoretical frequency-distribution curve should represent the expected relative frequency of x occurring in that interval. If this same reasoning is extended to several neighboring intervals, it follows that the area under such a curve between any two values of x should represent the expected relative frequency of x occurring inside the interval determined by those two values of x.

As an illustration, consider once more the two values $x = .4705$ and $x = .4905$ that have been indicated by arrows in Fig. 10. The observed relative frequency for x occurring inside this interval is given by the area of the rectangles lying inside this interval and was found to be .305. If it is assumed that the curve sketched in Fig. 10 represents a proper theoretical distribution, then the area under this curve between $x = .4705$ and $x = .4905$ will represent the relative frequency with which x would be expected to occur inside this interval. This area was found, by methods to be explained later, to be equal to .335.

In Chapter 3 probability was defined for discrete variables in such a manner that it was interpreted as expected relative frequency for the event in question. Although the definition and rules of probability were restricted to discrete variables for ease of explanation, the rules also apply to continuous variable events. Consequently, in view of the discussion in the preceding paragraphs, it follows that a theoretical frequency-distribution curve is a curve by means of which one can calculate the probability that x will lie inside any specified interval on the x axis. Thus, in the illustration related to Fig. 10, if it is assumed that the curve there represents the theoretical distribution, one can say that when a single sample value of x is taken the probability that the value of x will lie between .4705 and .4905 is .335. In symbols this would be written

$$P\{.4705 < x < .4905\} = .335.$$

This kind of statement is typical of probability statements for continuous variables; the events are usually concerned with the variable x lying inside some interval, or intervals, on the x axis. Such probabilities are given by areas under theoretical frequency distribution curves.

As in the case for discrete variables, if one chooses a realistic model one can expect the probabilities calculated on the basis of that model to be close to the corresponding observed relative frequencies that are obtained when the experiment is repeated a large number of times.

6. NORMAL DISTRIBUTION

The binomial distribution of section 2 is the most useful theoretical frequency distribution for discrete variables. The distribution that will be studied in this section is the most useful theoretical frequency distribution for continuous variables.

The histogram in Fig. 10 is typical of many distributions found in nature and industry. Such distributions are quite symmetrical, die out rather quickly at the tails, and possess a shape much like that of a bell. A theoretical distribution, which has proved very useful for distributions such as these and which will presently be seen as very important in other ways also, is called the *normal distribution*. The curve that has been sketched in Fig. 10 is the graph of a particular normal distribution. The graph of a general normal distribution is given in Fig. 11. Although a normal distribution is defined by the equation of its curve, this equation is not used explicitly in subsequent chapters and therefore it is not written

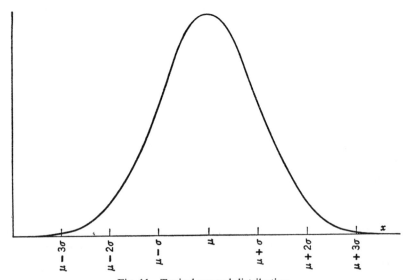

Fig. 11   Typical normal distribution.

down. The curve itself can be thought of as defining the distribution.

You may have heard of the normal curve in connection with the distribution of grades in large sections of certain courses. Grading on the basis of the normal curve assumes that the distribution of the mental output of students should be similar to the distribution of many of their physical characteristics, which are known to be approximately normally distributed. An instructor using such a grading scheme also usually assumes that the students in his course have the proper prerequisites and study the expected number of hours. An optimist at heart! One difficulty with this system is that it assigns grades on a relative rather than an absolute basis. Thus an unusually gifted class that works hard will be assigned the same distribution of grades as a class of lazy louts. Of course, the answer to this criticism is that students from year to year differ very little, and therefore it is highly unlikely that a large class will be made up of either brilliant workers or stupid loafers. If you have acquired a dislike for the normal curve on the basis of the grades it may have given you, realize that the normal curve is really not to blame and be charitable enough to approach its study here without prejudice. It is an exceedingly useful curve in many fields of application quite removed from school problems.

It will be recalled from Chapter 2 that the mean of a distribution represents the point on the x-axis at which a sheet of metal in the shape of the histogram of the distribution will balance on a knife-edge. This geometrical property of the mean makes it clear that when a histogram is symmetrical about a vertical axis the mean must be located at the symmetry point on the x-axis. This is true for the limiting value of the mean as well when the size of the sample is increased indefinitely and the class interval is made increasingly small. The limiting or theoretical, value of the mean is denoted by the Greek letter μ, just as for discrete variables. This explains why the symmetry point on the x-axis in Fig. 11 has been labeled μ. Whether a theoretical distribution is symmetrical or not, the symbol μ is used to designate the limiting, or theoretical, value of the mean.

If the standard deviation, as defined by formula (11), Chapter 2, were calculated for increasingly large samples and increasingly small class intervals, its value would also be expected to approach some value. This limiting, or theoretical, value is denoted by the Greek letter σ, just as for discrete variables.

The Greek letters μ and σ are used to represent the mean and standard deviation of theoretical frequency distributions, corresponding to $\bar{x}$ and s for sample frequency distributions, so that there will be no confusion as to which distribution is meant when the mean and standard deviation of a distribution are discussed. The two basic problems in statistics, namely estimation and hypothesis testing, involve problems of estimating μ and σ, and testing hypotheses about them by means of their sample estimates $\bar{x}$ and s.

Suppose, now, that the limiting form of the histogram for a frequency distribution, in the sense described earlier, is a normal curve. Then it can be shown by advanced mathematical methods that σ, the limiting value of s, has the following geometrical interpretation with respect to the limiting normal curve:

(7)   (a) The area under the normal curve between $\mu - \sigma$ and $\mu + \sigma$ is 68 per cent of the total area, to the nearest 1 per cent.

(b) The area under the normal curve between $\mu - 2\sigma$ and $\mu + 2\sigma$ is 95 per cent of the total area, to the nearest 1 per cent.

(c) The area under the normal curve between $\mu - 3\sigma$ and $\mu + 3\sigma$ is 99.7 per cent of the total area, to the nearest .1 per cent.

The axis in Fig. 11 has been marked off in units of σ, starting with the mean μ. It is clear from this sketch that there is almost no area under the curve beyond 3σ units from μ; however, the equation of the curve would show that the curve actually extends from $-\infty$ to $+\infty$.

The first two of the foregoing properties were used to give meaning to s in Chapter 2. Those two percentages were found there to be approximately correct for histograms whose shapes resemble a normal curve.

An interesting property of the normal curve is that its location and shape are completely determined by its values of μ and σ. The value of μ, of course, centers the curve, whereas the value of σ determines the extent of the spread. Since all normal curves representing theoretical frequency distributions have a total area of 1, as σ increases the curve must decrease in height and spread out. This is illustrated in Figs. 12 and 13 which give sketches of two normal curves with the same mean, namely 0, and standard deviations of 1 and 3, respectively. The fact that the shape of a normal curve is completely determined by its standard deviation enables one to reduce all normal curves to a standard one by a simple change of variable.

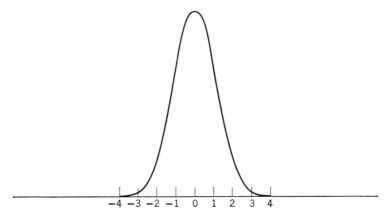

Fig. 12   A normal distribution with $\mu = 0$ and $\sigma = 1$.

For example, the curve of Fig. 12 can be made to look like the curve of Fig. 13 by changing the scale on the x-axis so that one unit on the Fig. 12 axis represents three units on the Fig. 13 axis. This corresponds, roughly, to taking the curve of Fig. 12, treating it and the area beneath it as though it were made of rubber, and stretching it out to three times its natural length with its area preserved. Conversely, Fig. 13 could be made to go into Fig. 12 by compressing Fig. 13 to one-third its natural length. This assumes that the long tails of these curves are cut off and ignored. Since the simplest normal curve with which to work is the one that has its mean at 0 and whose standard deviation is equal to 1, other normal curves are usually reduced to this standard one when there is need for a reduction. Now to any point on the x-axis of a normal curve there corresponds a point on the x-axis of the standard normal curve, and its value can be determined by stating how many standard deviations it is away from the mean point of the curve. Thus, the point $x = 6$ on Fig. 13 corresponds to the point $x = 2$ on the standard normal curve given by Fig. 12; therefore the value $x = 6$ can be obtained from Fig. 12 by stating that it is 2 standard deviations to the right of its mean 0. In general, if a point x

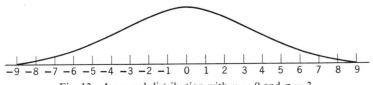

Fig. 13   A normal distribution with $\mu = 0$ and $\sigma = 3$.

on the axis of a normal curve with mean μ and standard deviation σ corresponds to a point z on the standard normal curve, then the point x is z standard deviations to the right of μ. The relationship between these corresponding points is therefore given by the formula

$$x = \mu + z\sigma.$$

Or, if z is expressed in terms of x,

(8)
$$z = \frac{x - \mu}{\sigma}.$$

This formula enables one to find the point z on the standard normal curve that corresponds to any point x on a nonstandard normal curve. Thus, the point $x = 4$ on Fig. 13 corresponds to the point $z = (4 - 0)/3 = 1\frac{1}{3}$ on Fig. 12. By this device of expressing all x values on a normal curve in terms of corresponding values on the standard normal curve, all normal curves can be reduced to a single standard one.

In the earlier discussions in Chapter 2 about the second moment, it was noted that the standard deviation is unaffected by adding a constant to the values of a set of measurements and that it is multiplied by c if each of the measurements is multiplied by c. This same property will hold for a random variable x and its theoretical standard deviation σ. That is, the variable $x - c$ will have the same standard deviation as the variable x, but the standard deviation for cx will be c times as large as for x. In view of these properties the standard deviation of $(x - \mu)/\sigma$ will be $1/\sigma$ times the standard deviation of $x - \mu$, or of x; therefore if σ is the standard deviation of x, the standard deviation of $z = (x - \mu)/\sigma$ must be 1. Since the mean of x is μ, subtracting μ from x will give a variable $x - \mu$ whose mean is 0. The mean of the variable $z = (x - \mu)/\sigma$ is therefore also 0, because multiplying a variable by a constant multiplies the mean by that constant, and multiplying 0 by $1/\sigma$ still gives 0. Thus, the variable $z = (x - \mu)/\sigma$ will possess the mean 0 and the standard deviation 1. The change of variable given by formula (8) will therefore change any variable x to one with mean 0 and standard deviation 1. This is true whether the variable x is a normal variable or not. A variable x that has been changed to the variable z by means of formula (8) is said to be measured in *standard units* after the change has been made.

Table IV in the appendix is a table for finding the area under any part of the normal curve for the variable z, that is for the normal curve that has

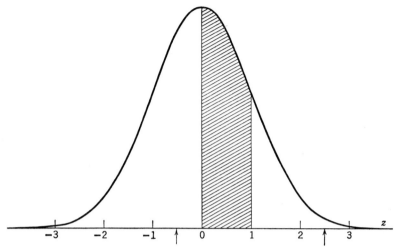

Fig. 14   Standard normal distribution.

mean 0 and standard deviation 1. The values of z in this table are given to two decimal places, with the second decimal place determining the column to use. As an illustration, suppose one wished to find the area under this standard normal curve from $z = 0$ to $z = 1.00$. The desired area is shown geometrically in Fig. 14. In Table IV one reads down the first column until the z value 1.0 is reached, then across to the entry in the column headed .00 to find .3413. This is the desired area. Table IV gives only areas from $z = 0$ to any specified positive value of z. If areas to the left of $z = 0$ are wanted, one must use symmetry and work with the corresponding right half of the curve.

Suppose now that one wishes to find the area under part of a normal curve with mean μ and standard deviation σ. For example, suppose one wishes to find the area from $x = \mu - \sigma$ to $x = \mu + \sigma$ in Fig. 11. It follows, by symmetry, that this area is twice the area from $x = \mu$ to $x = \mu + \sigma$, which is precisely the same as the corresponding area under the standard normal curve of Table IV that is sketched in Fig. 14. From formula (8), the values $x = \mu$ and $x = \mu + \sigma$ correspond to the values $z = 0$ and $z = 1$; consequently, the area from $x = \mu$ to $x = \mu + \sigma$ is the same as that under the standard normal curve from $z = 0$ to $z = 1$. Since this area was found to be .3413, the area from $x = \mu - \sigma$ to $x = \mu + \sigma$ is twice this number, or .6826. This, of course, is the number that gave rise to the normal distribution property (a) in (7).

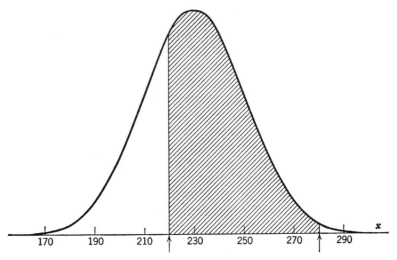

Fig. 15 A particular normal distribution.

As another illustration of the use of Table IV, suppose one wishes to find the area between $x = 220$ and $x = 280$ for x possessing a normal distribution with $\mu = 230$ and $\sigma = 20$. The desired area is shown in Fig. 15. First it is necessary to calculate the corresponding z values by means of (8). These are

$$z_1 = \frac{220 - 230}{20} = -.50$$

and

$$z_2 = \frac{280 - 230}{20} = 2.50.$$

These two z values are indicated by means of vertical arrows on Fig. 14. Now, the desired area is given by the area from $-.50$ to 2.50 under the standard normal curve. From Table IV, the area from $z = 0$ to $z = 2.50$ is .4938. By symmetry, the area from $z = -.50$ to $z = 0$ is the same as that from $z = 0$ to $z = .50$. The latter area is found in Table IV to be .1915; consequently, the desired area is the sum of these two areas, or .6853. Although the two normal curves in Figs. 14 and 15 would look quite different if the same scale were used on both axes, they purposely have been drawn to look alike so that the equivalence of corresponding areas will be apparent.

7. NORMAL APPROXIMATION TO BINOMIAL

Problems related to the binomial distribution are fairly easy to solve provided the number of trials, n, is not large. If n is large, the computations involved in using formula (1) become exceedingly lengthy; consequently, a good simple approximation to the distribution should prove to be very useful. Such an approximation exists in the form of the proper normal distribution. For the purpose of investigating this approximation, consider some numerical examples.

Let $n = 12$ and $p = \frac{1}{3}$ and construct the graph of the corresponding binomial distribution. By the use of formula (1), the values of $P\{x\}$ were computed, correct to three decimals, as

$$
\begin{array}{lll}
P\{0\} = .008 & P\{4\} = .238 & P\{8\} \ = .015 \\
P\{1\} = .046 & P\{5\} = .191 & P\{9\} \ = .003 \\
P\{2\} = .127 & P\{6\} = .111 & P\{10\} = .000 \\
P\{3\} = .212 & P\{7\} = .048 & P\{11\} = .000 \\
& & P\{12\} = .000.
\end{array}
$$

(9)

Although the graph used earlier for a binomial distribution was a line graph because of the discrete character of the variable x, this distribution will be graphed as a histogram in order to compare it more readily with normal-distribution histograms. The graph of the histogram for this distribution is shown in Fig. 16. The height of any rectangle is equal to

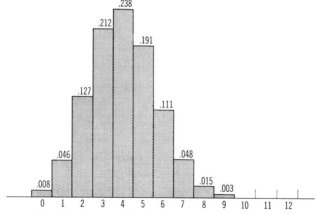

Fig. 16   Binomial distribution for $p = \frac{1}{3}$ and $n = 12$.

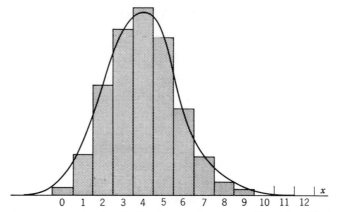

Fig. 17   Binomial distribution for $p = \frac{1}{3}$ and $n = 12$, with a fitted normal curve.

the probability given by (9) for the corresponding class mark. Since the base length of any rectangle is 1, the area of any rectangle is equal to its height, and therefore these probabilities are also given by the areas of the corresponding rectangles. The shape of this histogram resembles somewhat that of the histogram of Fig. 10, which has a normal curve fitted to it; therefore, it appears that this histogram could also be fitted fairly well by the proper normal curve.

Since a normal distribution curve is completely determined by its mean and standard deviation, the natural normal curve to use here is the one with the same mean and standard deviation as the binomial distribution. From the formulas given in (6), it follows that $\mu = 12 \cdot \frac{1}{3} = 4$ and $\sigma = \sqrt{12 \cdot \frac{1}{3} \cdot \frac{2}{3}} = 1.63$. A normal curve with this mean and standard deviation was superimposed on Fig. 16 to give Fig. 17. It appears that the fit is fairly good in spite of the fact that $n = 12$ is a small value of n and advanced theory promises a good fit only for large values of n.

As a test of the accuracy of the normal-curve approximation here and as an illustration of how to use normal-curve methods for approximating binomial probabilities, consider a few problems related to Fig. 17.

If the probability that a marksman will hit a target is $\frac{1}{3}$ and if he takes 12 shots, what is the probability that he will score at least 6 hits? The exact answer, correct to three decimals, is obtained by adding the values in (9) from $x = 6$ to $x = 12$, which is found to be .177. Geometrically, this answer is the area of that part of the histogram in Fig. 17 lying to the right of $x = 5.5$. Therefore, to approximate this probability by normal-curve methods, it is merely necessary to find the area under that part of the fitted normal curve lying to the right of 5.5. Since the fitted normal curve has $\mu = 4$ and $\sigma = 1.63$, it follows that

$$z = \frac{x - \mu}{\sigma} = \frac{5.5 - 4}{1.63} = 0.92.$$

Now, from Table IV, the area to the right of $z = 0.92$ is .179; therefore this is the desired approximation to the probability of getting at least 6 hits. Since the exact answer was just computed to be .177, the normal curve approximation here is certainly good.

To test the accuracy of normal-curve methods over a shorter interval, calculate the probability that the marksman will score precisely six hits in twelve shots. From (9) the answer, correct to three decimals, is .111. Since this is equal to the area of the rectangle whose base runs from 5.5 to 6.5, to approximate this answer it is necessary to find the area under the fitted normal curve between $x = 5.5$ and $x = 6.5$. Thus, by calculating the z values and using Table IV, one obtains

$$z_2 = \frac{6.5 - 4}{1.63} = 1.53, \qquad A_2 = .4370$$

$$z_1 = \frac{5.5 - 4}{1.63} = 0.92, \qquad A_1 = .3212.$$

Subtracting these two areas gives .116, which, compared to the exact probability value of .111, is also good. From these two examples it appears that normal-curve methods give good approximations even for some situations, such as the one considered here, in which n is not very large.

Suppose, now, that the value of $p = \frac{1}{3}$ is not changed but n is allowed to increase in size. The resulting histogram, like the one in Fig. 17, will move off to the right, spread out, and decrease in height. It is difficult to inspect such a histogram and to observe whether the proper normal curve would fit it well. These undesired changes in the histogram can be prevented by shifting to the corresponding variable in standard units. From (8) this means graphing the histogram for the variable

$$z = \frac{x - \mu}{\sigma} .$$

When formulas (6) are used, the standard variable z assumes the form

(10)
$$z = \frac{x - np}{\sqrt{npq}} .$$

Since the variable z possesses a distribution with mean 0 and standard deviation 1, the histogram for z will behave itself and not go wandering off and flatten out when n becomes large, as is the case of the histogram for x.

Figures 18 and 19 show the histograms for the variable z when $p = \frac{1}{3}$ and $n = 24$ and 48, respectively. They show how rapidly the distribution of z approaches the distribution of a normal variable with mean 0 and

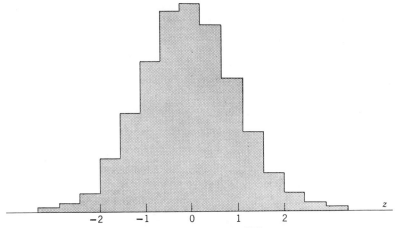

Fig. 18   Binomial distribution of $(x - np)/\sqrt{npq}$ for $p = \frac{1}{3}$ and $n = 24$.

standard deviation 1. It can be shown by advanced methods that if p is held fixed and n is allowed to become increasingly large, then the distribution of z will come increasingly close to the distribution of a normal variable with mean 0 and standard deviation 1. From a practical point of view, experience has shown that the approximation is fairly good as long as $np > 5$ when $p \leq \frac{1}{2}$ and $nq > 5$ when $p > \frac{1}{2}$.

The fact that the standard form of a binomial variable possesses a distribution approaching that of a standard normal variable implies that the binomial variable x possesses a histogram that can be fitted well by the proper normal curve when n is large. The proper normal curve is, of course, the one with mean and standard deviation given by formulas (6).

There are numerous occasions when it is more convenient to work with the proportion of successes, x/n, in n trials than with the actual number of successes, x. If the numerator and denominator in (10) are divided by n, z will assume the form

(11)
$$z = \frac{\dfrac{x}{n} - p}{\sqrt{\dfrac{pq}{n}}}.$$

The value of z has not changed, only the form in which it is written; consequently z still possesses an approximate normal distribution with

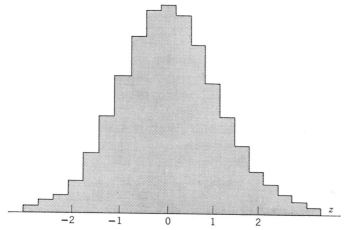

Fig. 19   Binomial distribution of $(x - np)/\sqrt{npq}$ for $p = \frac{1}{3}$ and $n = 48$.

mean and unit standard deviation when n is large This implies that the proportion of successes, x/n, possesses a histogram that can be fitted well by the proper normal curve when n is large. The proper normal curve is now the one with mean and standard deviation given by the formulas

(12)
$$\mu = p$$
$$\sigma = \sqrt{\frac{pq}{n}}.$$

As an illustration of the use of the normal-curve approximation to the binomial distribution in the form (11) consider the following problem. Suppose a politician claims that a survey in his district showed that 60 per cent of his constituents agreed with his vote on an important piece of legislation. If it is assumed temporarily that this percentage is correct, and if an impartial sample of 400 voters is taken in his district, what is the probability that the sample will yield less than 50 per cent in agreement?

If it is assumed that taking a sample of 400 voters is like playing a game of chance 400 times for which the probability of success in a single game is .6, this problem can be treated as a binomial-distribution problem with $p = .6$ and $n = 400$. For such a large value of n the normal curve approximation will be excellent. Using formula (11),

$$z = \frac{.5 - .6}{\sqrt{\dfrac{(.6)(.4)}{400}}} = -4.08.$$

Now the sample proportion, x/n, will be less than .5 provided that z is less than -4.08. The probability that $z < -4.08$ is by symmetry equal to the probability that $z > 4.08$, which is considered too small to be worth listing in Table IV. Thus, if it should happen that less than 50 per cent of the sample favored the politician, his claim of 60 per cent backing would certainly be discredited.

Objections may be raised, and rightfully so, that getting a sample of 400 voters is not equivalent to playing a game of chance 400 times. There are questions concerning the independence of the trials and the constancy of the probability that must be answered before one can be thoroughly happy with the binomial distribution model for this problem.

As a second illustration of the use of formula (11), the following problem will be solved. Past experience with an examination in freshman English has shown that only 50 per cent of the students pass it. If a new class of 200 freshmen takes the examination, what is the probability that at least 55 per cent will pass it? Here

$$z = \frac{.55 - .50}{\sqrt{\dfrac{(.5)(.5)}{200}}} = 1.41.$$

But $x \geq .55$ if, and only if $z \geq 1.41$; therefore by Table IV the probability of $x \geq .55$ is .08.

It should not be assumed from the preceding examples that all binomial-distribution problems can be treated satisfactorily by means of the normal approximation even though n may be fairly large. For example, if $n = 80$ and $p = \frac{1}{20}$, calculation of $P\{x\}$ values and a graph of those values will show that the distribution is not sufficiently symmetrical to permit a good fit by a normal curve. Since the mean is 4 here, and x cannot assume negative values, too much of the distribution is concentrated near zero for symmetry. Considerations such as these gave rise to the empirical rule for a good approximation, stated in the paragraph following (10).

▶ 8. BINOMIAL DISTRIBUTION DERIVATION

For those who have studied section 6 of Chapter 3, the correctness of formula (1) can be demonstrated as follows.

Consider an experiment of n trials and a particular sequence of outcomes that will produce precisely x successes and $n - x$ failures. One such sequence is the following in which all the successes occurred first, followed by all the failures:

$$\overbrace{SS \cdots S}^{x} \ \overbrace{FF \cdots F}^{n-x}.$$

Another such sequence is the following one in which a failure occurred first, followed by x consecutive successes, then by the remaining failures. Thus

$$FS\overbrace{S \cdots S}^{x} \ \overbrace{FF \cdots F}^{n-x-1}.$$

Because of the independence of the trials, the probability of obtaining the first of these two sequences is given by

$$\overbrace{p \cdot p \cdots p}^{x} \cdot \overbrace{q \cdot q \cdots q}^{n-x} = p^x q^{n-x}$$

The probability for the second sequence is given by

$$q \cdot \overbrace{p \cdot p \cdots p}^{x} \cdot \overbrace{q \cdot q \cdots q}^{n-x-1} = p^x q^{n-x}$$

Thus the probability for the two sequences is the same and will be the same for every sequence that satisfies the condition of having x successes and $n - x$ failures.

The number of ways in which the desired event can occur is equal to the number of different sequences that can be written down of the type just displayed, those containing x letters S and $n - x$ letters F. But this is equal to the number of ways of choosing x positions out of n available positions in which to place the letter S. The remaining $n - x$ positions will automatically be assigned the letter F. The n positions may be numbered and treated like n numbered cards. The problem then is to choose x of those cards. Since only the numbers on the cards are of interest and not the order in which they are drawn this is a combination problem. From the derivation in section 6 of Chapter 3, the number of ways of choosing x cards from n distinct cards is given by the combination formula (13) of Chapter 3, namely,

$$\binom{n}{x} = \frac{n!}{x!\,(n-x)!}\,.$$

This, therefore, is the number of sequences that produce exactly x successes.

Since each of these sequences represents one of the mutually exclusive ways in which the desired event can occur, and each such sequence has the same probability of occurring, namely $p^x q^{n-x}$, it follows that the desired probability is obtained by adding this probability as many times as there are sequences. But the number of such sequences was just found to be $\binom{n}{x}$; therefore $P\{x\}$ is obtained by multiplying $p^x q^{n-x}$ by $\binom{n}{x}$, which verifies formula (1).

9. REVIEW EXERCISES

A box contains the following nine cards: the three, four, and five of spades, the three and four of clubs, the three and four of hearts, and the four and five of diamonds. (*a*) If one card is to be drawn from the box and x is the random variable representing the number of black cards that will be obtained, find the distribution of x and graph it. (*b*) If one card is to be drawn and x represents the number on the card, find the distribution of x and graph it. (*c*) If two cards are to be drawn with the first card being replaced before the second drawing and x represents the number of black cards that will be obtained, find the distribution of x and graph it. (*d*) Work part (*c*) if the first card is not replaced. (*e*) If two cards are to be drawn without replacement and x represents the sum of the two numbers obtained, find the distribution of x and graph it. (*f*) Which of the preceding distributions, if any, are binomial distributions based on one or two trials, as the case may be? (*g*) Calculate the mean and standard deviation of the distribution in (*c*) by direct calculations and by using the binomial formulas. (*h*) If the experiment in (*a*) is to be repeated 10 times, with the drawn card always being replaced, and x denotes the number of black cards that will be obtained, find an expression for $P\{x\}$ which gives the distribution of x. (*i*) Use the result in (*h*) to calculate $P\{4 \leq x \leq 5\}$. (*j*) Use the normal approximation to approximate the value found in (*i*). (*k*) Calculate the approximate probability, using the normal approximation, that the proportion of black cards in 100 trials of the experiment in (*a*) will be less than .6. The solutions follow.

(*a*)

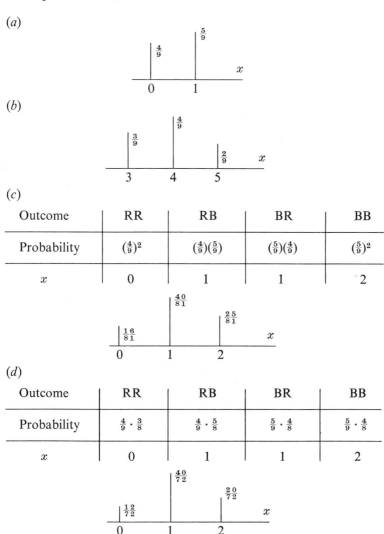

(*b*)

(*c*)

Outcome	RR	RB	BR	BB
Probability	$(\frac{4}{9})^2$	$(\frac{4}{9})(\frac{5}{9})$	$(\frac{5}{9})(\frac{4}{9})$	$(\frac{5}{9})^2$
x	0	1	1	2

(*d*)

Outcome	RR	RB	BR	BB
Probability	$\frac{4}{9} \cdot \frac{3}{8}$	$\frac{4}{9} \cdot \frac{5}{8}$	$\frac{5}{9} \cdot \frac{4}{8}$	$\frac{5}{9} \cdot \frac{4}{8}$
x	0	1	1	2

(e)

Outcomes: 33 43 53   Values of x: 6 7 8
           34 44 54   7 8 9
           35 45 55   8 9 10

Probabilities: $\frac{3}{9} \cdot \frac{2}{8}$ $\frac{4}{9} \cdot \frac{3}{8}$ $\frac{2}{9} \cdot \frac{3}{8}$

                $\frac{3}{9} \cdot \frac{4}{8}$ $\frac{4}{9} \cdot \frac{3}{8}$ $\frac{2}{9} \cdot \frac{4}{8}$

                $\frac{3}{9} \cdot \frac{2}{8}$ $\frac{4}{9} \cdot \frac{2}{8}$ $\frac{2}{9} \cdot \frac{1}{8}$

x	6	7	8	9	10
$P\{x\}$	$\frac{6}{72}$	$\frac{24}{72}$	$\frac{24}{72}$	$\frac{16}{72}$	$\frac{2}{72}$

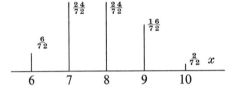

(f) (a) $n = 1$, $p = \frac{5}{9}$
    (c) $n = 2$, $p = \frac{5}{9}$.

(g)

x	$81P\{x\}$	$81xP\{x\}$	$81x^2P\{x\}$
0	16	0	0
1	40	40	40
2	25	50	100
		90	140

$$\mu = \frac{90}{81} = \frac{10}{9}$$

$$\sigma^2 = \frac{140}{81} - \left(\frac{10}{9}\right)^2 = \frac{40}{81}$$

$$\sigma = \frac{\sqrt{40}}{9}$$

$$\mu = np \doteq 2 \cdot \frac{5}{9} = \frac{10}{9}$$

$$\sigma = \sqrt{npq} = \sqrt{2 \cdot \frac{5}{9} \cdot \frac{4}{9}} = \frac{\sqrt{40}}{9}$$

(h) $n = 10, p = \dfrac{5}{9}$

$$P\{x\} = \frac{10!}{x!\,(10 - x)!}\left(\frac{5}{9}\right)^{x}\left(\frac{4}{9}\right)^{10-x}.$$

(i) $\qquad P\{4 \le x \le 5\} = P\{4\} + P\{5\}$

$$= \frac{10!}{4!\,6!}\left(\frac{5}{9}\right)^{4}\left(\frac{4}{9}\right)^{6} + \frac{10!}{5!\,5!}\left(\frac{5}{9}\right)^{5}\left(\frac{4}{9}\right)^{5}$$

$$= .39.$$

(j) $\mu = np = 10 \cdot \dfrac{5}{9} = \dfrac{50}{9} = 5.56$

$$\sigma = \sqrt{npq} = \sqrt{10 \cdot \frac{5}{9} \cdot \frac{4}{9}} = \frac{10}{9}\sqrt{2} = 1.57$$

$$z_1 = \frac{5.50 - 5.56}{1.57} = -\frac{.06}{1.57} = -.04$$

$$z_2 = \frac{3.50 - 5.56}{1.57} = -\frac{2.06}{1.57} = -1.31$$

$A_1 = .0160, \; A_2 = .4049, \; A_2 - A_1 = .3889;$ hence

$$P\{4 \le x \le 5\} \doteq .3889, \text{ or } .39.$$

(k) $\qquad z = \dfrac{\dfrac{x}{n} - p}{\sqrt{\dfrac{pq}{n}}} = \dfrac{.60 - .556}{\sqrt{\dfrac{\frac{5}{9} \cdot \frac{4}{9}}{100}}} = \dfrac{.044}{.050} = .88$

$A = .31$; hence $P\left\{\dfrac{x}{10} < .6\right\} = .50 + .31 = .81.$

EXERCISES

1. Toss 3 coins simultaneously and record the number of heads obtained. Perform this experiment 100 times and then compare your experimental relative frequencies with those given by theory in Fig. 6.

2. Roll a die 3 times, or roll 3 dice simultaneously, and record the number of aces obtained. Perform this experiment 100 times and compare your experimental relative frequencies with those given by theory in Fig. 8.

3. A box contains three cards consisting of the two, three, and four of hearts. Two cards are drawn from the box, with the first card drawn returned to the box before the second drawing. Let x denote the sum of the numbers obtained on the two cards. Use the enumeration of events technique to derive the distribution of the random variable x.

4. Work problem 3 under the assumption that the first card is not returned to the box.

5. Verify the values given in the text in Table 3 by means of formula (1).

6. Use the method of enumeration of possible outcomes with their corresponding probabilities to derive the binomial distribution for the number of heads obtained in tossing a coin 4 times. Check your results by means of formula (1).

7. Work problem 6 for the number of aces obtained in rolling a die 4 times.

8. A coin is tossed 5 times. Using formula (1), calculate the values of $P\{x\}$, where x denotes the number of heads, and graph $P\{x\}$ as a line chart.

9. If the probability that you will win a hand of bridge is $\frac{1}{3}$ and you play 6 hands, calculate the values of $P\{x\}$, where x denotes the number of wins, by means of formula (1).

10. For the binomial variable for which $n = 6$ and $p = \frac{1}{4}$, calculate the mean and standard deviation and verify your results by means of formulas (6).

11. For problem 9, calculate the mean and standard deviation for the variable x and verify your results by means of formulas (6).

12. Given that x is normally distributed with mean 10 and standard deviation 2, use Table IV to calculate the probability that $(a)\, x > 12$, $(b)\, x > 11$, $(c)\, x < 9$, $(d)\, x < 9.5$, $(e)\, 9 < x < 12$.

13. Assuming that stature (x) of college males is normally distributed with mean 69 inches and standard deviation 3 inches, use Table IV to calculate the probability that $(a)\, x < 65$ inches, $(b)\, 65$ inches $< x < 70$ inches.

14. Suppose your score on an examination in standard units (z) is .8 and scores are assumed to be normally distributed. What percentage of the students would be expected to score higher than you?

15. A high-school gym teacher announces that he grades individual athletic events by achievement relative to all his classes. If he gives 20 per cent A's and if experience has shown that the mean is 4 feet 8 inches and the standard deviation is 4 inches for the high jump, how high should a student plan to jump if he expects to get an A? Assume that jumps are normally distributed.

16. A coin is tossed 8 times. Find the probability, both exactly by means of formula (1) and approximately by means of the normal-curve approximation, of getting (a) 5 heads, (b) at least 6 heads.

17. If the probability of your winning at pinochle is .4, find the probability, both exactly by means of formula (1) and approximately by means of the normal-curve approximation, of winning 3 or more of 6 games played.

18. If 30 per cent of students have defective vision, what is the probability that at least half of the members of a class of 20 students will possess defective vision? Use the normal curve approximation.

19. If 10 per cent of television picture tubes burn out before their guarantee has expired, (a) what is the probability that a merchant who has sold 100 such tubes will be forced to replace at least 20 of them? (b) What is the probability that he will replace at least 5 and not more than 15 tubes? Use the normal curve approximation.

20. If 20 per cent of the drivers in a certain city have at least 1 accident during a year's driving, what is the probability that the percentage for 300 customers of an insurance company in that city will exceed 25 per cent during the next year? Use the normal curve approximation.

21. If 10 per cent of the cotter pins being manufactured are defective, what is the approximate probability that the percentage of defectives in a box of 200 will exceed 15 per cent?

22. Would you expect the binomial distribution to be applicable to a calculation of the probability that the stock market will rise at least 20 of the days during the next month if you have a record for the last 5 years of the percentage of days that it did rise? Explain.

23. Explain why it would not be strictly correct to apply the binomial distribution to a calculation of the probability that it will rain at least 10 days during next January if each day in January is treated as a trial of an event and one has a record of the percentage of rainy days in January.

24. Suppose $n = 30$ and $p = \frac{1}{10}$. Calculate $P\{0\}$, and on the basis of its value argue that a good normal curve fit to the entire distribution would not be expected here.

25. For problem 24, calculate $P\{x \leq 0\}$ by means of the normal curve approximation.

26. Give an example of a binomial distribution for which $n > 100$ and p is not small but for which there will not be a good normal approximation.

27. A box contains four black cards numbered 1, 2, 3, and 4, three red cards numbered 2, 3, and 4, and three white cards numbered 3, 4, and 5. Work parts (a) through (g) of the illustrative review exercise in section 9. (h) If the experiment in (a) is repeated eight times, with the drawn card always replaced, and x denotes the number of black cards obtained, find an expression for $P\{x\}$. (i) Use the result in (h) to calculate $P\{3 \leq x \leq 5\}$. (j) Use the normal approximation to solve (i). (k) Calculate the probability, using the normal approximation, that the proportion of black cards will be greater than $\frac{1}{2}$ if the experiment is conducted 50 times.

▶28. Derive the formula $\mu = np$ for the general binomial distribution $P\{x\}$ given by (1) by writing out the terms in $\sum_{x=0}^{n} xP\{x\}$, then factoring out the common factor np, then calculating $\sum_{x=0}^{n-1} Q(x)$ where $Q(x)$ is the same as $P\{x\}$ for $n - 1$ trials, and finally recognizing that this last sum, which has the value 1, is the other factor in $\Sigma \, xP\{x\}$. The formula seems obvious but its algebraic derivation is not.

▶29. Consult a more advanced statistics text to observe the algebraic technique used to derive the formula $\sigma = \sqrt{npq}$.

CHAPTER 5

Sampling

1. RANDOM SAMPLING

The preceding chapters have been concerned with empirical and theoretical frequency distributions. As explained in Chapter 4, a theoretical frequency distribution, such as the normal distribution, is thought of as the limiting form of a sample frequency distribution as the sample size increases indefinitely.

In the discussion of samples and sample frequency distributions it was assumed that random samples were always taken. Random sampling was defined in Chapter 2 as a sampling procedure in which every member of the population has the same chance of being selected. In terms of probability this implies that the probability of any particular member being selected is equal to $1/N$, where N denotes the number of individuals in the population. More generally, if the sample is to contain r individuals, in which case the sample is said to be of size r, the sampling is defined to be random if every combination of r individuals in the population has the same chance of being selected. In terms of probability and the formula $\binom{N}{r}$ for the number of ways of selecting a set of r individuals from N individuals, this implies that the probability of any particular group of r individuals being selected is equal to $1 / \binom{N}{r}$.

In Chapter 2 random sampling was advocated on the grounds that it is a method of sampling for which one can expect the samples and their distribution to represent the population distribution correctly. There are, however, additional reasons for advocating it. The most important of these is that random sampling lends itself to probability models for distributions.

117

Since the conclusions to be drawn about populations by means of samples are to be based upon probabilities, samples must be selected in such a manner that the rules of probability can be applied to them. For the purpose of seeing why this is so, return to the problem discussed at the end of Chapter 4. There it was assumed that a sample of 400 voters could be treated as 400 independent trials of an experiment for which the probability of success in a single trial is .6. This assumption permitted the problem to be treated as a binomial-distribution problem; hence it also permitted the calculation of probabilities of various possible outcomes by means of the binomial distribution formula and its normal curve approximation.

The two important features that are necessary to enable the binomial distribution to be applied to practical problems such as this, namely that the samples are independent and that the probability of success is the same for all samples, should be stressed. Since these two properties are satisfied by random sampling and are usually possessed by games of chance, such as tossing coins or rolling dice, it follows that a satisfactory way of obtaining samples is to introduce a game of chance to make the selection. For the illustration being discussed, consider how this could be done to obtain a sample of 400 voters from the registered voters of a given district.

A cumbersome but satisfactory way of introducing a game-of-chance selection would be to write the name of each voter on a slip of paper, mix the slips well in a large container, and then draw 400 slips from the container, which is thoroughly mixed after each individual drawing. The purpose of the thorough mixing is to insure independence of the trials. If there were no mixing and the name of a voter in a section of a district consisting largely of members of the same political party had been drawn, then in the next drawing the chances of getting another member of this same political party would be increased because of the proximity of the slips for that section and the natural tendency to draw slips from the same part of the container. Although the thorough mixing insures the independence of the trials, it does not strictly guarantee that the probability of success will not change from trial to trial. If the total number of registered voters is not large and if the first 100 samples produced members of only one political party, then the probability of getting another member of that same political party on the next draw would be considerably smaller than it was before any drawings had been made. However, if the population being sampled is large compared to the size of the sample being taken, then under thorough mixing the probability will change very little, and for all practical purposes it may be assumed to be constant. This is the usual situation in statistical problems.

A method of drawing 400 names from a register which is simpler and better than using slips and containers is to employ a table of random sampling numbers. Such a table could be constructed by writing the digits 0 to 9 on ten slips of paper, mixing them thoroughly between each drawing, replacing the slip drawn each time, and recording the digit drawn each time. The table of random numbers given in Table II of the appendix was obtained by a more refined method than with slips of paper, however. Suppose now that there were exactly 10,000 registered voters in the district being sampled and each voter had a number, 0000 to 9999, assigned him. Then, to obtain a sample of 400 names, it would merely be necessary to select 400 sets of four-digit numbers from Table II. Since these numbers occur in groups of five, one would select only the first four digits of a group to yield a name. There are fifty rows to each column; hence it would suffice to select eight columns. From the manner in which random numbers are formed, it follows that every four-digit number has the same probability of being formed at any specified place in the table; therefore, one can just as well choose the numbers systematically by reading down a column as by jumping around in the table. It might well happen, of course, that one or more individuals in the population would be selected more than once when random sampling numbers are used because these numbers were formed independently and therefore a particular four-digit number may occur several times in the table. If there had been only 7500 registered voters in the district, then one would discard any four-digit number obtained from the table that is larger than 7499 because there would be no voters associated with those numbers. Any size sample can be extracted from any population of reasonable size in a similar manner by using a little ingenuity.

Since tables of random numbers are expected to yield samples that possess the defining property of random sampling, samples obtained by using tables of random numbers are considered to be random samples. Strictly speaking, one should talk only about the method of sampling and not about the results of the method. If the method of sampling insures that the property required for random sampling is being satisfied, it is called random sampling and any sample obtained by employing this method is therefore called a random sample. Thus, if a table of random numbers yielded a sample of 400, all of whom belonged to the same political party, the sample would still be called random because it had been obtained by a random-sampling process.

Since one can only approximate ideal conditions in real life, no table of random numbers or game of chance can guarantee random sampling; however, the approximation is usually sufficiently good that one need not be afraid to wager some of his own money on outcomes based on the assumption that such devices yield random samples.

It would appear that a great deal of effort is being expended on getting random samples when other methods that are simpler to use might yield samples just as satisfactory in many respects. For example, it would be much cheaper to take a sample of 400 voters in a district by selecting, say, 20 voters on a single street and then selecting 20 streets in the district. One might go a step further, for the purpose of obtaining a good cross section of the district, by selecting the 20 streets from poor, middle class, and wealthy sections in proportions approximately equal to the proportions of such voters. Unfortunately, being clever in designing sampling methods that give highly representative samples of the population being sampled is of no avail in statistics unless the methods possess the essential features of random sampling because the probability models of statistics apply only to random samples. One cannot, in general, make valid probability statements about the outcomes of other types of sampling methods. It is for this reason that statisticians insist that samples be randomly selected. It will be assumed, hereafter, that samples are always obtained by a random sampling method, and the adjective random will be omitted.

There are many examples, in public life, of fiascos that have occurred because conclusions were based on nonrandom samples. For example, in 1936 the *Literary Digest* conducted a poll by mail for the purpose of predicting the forthcoming presidential election. It sent out 10,000,000 ballots and on the basis of more than 2,000,000 returns predicted that Landon would be elected. Actually, Roosevelt received approximately 60 per cent of the votes cast in that election. Newspapers regularly report the opinions and predictions of politicians as though their statements possessed much merit, even when the politician declares that his opinions are based upon "sounding out" his constituents. Businessmen frequently make incorrect decisions in such fields as marketing when their decisions are based on faulty information obtained from poor samples.

Even though one may be aware of the importance of taking random samples, one may not be able to do so because of prohibitive costs. Thus, on a limited budget, one might not be able to afford to take a random sample of 400 voters in a district of 10,000 voters. The problem of how to select a random sample in practical situations is difficult enough, but the problems of statistical inference when a compromise on randomness must be made are considerably more difficult.

2. MODIFIED RANDOM SAMPLING

The type of random sampling that has been discussed thus far is known as simple random sampling. There are other fancier methods which have proved more useful than simple random sampling for certain kinds of problems. For example, suppose you wished to estimate the mean income of a group of 100 employees of a firm and the group consisted of 10 supervisors and 90 laborers. Suppose further that all 10 supervisors had the same salary, say, A dollars, and that all 90 laborers received the same pay, say, B dollars, where B is considerably smaller than A. Then the mean income, in dollars, of the entire group would be

$$\mu = \frac{10A + 90B}{100} = \frac{A + 9B}{10}.$$

Now if the estimate of μ were to be based on a sample of size 10 and if this sample were obtained by taking a random sample of size 9 from the 90 laborers and a random sample of size 1 from the 10 supervisors, the sample mean would estimate μ perfectly because the sample mean would be given by the second expression for μ. A simple random sample of size 10 taken from the entire population of 100 ordinarily would not yield exactly 9 laborers and 1 supervisor, and therefore it ordinarily would not estimate μ perfectly. Calculations show that this particular division of a random sample of size 10 would occur less than half the time. Although the setup in this problem is very artificial, because it is unlikely that all employees in the same category will have exactly the same income, nevertheless the modified random sampling in which the sizes of the two samples are made proportional to the sizes of the two groups will usually be more accurate for estimating the mean than a simple random sample of the same total size. This modified type of random sampling is called *proportional sampling*. It is a special case of what is known as *stratified sampling*. In this type of sampling the population is divided into groups, or strata, and random samples are taken separately from each of the groups. In proportional sampling the size of the sample from each group is made proportional to the size of the group, but for other kinds of stratified sampling this is not the case. When the members of individual groups are very homogeneous but the groups differ considerably, stratified sampling is considerably better than simple random sampling for estimating the mean of the population.

The following problem is an illustration of a situation for which the advantage of stratified random sampling would be quite pronounced. Suppose the mean weight of the children in an elementary school is to be estimated by means of a sample of size 200. Suppose there are six grades in the school and the number of pupils in each of the grades is known and is given as 200, 200, 180, 160, 140, and 120, respectively. Since there are 1,000 pupils in the school, these enrollments yield the proportions .20, .20, .18, .16, .14, and .12, respectively. Under proportional sampling, for a total sample of 200 one would therefore choose random samples in each grade of sizes 40, 40, 36, 32, 28, and 24, respectively. After calculating the means of those samples, which will be denoted by $\bar{x}_1, \bar{x}_2, \ldots, \bar{x}_6$, one would estimate the mean of the entire school by using the formula

$$.2\bar{x}_1 + .2\bar{x}_2 + .18\bar{x}_3 + .16\bar{x}_4 + .14\bar{x}_5 + .12\bar{x}_6.$$

Since the weights in a given grade are likely to be fairly homogeneous as contrasted to the variation in weights for the entire school, the estimates $\bar{x}_1, \bar{x}_2, \ldots, \bar{x}_6$ are likely to be fairly accurate estimates of the true mean weights for those grades and, therefore, since these individual estimates have been weighted properly to represent the enrollments in the various grades, the preceding estimate based on this proportional weighting would be expected to be an accurate estimate of the true mean weight for the entire school as compared to the estimate $\bar{x}$ based on a simple random sample of 200 taken from the entire school population. It is not possible at this stage to discuss how one determines the extent to which one estimate is better than another; however, assuming for the moment that a method of comparison is available, experience has shown that proportional sampling for a problem of the foregoing type often requires less than one-half as large a sample as a corresponding simple random sample.

The problem of how to obtain random samples from human populations that are widely dispersed is especially difficult. It would be very difficult and expensive, for example, to obtain a random sample of size 1,000 from the population of California. For problems of this type, it is customary to divide the entire region into small regions and to choose a random sample of those regions. They in turn can be broken down into smaller subregions for further random sampling. This procedure can be continued until convenient sampling units of individuals have been obtained. This type of sampling is called *cluster* sampling.

Although many practical problems require the use of modified random sampling methods rather than simple random sampling, they all employ simple random sampling at some stage, and therefore it is essential to understand simple random sampling before becoming interested in more elaborate methods. The discussion hereafter is therefore confined to simple random sampling.

The method of obtaining samples by means of a table of random numbers can be employed whether the variable of interest is discrete or continuous. In the problem of selecting 400 voters the variable was discrete, since interest was centered on the number of voters favoring the politician. In the earlier problem of selecting 120 dormitory students the variable was the continuous variable weight. In either case each member of the population can be associated with a different number, and the desired size sample can then be drawn by means of a table of random numbers. The resulting numbers determine the individuals to be selected. If the variable is a continuous variable, such as weight, the values of the continuous variable for those individuals selected then constitute the desired random sample.

In the next section a hypothetical sampling experiment will be conducted to obtain some theory on how sample means behave in repeated sampling experiments. After the hypothetical experiment conclusions have been obtained, an actual sampling experiment will be conducted to verify that the theory works in practice.

3. SAMPLING DISTRIBUTION OF $\bar{x}$

For the purpose of explaining the material of this section, consider the following problem. Let x represent the height of an individual selected at random from a population of adult males. Assume that x possesses a theoretical normal distribution with mean $\mu = 68$ inches and standard deviation $\sigma = 3$ inches. This means that the histogram of the population distribution of height can be fitted well by a normal curve having those values for the mean and standard deviation. The problem to be solved may now be stated: if a random sample of size $n = 25$ is taken from this population, what is the probability that the sample mean $\bar{x}$ will fall inside the interval 67–69 inches?

If the experiment of taking a random sample of 25 were repeated a large number of times, a large number of values of $\bar{x}$ would be available for classifying into a sample frequency distribution of $\bar{x}$. If this experiment were repeated indefinitely and the class interval chosen were very small, the upper boundary of the histogram representing the sample frequency distribution would be expected to smooth out and approximate a smooth curve. This limiting curve would represent a theoretical frequency distribution for the variable $\bar{x}$. By means of this distribution the desired probability of $\bar{x}$ lying inside the interval 67–69 could be calculated.

Since the population is finite, repeated sampling experiments would eventually exhaust the population, unless the sampled individuals were returned to the population each time. It is therefore necessary to assume that individuals are returned or that the population is so large that a long run of sampling experiments will have no appreciable effect on the population.

For the purpose of becoming acquainted with the notion of a sampling distribution for a sample mean, a small sampling experiment similar to the kind just described will be carried out. However, rather than taking samples of size 25 from a normal population with mean 68 and standard deviation 3, samples of size 4 will be taken from a discrete approximation to the standard normal distribution. This approximation is obtained by using Table IV to calculate the percentage of area under a normal curve corresponding to an interval of length 1 standard deviation, with the middle interval centered at the origin. The resulting percentages, written as decimal fractions, are shown in Fig. 1, which gives the histogram for this approximate normal distribution.

Incidentally, the percentages obtained from Fig. 1, when the two end interval percentages are combined on each side, give the percentages that are often used by instructors who "grade on the curve" to determine the percentage of letter grades A, B, C, D, and F to assign.

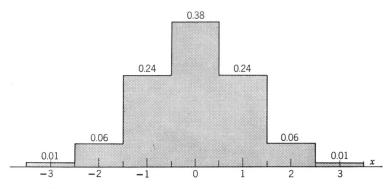

Fig. 1   An approximation to the standard normal distribution.

Samples of size 4 were taken from this discrete distribution by means of the random numbers found in Table II. First, a tabulating form of the type shown in Table 1 was constructed. By this procedure all pairs of random digits were divided into seven groups according to the proportions shown in Fig. 1 and associated with the class marks of Fig. 1. For example, $x = -3$ is assigned to the pair 00, which is 1 per cent of all such pairs, and the value $x = -2$ is assigned to the pairs from 01 to 06 inclusive, which include 6 per cent of all random-number pairs. Four such pairs of random numbers are read from Table II and recorded in the proper class interval to form one experiment. The results of the first three such experiments are shown in Table 1. This experiment was repeated 50 times. Next, the mean for each experiment was calculated and recorded in the last row of Table 1, labeled $\bar{x}$. The sample means for the 50 experiments that were carried out here are shown in Table 2.

TABLE 1

x	Random numbers	1	2	3	$\cdots$
−3	00				
−2	01–06		/	/	
−1	07–30	/			
0	31–68	//	/	///	
1	69–92	/	/		
2	93–98		/		
3	99				
$\bar{x}$		0	$\frac{1}{4}$	$-\frac{1}{2}$	$\cdots$

TABLE 2

Experiment number	1	2	3	4	5	6	7	8	9	10	11	12	13	14
Value of $\bar{x}$	0	$\frac{1}{4}$	$-\frac{2}{4}$	$\frac{2}{4}$	$\frac{1}{4}$	$\frac{2}{4}$	0	$\frac{1}{4}$	$-\frac{3}{4}$	$\frac{1}{4}$	$-\frac{3}{4}$	$-\frac{2}{4}$	$-\frac{2}{4}$	$-\frac{1}{4}$

15	16	17	18	19	20	21	22	23	24	25	26	27	28	29	30	31	32
$\frac{1}{4}$	0	$-\frac{2}{4}$	0	$-\frac{2}{4}$	$-\frac{2}{4}$	0	$-\frac{1}{4}$	$\frac{1}{4}$	0	$-\frac{1}{4}$	$\frac{3}{4}$	$\frac{2}{4}$	$-\frac{2}{4}$	$\frac{1}{4}$	$-\frac{2}{4}$	$-\frac{1}{4}$	0

33	34	35	36	37	38	39	40	41	42	43	44	45	46	47	48	49	50
$\frac{2}{4}$	0	$-\frac{1}{4}$	$\frac{2}{4}$	0	0	$-\frac{5}{4}$	$\frac{1}{4}$	0	$\frac{3}{4}$	$-\frac{3}{4}$	$\frac{5}{4}$	$-\frac{4}{4}$	0	0	$\frac{2}{4}$	0	$\frac{1}{4}$

The values of $\bar{x}$ were next tabulated to yield the frequency table shown in Table 3 in which the third row gives the percentages in decimal-fraction form of the corresponding absolute frequencies.

Finally, this frequency table was graphed as a histogram. Since total areas must be equal to 1 in comparing probability distributions, and since the class interval in this table is $\frac{1}{4}$, it is necessary to draw rectangles that are four times as high as the $f/50$ values. The resulting histogram, with area 1, is shown in Fig. 2.

On comparing Figs. 1 and 2, it is apparent that sample means based on four measurements each do not vary as much as do individual sample values. This is certainly to be expected because, for example, a large value of $\bar{x}$ would require four large values of x, and the probability of getting four large values is much smaller than the probability of getting one large value. The standard deviation of the $\bar{x}$ distribution is obviously considerably smaller than that for the x distribution. Furthermore, it appears that the $\bar{x}$ distribution possesses a mean that is close to 0, which is the mean of the x distribution. Finally, except for one rather pronounced irregularity for the interval centered at $-\frac{1}{4}$, it appears that the distribution of $\bar{x}$, except for the difference in spread, possesses a distribution of the same approximate normal type as the x distribution.

TABLE 3

$\bar{x}$	$-\frac{5}{4}$	$-\frac{4}{4}$	$-\frac{3}{4}$	$-\frac{2}{4}$	$-\frac{1}{4}$	0	$\frac{1}{4}$	$\frac{2}{4}$	$\frac{3}{4}$	$\frac{4}{4}$	$\frac{5}{4}$
f	1	1	3	8	5	14	9	6	2	0	1
$f/50$	.02	.02	.06	.16	.10	.28	.18	.12	.04	.00	.02

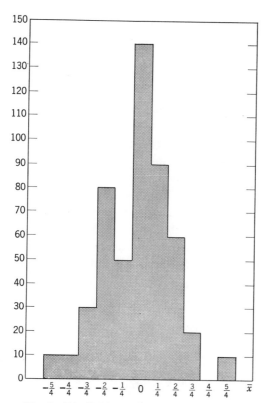

Fig. 2   Distribution of $\bar{x}$ for samples of size 4 from the distribution of Fig. 1.

Calculations of the mean and standard deviation for the $\bar{x}$ distribution were made by means of the Table 3 values. Those calculations yielded the values $-.035$ and $.48$, respectively. Thus, the mean of the $\bar{x}$ distribution is very close to the mean of the x distribution, whereas the standard deviation of the $\bar{x}$ distribution is approximately one-half the standard deviation of the x distribution, because the latter distribution approximates a normal distribution with $\sigma = 1$.

If this sampling experiment had been carried out, say, 500 times rather than just 50, irregularities such as those in Fig. 2 would disappear and it would be found that the properties of the $\bar{x}$ distribution just discussed would become increasingly apparent. Thus, it would be found that the histogram could be fitted very well with a normal curve, that the mean of the $\bar{x}$ distribution would be very close to 0, and that the standard deviation of the $\bar{x}$ distribution would have a value very close to one-half the value of the standard deviation of the x distribution. Although the samples here were taken from an approximate normal distribution as given by Fig. 1 rather than from an exact normal distribution, similar results would be obtained if the approximation were made increasingly good by choosing a very small class interval.

Fortunately, it is not necessary to carry out such repeated sampling experiments to arrive at the theoretical frequency distribution for $\bar{x}$. By using the rules of probability and advanced mathematical methods, it is possible to derive the equation of the curve representing the distribution of $\bar{x}$ when the sampling is from the exact normal distribution rather than an approximation. This corresponds to what was done in Chapter 4 to arrive at the theoretical distribution for binomial x without performing any sampling experiments. It turns out that $\bar{x}$ will possess a normal distribution if x does, with the same mean as x but with a standard deviation that is $1/\sqrt{n}$ times the standard deviation of x. These mathematical results are expressed in the form of a theorem:

(1)   **Theorem.** *If* x *possesses a normal distribution with mean* μ *and standard deviation* σ, *then the sample mean* $\bar{x}$, *based on a random sample of size* n, *will also possess a normal distribution with mean* μ *and standard deviation* $\sigma/\sqrt{n}$.

The distribution of $\bar{x}$ given by this theorem is often called the sampling distribution of $\bar{x}$ because of its connection with repeated sampling experiments, even though it is derived by purely mathematical methods.

This theorem is a purely mathematical theorem about ideal distributions corresponding to smooth curves; however, the conclusions can be expected to hold well for actual populations, provided the population is large and provided the population histogram can be fitted well by a normal curve. This means that if one starts with a population whose histogram can be fitted well with a normal curve and if one takes a large number of samples each of size n and calculates the value of $\bar{x}$ for each sample, then the histogram for the $\bar{x}$ values will be fitted well by the normal curve specified in the theorem.

The results of the sampling experiment just completed appear to be in agreement with this theorem. The histogram of Fig. 2 looks like the type of histogram that one gets from samples from a normal population, and since $\sigma \doteq 1$ and $n = 4$ here, its mean and standard deviation are in

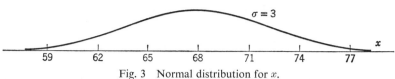

Fig. 3   Normal distribution for x.

agreement with the theoretical values of 0 and $\sigma/\sqrt{4} \doteq \frac{1}{2}$ given by the theorem. From this theorem one can draw the conclusion that the means of samples of size 4 from a normal population possess only one-half the variability about the mean of the population that the individual measurements do.

The problem introduced at the beginning of this section is now used to illustrate this theorem. Since $\mu = 68$, $\sigma = 3$, and $n = 25$ here, the theorem states that $\bar{x}$ will possess a normal distribution with mean 68 and standard deviation given by

$$\sigma_{\bar{x}} = \frac{\sigma}{\sqrt{n}} = \frac{3}{\sqrt{25}} = .6.$$

Figures 3 and 4 show the relationship between the distributions of x and $\bar{x}$.

The problem of calculating the probability that $\bar{x}$ will lie inside the interval (67, 69) is now easily solved by the methods introduced in Chapter 4 by means of Fig. 4 and Table IV of the appendix. The values of z

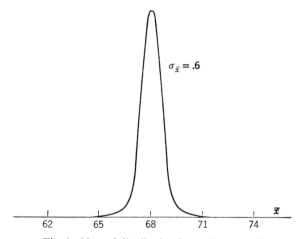

Fig. 4   Normal distribution for $\bar{x}$ when $n = 25$.

corresponding to $\bar{x}_1 = 67$ and $\bar{x}_2 = 69$ are given by

$$z_1 = \frac{67 - 68}{.6} = -1.67, \qquad z_2 = \frac{69 - 68}{.6} = 1.67.$$

Since, from Table IV, the probability that z will lie between -1.67 and 1.67 is equal to .90, this value is also the probability that $\bar{x}$ will lie inside the interval (67, 69).

The quantity $\sigma/\sqrt{n}$ is often called the standard error of the mean; however, that name is somewhat unfortunate because there is really no error involved here. This quantity is merely the standard deviation of the random variable $\bar{x}$ and therefore measures the natural variation of that variable. If, however, μ represented the length of a building, say, and x its measured length, then it would be proper to speak of errors of measurement and the standard deviation of a mean of such measurements as the standard error of the mean.

Suppose now that the variable x does not possess a normal distribution. What then can be said about the distribution of $\bar{x}$? A number of statisticians have conducted sampling experiments with different kinds of nonnormal distributions for x to see what effect the nonnormality would have on the distribution for $\bar{x}$. The surprising result has always been that if n is larger than about 25 the distribution of $\bar{x}$ will appear to be normal in spite of the population distribution chosen for x. Several years ago an instructor of an advanced statistics course challenged his students to construct a distribution as nonnormal as they could and wagered them that if he took samples of size 25 from their population the resulting $\bar{x}$ distribution would check out as a normal distribution. After agreement on the rules of the contest, the experiment was conducted. That evening the instructor ate in style at the students' expense. If the distribution for x does not differ too widely from a normal distribution, the distribution of $\bar{x}$ will often appear to be normal for n as small as 5. This remarkable property of $\bar{x}$ is of much practical importance because a large share of practical problems involve samples sufficiently large to permit one to assume that $\bar{x}$ is normally distributed and thus permit the use of familiar normal-curve methods to solve problems related to means without being concerned about the nature of the population distribution.

A well-known mathematical theorem, known as a "central limit theorem," essentially states that under very mild assumptions the distribution of $\bar{x}$ will approach a normal distribution as the sample size, n, increases. This theorem, together with the results of sampling experiments of the type already discussed, can be expressed in the following manner:

(2)   **Theorem.** *If x possesses a distribution with mean μ and standard deviation σ, then the sample mean x̄, based on a random sample of size n, will possess an approximate normal distribution with mean μ and standard deviation $\sigma/\sqrt{n}$, the approximation becoming increasingly good as n increases.*

For the purpose of demonstrating that $\bar{x}$ may possess an approximate normal distribution with mean μ and standard deviation $\sigma/\sqrt{n}$, even though x is not normally distributed, the following sampling experiment was conducted. Random samples of size 10 were chosen from the population represented by the histogram in Fig. 5. The variable x here is a discrete variable that can assume only the integer values 1 to 6, with the corresponding probabilities indicated on the histogram. It is considerably easier to conduct a sampling experiment with a simple discrete variable, such as the one being used here, than with a continuous type variable, such as height. The theorem in (2) does not require that x be a continuous variable. A histogram is used in place of a line chart merely to display the lack of normality better.

Two-digit random numbers from Table II were divided into six groups, corresponding to the six possible values of x. The first 25 per cent of these numbers, namely all those from 00 to 24, were assigned the x value 1. The next 25 per cent, those from 25 to 49, were assigned the x value 2, the next 20 per cent, those from 50 to 69, the x value 3, etc. After these assignments had been made, a column of two-digit random numbers was

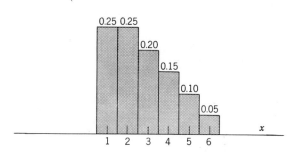

Fig. 5 Population distribution for sampling experiment.

selected. The first 10 numbers in that column yielded the first sample of size $n = 10$ from the x population. The second set of 10 numbers in that column yielded the second sample of 10, etc. This was continued, with as many columns as needed, until 100 samples had been drawn.

In the next step of the experiment the values of $\bar{x}$ for those 100 samples were calculated. The results of those computations are shown in Table 4. After the $\bar{x}$ values had been calculated, they were classified in a frequency table by using a class interval of length .2, just as was done for samples in Chapter 2. The results of this classification are shown in Table 5 and Fig. 6. The class boundaries in Table 5 do not appear to agree with the type advocated in Chapter 2, but that is because the variable here is discrete, and there are only two possible values in each class interval. The histogram of Fig. 6 certainly has the appearance of one that might have been obtained from sampling a normal population. Thus the claim in (2) that $\bar{x}$ should have an approximate normal distribution seems to have been fulfilled here.

Finally, the values of the sample mean and the sample standard

TABLE 4

Sample number	1	2	3	4	5	6	7	8	9	10	11	12	13	14
Value of $\bar{x}$	3.3	3.2	2.6	2.4	2.1	2.2	2.7	2.7	2.9	3.1	3.7	2.8	2.7	2.8

15	16	17	18	19	20	21	22	23	24	25	26	27	28	29	30	31
2.3	2.5	3.7	2.4	2.6	3.0	3.4	2.5	2.8	3.6	2.9	2.7	3.3	2.9	2.3	2.4	3.4

32	33	34	35	36	37	38	39	40	41	42	43	44	45	46	47	48
2.7	1.9	2.4	2.3	2.1	3.4	3.1	2.7	2.5	2.2	2.6	2.8	3.1	3.4	3.1	2.9	2.5

49	50	51	52	53	54	55	56	57	58	59	60	61	62	63	64	65
2.2	3.1	2.5	2.7	3.0	2.9	2.4	2.5	2.8	2.3	2.9	2.3	2.8	3.1	2.6	2.4	2.9

66	67	68	69	70	71	72	73	74	75	76	77	78	79	80	81	82
3.1	2.9	2.3	3.2	2.8	3.1	3.2	3.2	3.1	2.5	3.0	3.0	2.7	2.8	1.5	3.2	2.7

83	84	85	86	87	88	89	90	91	92	93	94	95	96	97	98	99	100
2.0	2.9	2.9	3.4	3.3	2.2	2.9	2.7	2.5	2.8	2.5	3.3	3.0	2.6	2.5	2.6	2.1	2.4

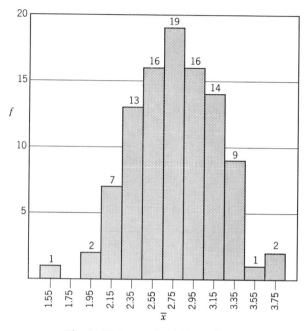

Fig. 6   Histogram for 100 sample means.

deviation for the data of Table 5 were calculated by the methods explained in Chapter 2, with the following results:

$$\text{sample mean for } \bar{x} = 2.77$$

(3)

$$\text{sample standard deviation for } \bar{x} = .41.$$

These values need to be compared with the values expected from the
theory in (2). In order to make this comparison, it is necessary to know
the values of μ and σ for the x population being sampled. Calculations by
standard methods for the frequency distribution given by Fig. 5 yielded
the values $\mu = 2.75$ and $\sigma = 1.48$, correct to two decimal places. Since
$n = 10$ in this experiment, the theory in (2) states that the theoretical
normal distribution approximating the actual distribution of $\bar{x}$ will have as
mean and standard deviation the quantities

$$\mu_{\bar{x}} = \mu = 2.75$$

(4)

$$\sigma_{\bar{x}} = \frac{\sigma}{\sqrt{n}} = \frac{1.48}{\sqrt{10}} = .47.$$

The values actually obtained from the experiment, given in (3), appear to
agree reasonably well with the theoretical values given in (4). The theoretical values given in (4) are those that should be approached by the
values in (3) if the sampling experiment were continued indefinitely
instead of stopping after 100 such experiments.

TABLE 5

Interval	Tally	$\bar{x}$	f
1.5–1.6	/	1.55	1
1.7–1.8		1.75	0
1.9–2.0	//	1.95	2
2.1–2.2	₦₦ //	2.15	7
2.3–2.4	₦₦ ₦₦ ///	2.35	13
2.5–2.6	₦₦ ₦₦ ₦₦ /	2.55	16
2.7–2.8	₦₦ ₦₦ ₦₦ ////	2.75	19
2.9–3.0	₦₦ ₦₦ ₦₦ /	2.95	16
3.1–3.2	₦₦ ₦₦ ////	3.15	14
3.3–3.4	₦₦ ////	3.35	9
3.5–3.6	/	3.55	1
3.7–3.8	//	3.75	2
			100

Since $n = 10$ is a small sample size and since the population distribution
for x is far removed from being normal, one could hardly have expected
the distribution of $\bar{x}$ to fit the theory in (2) too well, and yet it appears to
do so very well.

▶4. SMALL POPULATION SAMPLING

In the foregoing theory it was assumed that individuals were selected
from the population by means of random-sampling numbers or other
sampling methods in which each selected individual was returned to the
population for a possible repeat selection, or that the population was so
large in relation to the size of the sample that the removal of the sample
had no appreciable effect on the composition of the population. Now,
in many real-life sampling problems this is not the case. Most sampling
plans do not permit an individual to be selected twice in a given sample;
consequently, if the population is not large in relation to the size of the
sample, the theory will not be strictly correct. The difficulty arising in
such situations can be overcome by modifying the formula for the standard
deviation of $\bar{x}$.

If N denotes the size of the population being sampled and n denotes the size of the sample taken without replacement, then it can be shown that the formula $\sigma_{\bar{x}} = \sigma/\sqrt{n}$ must be replaced by the formula

$$\sigma_{\bar{x}} = \frac{\sigma}{\sqrt{n}} \sqrt{\frac{N-n}{N-1}} .$$

To see what effect the correction factor $\sqrt{(N-n)/(N-1)}$ has, consider sample and population sizes for which (a) $n = 5$ per cent of N, (b) $n = 10$ per cent of N, (c) $n = 20$ per cent of N. Since there is seldom any point in taking samples from populations of less than 100 and since $N - 1$ will differ from N by less than 1 per cent then, the foregoing correction factor may be written in the approximate form

$$\sqrt{\frac{N-n}{N}} = \sqrt{1 - \frac{n}{N}} .$$

Calculations for the three cases under consideration here yielded the following values for this correction factor: (a) .97, (b) .95, and (c) .89. From these results, it is safe to conclude that the original formula $\sigma_{\bar{x}} = \sigma/\sqrt{n}$ will be in error by less than 10 per cent, unless the sample constitutes at least 20 per cent of the population, and therefore that one need not worry too much about the size of the population unless the sample constitutes at least 20 per cent of the population. A more conservative viewpoint would be to refrain from worrying unless the sample constitutes at least 10 per cent of the population.

This same correction factor should be applied to the standard deviation of a proportion given by formula (12), Chapter 4, when the population size is small enough to justify it. Thus formula (12), Chapter 4, would be replaced by the formula

$$\sigma_{p'} = \sqrt{\frac{pq}{n}} \sqrt{\frac{N-n}{N-1}} .$$

EXERCISES

1. Suggest how to take a random sample of 100 students from the students at a university.

2. Suggest how you might set up an approximate random-sampling scheme for drawing samples of (a) trees in a forest, (b) potatoes in a freight car loaded with sacks of potatoes, (c) children of a community under 5 years of age who have had measles. In each case indicate some variable that might be studied.

3. Give reasons why taking every tenth name from the names under the letter A in a telephone book might or might not be considered a satisfactory random-sampling scheme for studying the income distribution of adults in a city.

4. Give an illustration of a population for which taking every twenty-fifth number in its listed order would probably yield a satisfactory approximation to random sampling for studying a particular attribute of the population.

5. Airlines often leave questionnaires in the seat pockets of their planes to obtain information from their customers regarding their services. Criticize this method of obtaining information.

6. During a prolonged debate on an important bill in the United States Senate, Senator A received 300 letters commending him on his stand and 100 letters reprimanding him for his stand. Senator A considered these letters as a fair indication of public sentiment on this bill. Comment on this.

7. A business firm sent out questionnaires to a random sample of 1000 house-wives in a certain city concerning their views about paper napkins. Of these, 400 replied. Would these 400 replies be satisfactory for judging the general views of housewives on napkins?

8. How could you use random numbers to take samples of wheat in a wheat field if the wheat field is a square, each side of which is 1000 feet long, and if each sample is taken by choosing a random point in the square and harvesting the wheat inside a hoop 5 feet in diameter whose center is at the random point?

9. Suppose there are 190 lawyers listed in a city directory and you desire a random sample of 30 of them. How can you use random numbers to obtain the sample without discarding a large share of the random numbers obtained? That is, do not associate lawyers only with the first 190 three-digit random numbers, thereby discarding all other three-digit random numbers.

10. How would you use random numbers to take a sample of 25 food markets in a city?

11. How would you take a sample of 25 clerks from the population of clerks working in food markets in a city, using proportional sampling?

12. Give an illustration of a population for which you believe stratified sampling would be considerably cheaper or better than random sampling.

13. An agency wishes to take a sample of 200 adults in a certain residential section of a city. It proposes to do so by taking a random sample of 200 house-holds obtained from a listing of all households in that district and then selecting at random 1 adult from each such household. Why, or why not, will this pro-cedure yield random samples?

14. Given that x is normally distributed with mean 20 and standard deviation 4, calculate the probability that the sample mean, $\bar{x}$, based on a sample of size 64, will (a) exceed 21, (b) exceed 20.5, (c) lie between 19 and 21, (d) exceed 25, (e) exceed 18.

15. Given that x is normally distributed with mean 30 and standard deviation 8, calculate the probability that the sample mean, $\bar{x}$, based on a sample of size 16, will (a) be less than 32, (b) exceed 36, (c) exceed 28, (d) be less than 25, (e) lie between 33 and 34.

16. Sketch on the same piece of paper the graph of a normal curve with mean 6 and standard deviation 2 and the graph of the corresponding mean curve for a sample of size 9.

17. What would the graph of the $\bar{x}$ curve in problem 16 have looked like if the sample size had been 36?

18. If the standard deviation of weights of first-grade children is 5 pounds, what is the probability that the mean weight of a random sample of 100 such children will differ by more than 1 pound from the mean weight for all the children?

19. Have each member of the class perform the following experiment 10 times. From Table II in the appendix select 10 one-digit random numbers and calculate their mean. Bring these 10 experimental means to class, where the total set of experimental means may be classified, the histogram drawn, and the mean and standard deviation computed. These results should then be compared with theory in the same manner as in the experiment in the text. The population distribution here has $\mu = 4.5$ and $\sigma = 2.87$.

20. Verify the values of $\bar{x}$ and s given in (3) of the text.

21. Verify the values of μ and σ used in (4) of the text by deleting the decimal points in Fig. 5 and treating the resulting numbers as observed frequencies for a sample of 100 from that distribution.

22. Suggest different criteria that might be useful in enabling one to take stratified samples for estimating the mean annual expenditure on meat by families of a large city.

23. Explain how Theorem (2) justifies the assumption made in Chapter 4 to the effect that the normal distribution is a good approximation to the binomial distribution if n is sufficiently large. Do this by considering the binomial distribution for a sample of size one in which case $x = 0$ or 1 with probabilities p and q, respectively, and using formula (11) of Chapter 4 with $x/n = \bar{x}$.

24. Perform a sampling experiment of the type used to make Theorem (2) seem plausible by taking 50 samples of size 5 from the discrete distribution given by

x	0	1	2
$P\{x\}$	.4	.2	.4

Graph the histogram of the $\bar{x}$ distribution and calculate its mean and standard deviation. Calculate the mean and standard deviation of the x distribution and compare your $\bar{x}$ results with those expected from Theorem (2). Since n is very small here and the x distribution is far from being normal, you should not expect the $\bar{x}$ distribution to look too much like a normal distribution.

▶25. Work problem 18 if the total number of children is only 500.

▶26. Work problem 14 under the assumption that the population here consists only of $N = 500$ individuals and that Theorem (1) is still applicable. Compare your results with those of problem 14.

▶27. Work problem 15 under the assumption that the population here consists only of $N = 100$ individuals and that Theorem (1) is still applicable. Compare your results with those of problem 15.

CHAPTER 6

Estimation

1. POINT AND INTERVAL ESTIMATES

The introduction in Chapter 1 stated that one of the fundamental problems of statistics is the estimation of properties of populations. Now that frequency distributions have been studied, to a limited extent at least, it is possible to discuss the properties of populations that can be estimated. The two population frequency distributions that have been studied thus far are the binomial distribution and the normal distribution; therefore their properties will be investigated first.

The binomial distribution given by formula (1), Chapter 4, is completely determined by the number of trials, n, and the probability of success in a single trial, p. The symbols n and p are called the *parameters* of the distribution. The values assigned to the parameters determine the particular binomial distribution desired. Since the parameters n and p completely determine the binomial distribution, any property of a binomial distribution is also completely determined by them. Furthermore, since the number of trials, n, is almost always chosen in advance in estimation problems, the problems of estimation for binomial distributions can usually be reduced to the problem of estimating p.

The normal distribution given by Fig. 11, Chapter 4, is completely determined by the two parameters μ and σ. Problems of estimation for normal populations can therefore usually be reduced to the problems of estimating μ and σ.

There are two types of estimates of parameters in common use in statistics. One is called a point estimate and the other is called an interval estimate. A point estimate is the familiar kind of estimate; that is, it is a number obtained from computations on the sample values that serves as an approximation to the parameter being estimated. For example, the sample proportion, x/n, of voters favoring a certain candidate is a point estimate of the population proportion p. Similarly, the sample mean $\bar{x}$ is a point estimate of the population mean μ. An interval estimate for a parameter is an interval, determined by two numbers obtained from computations on the sample values, that is expected to contain the value of the parameter in its interior. The interval estimate is usually constructed in such a manner that the probability of the interval's containing the parameter can be specified. The advantage of the interval estimate is that it shows how accurately the parameter is being estimated. If the length of the interval is very small, high accuracy has been achieved. Such interval estimates are called *confidence intervals*. Both point and interval estimates are determined for binomial and normal distribution parameters in this chapter.

2. ESTIMATION OF μ

Consider the following problem. A manufacturer of bricks has found from experience that the crushing strength of his bricks for a given batch is approximately normally distributed. He has also found that the mean crushing strength varies from batch to batch but the standard deviation remains fairly constant at the value $\sigma = 20$. He wishes to estimate the mean crushing strength for a new batch, so he tests a random sample of 25 bricks and finds that their mean crushing strength is $\bar{x} = 300$. With these data available, three types of estimation problems will be solved.

(*a*) How accurate is $\bar{x} = 300$ as a point estimate of the batch mean μ? To solve this problem, use is made of the theory presented in the preceding chapter. From the theory given in (2), Chapter 5, it follows that the sample mean $\bar{x}$ may be assumed to be normally distributed with mean μ and standard deviation given by

$$\sigma_{\bar{x}} = \frac{\sigma}{\sqrt{n}} = \frac{20}{\sqrt{25}} = 4.$$

A sketch of this distribution is given in Fig. 1. Since the probability is .95 that a normal variable will assume some value within two standard deviations of its mean (more accurately 1.96 standard deviations correct to two decimals by Table IV in the appendix), it follows that the probability is .95 that $\bar{x}$ will assume some value within 8 units of μ. Since $\bar{x} = 300$ is the observed value here, the manufacturer can feel quite confident that

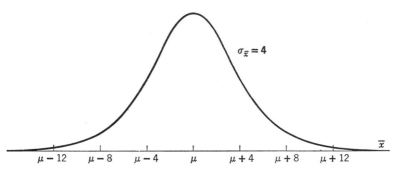

Fig. 1   Distribution of $\bar{x}$ for the crushing strength of bricks.

this value differs from the population value μ by less than 8 units because in the long run in only 5 per cent of such sampling experiments will the sample value $\bar{x}$ differ by more than 8 units from μ. The magnitude of the difference $\bar{x} - \mu$ is called the error of estimate. In terms of this language, one can say that the probability is .95 that the error of estimate will be less than 8 units. If higher probability odds were desired, one could use, say, a three-standard deviation interval on both sides of μ and then state that the probability is .997 that the error of estimate will be less than 12 units.

Since $\bar{x}$ is based on a sample it is not possible to state how close $\bar{x}$ is to the population mean μ when μ is unknown; it is only possible to state in probability language how close $\bar{x}$ is likely to be to μ. Thus, the exact error of estimate, namely $|\bar{x} - \mu|$, is known only when μ is known. Since the problem of estimation arises only when μ is unknown, one must introduce probabilities in order to discuss the magnitude of an error of estimate in statistical problems. Even though the true value μ is not known, one can still speak of how close $\bar{x}$ is to μ and therefore one can say something about the magnitude of the error of estimate, $|\bar{x} - \mu|$, provided the statement is couched in the proper probability language.

(b) Suppose the manufacturer is not satisfied with the accuracy of his estimate based on the sample of 25. How large an additional sample should he take so that he can be reasonably certain, say with a probability of .95, that his estimate will not be in error by more than 5 units? Now, as n is increased, the normal curve for $\bar{x}$ will become taller and narrower, concentrating more and more area in the neighborhood of the mean μ. This is shown, for example, in Figs. 3 and 4, Chapter 5, where n goes from 1 to 25. A stage will be reached when 95 per cent of the area, centered at μ, is found to lie within the interval extending 5 units on both sides of μ. This value of n is the desired sample size. Since 95 per cent of the central area corresponds to 1.96 standard deviations on both sides of μ, it follows that n must be such that 1.96 standard deviations for $\bar{x}$ equals 5. Thus n must satisfy the equation

$$1.96\sigma_{\bar{x}} = 5.$$

Since $\sigma = 20$ here, this equation is equivalent to

$$1.96\frac{20}{\sqrt{n}} = 5.$$

Solving for n gives the result $n = 61.5$. The manufacturer therefore must take an additional 37 samples, since he has taken 25 already, in order to attain the desired accuracy of estimate.

Since 1.96 is an inconvenient number to use in equations of this type, it usually suffices to replace it by 2. The solution of the equation then becomes $n = 64$. Although this approximation does yield a difference of 2 in the answer, that is hardly a large number to worry about in a total sample of 64. Furthermore, the objective here is to learn the methods of statistics and any saving of calculating energy which hopefully will be applied to thinking energy is well worth the sacrifice in accuracy of computation.

If one wants the probability that the error of estimate will not exceed 5 to be something other than .95, then it is necessary to replace the factor 1.96 (or 2) in the preceding equation by the proper z value found in Table IV corresponding to the desired probability. Thus, if the probability .90 were selected, the Table IV value of z would be 1.64. This follows from the fact that 90 per cent of the area of a normal curve lies within 1.64 standard deviations of the mean. The equation to be solved for n would then become

$$1.64\frac{20}{\sqrt{n}} = 5.$$

The solution of this equation is $n = 43$.

Since it is bothersome to have to solve an equation like this each time, a formula which yields n more directly will be obtained. If the maximum allowable error of estimate is denoted by e and the z value corresponding to the desired probability is denoted by z_0, then the equation that must be solved for n is given by

$$z_0\frac{\sigma}{\sqrt{n}} = e.$$

The solution of this equation, and therefore the desired formula, is given by

$$n = \frac{z_0^2 \sigma^2}{e^2}.$$

This formula enables one to determine how large a sample is needed in order to estimate μ to any desired degree of accuracy before a single sample has been taken, provided the value of σ is known. It is not necessary to have a preliminary sample available, as in the problem solved four paragraphs back. If, however, one does not know σ from other sources, nor has a good estimate of it, then it is necessary to take a preliminary sample in order to obtain an estimate of σ that can be used in the formula for determining how large n must be.

(c) Consider a third type of estimation problem for this same example. What is a 95 per cent confidence interval for μ based on the original sample of 25? If it is assumed that x is exactly normally distributed, it is clear from the theory given in (1), Chapter 5, or Fig. 1, that one can write

(1) $$P\{\mu - 8 < \bar{x} < \mu + 8\} = .95.$$

This is an algebraic probability statement of what was stated in geo-metrical language in problem (a), namely, that the probability is .95 that the point on the $\bar{x}$ axis of Fig. 1 corresponding to a sample mean $\bar{x}$ will not be more than 8 units away from the point representing the population mean μ. Now it is possible to turn this geometry, and hence the algebra, around and state that the probability is .95 that the point μ will not be more than 8 units away from the point corresponding to a sample mean $\bar{x}$. The relationship here is relative; if one point is within 8 units of a second point, the the second point will be within 8 units of the first point. This reversing of the roles of the two points will now be done algebraically by the use of inequality properties.

An inequality such as $\bar{x} < \mu + 8$ can be rearranged in the same manner as an equality, except that multiplying both sides of an inequality by a negative number will reverse the inequality sign. Thus, the inequality $2 < 5$ becomes the inequality $-2 > -5$ when it is multiplied through by -1. The inequality $\bar{x} < \mu + 8$ is seen to be equivalent to the inequality $\bar{x} - 8 < \mu$ by adding -8 to both sides of the first inequality. Similarly, $\mu - 8 < \bar{x}$ is equivalent to $\mu < \bar{x} + 8$. If these two results are combined, it will be seen that the double inequality

$$\mu - 8 < \bar{x} < \mu + 8$$

is equivalent to the double inequality

$$\bar{x} - 8 < \mu < \bar{x} + 8.$$

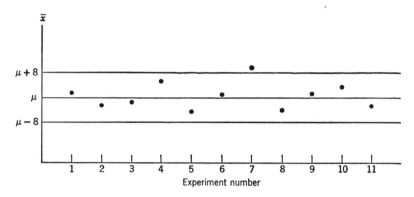

Fig. 2   Repeated sampling experiments for $\bar{x}$.

As a consequence, the probability statement (1) is equivalent to the probability statement

(2) $$P\{\bar{x} - 8 < \mu < \bar{x} + 8\} = .95.$$

In words, this says that the probability is .95 that the population mean μ will be contained inside the interval that extends from $\bar{x} - 8$ to $\bar{x} + 8$. This interval is written in the form $(\bar{x} - 8, \bar{x} + 8)$.

Although (1) and (2) are equivalent probability statements, they possess slightly different interpretations in terms of relative frequencies in repeated runs of this sampling experiment. For each such sampling experiment, a value of $\bar{x}$ is obtained. If these values of $\bar{x}$ are plotted as points, as shown in Fig. 2, then the frequency interpretation of (1) is that in such repeated sampling experiments 95 per cent of the points will fall within the band shown in Fig. 2.

A frequency interpretation for (2) requires that the interval extending from $\bar{x} - 8$ to $\bar{x} + 8$, corresponding to each sampling experiment, be plotted. This has been done in Fig. 3 for the experiments that yielded

Fig. 2. The frequency interpretation of (2), then, is that in such repeated sampling experiments 95 per cent of the intervals will contain μ. Geometrically, it is clear from Figs. 2 and 3 that an interval in Fig. 3 will contain μ if, and only if, the corresponding point in Fig. 2 lies inside the band displayed there. This is very much like saying that a chalk line on the floor (μ) will be within 8 feet of you ($\bar{x}$) if, and only if, you are within

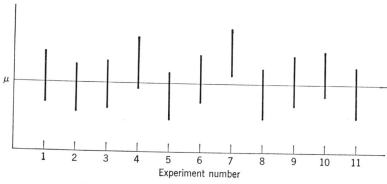

Fig. 3   Intervals for repeated sampling experiments.

8 feet of the line.   The advantage of the interval interpretation is that in practice one never knows what the value of μ is; otherwise there would be no point of estimating it, and therefore it is not possible to construct the band given by $\mu - 8$ and $\mu + 8$ in Fig. 2; however, it is always possible to construct the intervals given by $\bar{x} - 8$ and $\bar{x} + 8$ in Fig. 3.

Now, in practice, only one sampling experiment is conducted; therefore, only the first point and the first interval are available from Figs. 2 and 3. On the basis of this one experiment, the claim is made that the interval from $300 - 8$ to $300 + 8$, or from 292 to 308, contains the population mean μ. Using inequality symbols, this is written in the form

$$292 < \mu < 308.$$

If for each such sampling experiment the same claim is made for the interval corresponding to that experiment, then 95 per cent of such claims will be true in the long run of such experiments.   In view of this property, the interval from 292 to 308 is called a 95 per cent *confidence interval* for μ.   The end points of the interval, namely 292 and 308, are *confidence limits* for μ.

It should be clearly understood that one is merely betting on the correctness of the rule of procedure when applying the confidence interval technique to a given experiment. It is incorrect to make the claim that the probability is .95 that the interval from 292 to 308 will contain μ. The latter probability is either 1 or 0, depending upon whether μ does or does not lie in this fixed interval. Nontrivial probability statements are made only about variables and not about constants. It is only when one considers the variable interval from $\bar{x} - 8$ to $\bar{x} + 8$, before a numerical value of $\bar{x}$ has been obtained, that one can make probability statements such as that in (2).

The advantage of a confidence interval for μ over a point estimate of μ is that the confidence interval gives one an idea of how closely μ is being estimated, whereas the point estimate $\bar{x}$ says nothing about how good the estimate is. Thus, the confidence interval (292, 308) gives one assurance (confidence) that the true mean μ is very likely at least as large as 292 and very likely not larger than 308.

The three types of problems just solved in connection with the example introduced at the beginning of this section are the three major problems arising in the estimation of μ. They may be listed as (a) determining the accuracy of $\bar{x}$ as an estimate of μ, (b) determining the size sample needed to attain a desired accuracy of estimate of μ, and (c) determining a confidence interval for μ.

The methods for solving these problems were quite simple because it was assumed that the variable x was approximately normally distributed and that the value of σ was known. Now, by the theory in (2), Chapter 5, it follows that it would have been safe to treat $\bar{x}$ as a normal variable, even though x had not been assumed to be normally distributed, because n is large here. The problem of what to do when σ is not known is not so simple. If the sample is large, say 25 or more, it is usually safe to replace σ by its sample estimate s in the formulas used to solve the problems.

As an illustration of what to do when σ is not known, the following problem will be worked. A random sample of 100 students is selected from a certain school. They are given an intelligence test to determine their intelligence-quotient scores. The scores on this test yielded the sample values $\bar{x} = 112$ and $s = 11$. What is a 95 per cent confidence interval for the school mean intelligence quotient based on these sample values? The problem is solved in the same manner as before, except that s is used in place of σ.

As before, it follows from Table IV that the probability is .95 that a standard normal variable z will satisfy the inequalities

$$-1.96 < z < 1.96.$$

But if $\bar{x}$ is a normal variable, the quantity

$$\frac{\bar{x} - \mu}{\sigma_{\bar{x}}} = \frac{\bar{x} - \mu}{\sigma/\sqrt{n}} = \frac{\bar{x} - \mu}{\sigma}\sqrt{n}$$

will be a standard normal variable, and therefore the probability is .95 that it will satisfy the inequalities

$$-1.96 < \frac{\bar{x} - \mu}{\sigma}\sqrt{n} < 1.96.$$

If these inequalities are solved for μ, they will reduce to the following inequalities:

$$(3) \qquad \bar{x} - 1.96\frac{\sigma}{\sqrt{n}} < \mu < \bar{x} + 1.96\frac{\sigma}{\sqrt{n}}.$$

This result can be used as a formula for obtaining 95 per cent confidence intervals for population means.

For the problem being considered, $n = 100$, $\bar{x} = 112$, and $s = 11$. Since the value of σ is not known here, it must be approximated by its sample estimate $s = 11$. If these values are substituted into (3), it will assume the form

$$112 - 1.96\frac{11}{\sqrt{100}} < \mu < 112 + 1.96\frac{11}{\sqrt{100}}.$$

These quantities reduce to 109.8 and 114.2; hence the desired approximate 95 per cent confidence interval for μ is given by

$$109.8 < \mu < 114.2.$$

This is only an approximate 95 per cent confidence interval because σ was replaced by its sample approximation s and x was not assumed to be normally distributed. For a sample as large as 100, the errors arising because of these approximations will be negligible.

If one desired, say, a 90 per cent confidence interval rather than a 95 per cent confidence interval, it would merely be necessary to replace the number 1.96 by the number 1.64 in the preceding formulas, just as in the earlier problem of determining n. In the preceding problem the limits would then become

$$112 - 1.64 \frac{11}{\sqrt{100}} < \mu < 112 + 1.64 \frac{11}{\sqrt{100}}.$$

If these inequalities are simplified, the desired approximate 90 per cent confidence interval for μ will become

$$110.2 < \mu < 113.8.$$

Any other percentage confidence interval can be obtained in a similar manner by means of Table IV.

The methods of estimation explained in this section are called large sample methods whenever σ is replaced by its sample estimate because they are then strictly valid only for large samples. If the sample is smaller than about 25 and the value of σ is unknown, these methods are of questionable accuracy, and therefore a more refined method is needed. A method designed to solve such small sample problems is presented next.

3. STUDENT'S t DISTRIBUTION

Consider once more the problem that was solved three paragraphs back, with the modification that the sample size is given to be 10 rather than 100. Thus, $\bar{x} = 112$ and $s = 11$ for a sample of size 10. To avoid the error involved in replacing σ by s when s is based on such a small sample, a new variable, called *Student's t variable* is introduced. It is defined by the formula

$$(4) \qquad\qquad t = \frac{\bar{x} - \mu}{s} \sqrt{n}.$$

This variable resembles the standard normal variable introduced in section 2, namely,

$$z = \frac{\bar{x} - \mu}{\sigma} \sqrt{n}.$$

However, it differs from z in that it involves the sample standard deviation, s, in place of the population standard deviation, σ. Since t does not require a knowledge of σ, as is the case with z, its value can be computed from sample data, whereas the value of z cannot be computed unless σ is known. This is the reason why t can be used to solve problems without the necessity of introducing approximations to population parameters.

If a large number of sampling experiments were carried out in which a sample of size n were selected from a normal population and the value of t computed, a large number of values of t would be available for classifying into a frequency table to obtain a good estimate of the limiting, or theoretical, distribution of t. Mathematical methods, however, yield the exact distribution. It turns out that the distribution of t depends only upon the value of n, provided that the basic variable x possesses a normal distribution. Furthermore, the distribution of t is very close to the distribution of a standard normal variable z, except for very small values of n. Figure 4 shows the graph of the distribution of t for $n = 5$ and the graph of a standard normal variable z.

Table V in the appendix gives values of the variable t corresponding to what is called the number of "degrees of freedom," denoted by ν, and various probabilities. For the problem being considered here, the number of degrees of freedom is given by the formula $\nu = n - 1$. This corresponds to using the divisor $n - 1$ rather than n in defining the sample standard deviation in Chapter 2. The t distribution is used for other types of problems also in which the parameter ν is not equal to $n - 1$; otherwise this mysterious phrase would not need to be introduced here. Any column heading, such as .05, indicates the probability of t numerically exceeding the value of t listed in that column. This means that each tail of the curve cut off by the value of t, and its negative value, contains $2\frac{1}{2}$ per cent of the area under the curve. Thus for the above problem, since $n = 10$, one reads the entry in the row corresponding to 9 degrees of freedom and

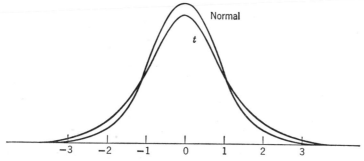

Fig. 4 Standard normal distribution and a Student's t distribution.

in the column headed .05, and finds $t = 2.26$. The probability is therefore .95 that t will satisfy the inequalities

(5) $-2.26 < t < 2.26.$

If this is applied to (4), it will follow that the probability is .95 that

$$-2.26 < \frac{\bar{x} - \mu}{s} \sqrt{n} < 2.26.$$

These inequalities can be solved for μ in the same manner as formula (3) was obtained. The result is

(6) $\bar{x} - 2.26 \frac{s}{\sqrt{n}} < \mu < \bar{x} + 2.26 \frac{s}{\sqrt{n}}.$

The desired 95 per cent confidence interval for μ is obtained by substituting the sample values $n = 10$, $\bar{x} = 112$, and $s = 11$ into these inequalities. The result of this substitution is

$$112 - 2.26 \frac{11}{\sqrt{10}} < \mu < 112 + 2.26 \frac{11}{\sqrt{10}}.$$

This simplifies into

(7) $104 < \mu < 120.$

It is important to realize the distinction between this new method of finding a confidence interval for μ and the earlier large sample method. This method does not require one to approximate σ by s, as is true for the large sample method, and therefore it gives an exact rather than an approximate solution to the problem.

Formula (6) cannot be used to find a 95 per cent confidence interval for μ unless the sample size is 10, because from Table V it will be found that (5) holds only for $\nu = 9$. If t_0 is used to denote the value of t found in the .05 column of Table V opposite ν degrees of freedom, then a general formula for a 95 per cent confidence interval for μ is given by the inequalities

(8) $\bar{x} - t_0 \frac{s}{\sqrt{n}} < \mu < \bar{x} + t_0 \frac{s}{\sqrt{n}}.$

This formula is also valid for percentages other than 95 if the corresponding value of t_0 is employed. Thus a 90 per cent confidence interval is obtained if one replaces t_0 by the t value in the .10 column of Table V, which is opposite the desired degrees of freedom value.

For the purpose of comparing the old method with the new, it is necessary to calculate a 95 per cent confidence interval by means of formula (3). If σ is estimated by s and the sample values $n = 10$, $\bar{x} = 112$, and $s = 11$ are substituted in (3), the desired approximate 95 per cent confidence interval is given by

$$112 - 1.96\frac{11}{\sqrt{10}} < \mu < 112 + 1.96\frac{11}{\sqrt{10}}.$$

This simplifies into

$$105 < \mu < 119.$$

It will be noted that this interval is somewhat narrower than that given by the small-sample method and displayed in (7). The large-sample method always gives a confidence interval that is somewhat too narrow; however, the error decreases rapidly as n grows and is hardly noticeable for n larger than 20.

Since the small-sample method based on the t distribution is an exact method, it would seem that one should always use it when σ is unknown. Unfortunately, however, the theory behind the t distribution requires one to assume that the basic variable x possesses a normal distribution; therefore unless one can be assured that x is at least approximately normally distributed, the t distribution may not be justified. The large-sample method requires only that $\bar{x}$ be normally distributed and that s be a good estimate of σ. Now $\bar{x}$ will be approximately normally distributed even though x is not, even for fairly small samples, as was shown by the sampling experiments in the preceding chapter. As a result, the large-sample methods cannot be completely displaced by the small-sample t approach.

The next estimation problems logically to be considered should be those related to σ. Since such problems require some additional theory, they will be postponed to a later chapter.

4. ESTIMATION OF p

Section 2 was concerned with the estimation of the parameter μ for continuous-variable distributions. This section explains how to solve similar types of problems for the parameter p associated with binomial distributions. The methods presented here are large-sample methods because they require the replacement of p by its sample estimate and also because they assume that the normal-curve approximation to the binomial distribution is satisfactory.

As an example to illustrate the various types of estimation problems to be solved, consider the problem of estimating the percentage of adult males in a certain city who smoke at least one pack of cigarettes a day. Suppose a random sample of size 300 yielded 36 such individuals. By using these data, the following three problems can be solved: (a) What is the accuracy of the sample proportion as an estimate of p? (b) How large a sample would be needed if the probability is to be .95 that the error of estimate will not exceed .02 units? (c) What is a 95 per cent confidence interval for p? All of these problems are solved in the same manner as in section 2 because the sample size here is large enough to justify the use of normal-curve methods.

(a) From formula (11), Chapter 4, it follows that the sample proportion, x/n, which will be denoted by p', may be assumed to be approximately normally distributed with mean p and standard deviation

$$\sqrt{\frac{pq}{n}} = \sqrt{\frac{pq}{300}}.$$

As a result, the probability is approximately .95 that p' will lie within 1.96 such standard deviations of p. Thus the probability is approximately .95 that the error of estimate will be less than

$$(9) \qquad\qquad 1.96\sqrt{\frac{pq}{300}}.$$

Since p is unknown, it must be estimated by

$$p' = \frac{x}{n} = \frac{36}{300} = .12.$$

The value of (9) then assumes the approximate value

$$1.96\sqrt{\frac{(.12)(.88)}{300}} = .037.$$

It can therefore be stated that the probability is approximately .95 that the sample estimate p' will not differ from p by more than .037 units. This result gives one a good idea of the accuracy of the sample value .12 as an estimate of p.

(b) To solve the problem of how large a sample is needed to attain a given accuracy of estimate for p, one uses the same reasoning as that used in section 2 for μ. This means that n must be chosen so that the proper number of standard deviations of p' will equal the desired maximum error of estimate. As before, let e denote the selected maximum error of estimate and let z_0 denote the value of z corresponding to the desired probability of not exceeding this maximum error. Then n must satisfy the equation

$$z_0 \sqrt{\frac{pq}{n}} = e.$$

Solving this equation for n will yield the formula

(10) $$n = \frac{z_0^2 pq}{e^2}.$$

For the particular problem being considered here, $e = .02$ and $z_0 = 1.96$. Since p is unknown, it must be estimated by the sample value $p' = .12$. If these values are substituted in (10), the value of n will be found to be approximately 1014; hence an additional sample of approximately 714 will be needed to obtain the desired accuracy of estimation.

(c) To find a confidence interval for p, one also uses the same reasoning as for μ. Since p' takes the place of $\bar{x}$, an approximate 95 per cent confidence interval for p is given by the inequalities

$$p' - 1.96 \sqrt{\frac{pq}{n}} < p < p' + 1.96 \sqrt{\frac{pq}{n}}.$$

Replacing p by p' in the two radical terms and substituting the values of $n = 300$ and $p' = .12$, one obtains the approximate interval

$$.12 - .037 < p < .12 + .037.$$

These limits reduce to .083 and .157; consequently an approximate 95 per cent confidence interval for p is given by the inequalities

$$.083 < p < .157.$$

Repetition may be boring, yet it is worth repeating that all three solutions are based on large-sample methods. Fortunately, these methods are quite good, even for small samples, provided that $np > 5$ for $p < \frac{1}{2}$ and $nq > 5$ for $p > \frac{1}{2}$.

A final illustration of the methods for estimating p is given because of its interest to those who enjoy politics. A well-known pollster claims that his estimate of the proportion of the voters favoring a certain presidential candidate is not in error by more than .03 units. In a close presidential race, how large a sample would he need to take to be certain, with a probability of .997, of being correct in his claim?

From Table IV in the appendix, 99.7 per cent of the central area of a normal distribution lies within three standard deviations of the mean; therefore $z_0 = 3$ here. Since the race is very close, it may be assumed that $p = \frac{1}{2}$; hence formula (10) yields the result

$$n = \frac{9 \cdot \frac{1}{2} \cdot \frac{1}{2}}{(.03)^2} = 2500.$$

A random sample of this size taken from over the country should therefore suffice to give him the desired accuracy.

The use of $p = \frac{1}{2}$ in the foregoing problem may appear to be arbitrary, particularly if the election is not really close. However, it is easy to show that pq assumes its maximum value when $p = \frac{1}{2}$, and hence that the maximum value of n in (10) occurs when $p = \frac{1}{2}$. This is done by first verifying that

$$pq = p(1 - p) = p - p^2 = \frac{1}{4} - \left(\frac{1}{2} - p\right)^2.$$

Next, pq will be as large as possible, namely $\frac{1}{4}$, when the term $(\frac{1}{2} - p)^2$ which is being subtracted from $\frac{1}{4}$ has the value 0. But this will occur when $p = \frac{1}{2}$. This implies that when one is determining the size of the sample necessary for a specified accuracy of estimate the value of n for $p = \frac{1}{2}$ will be larger than for any other value of p. As a result, the use of $p = \frac{1}{2}$ in such problems assures one that the resulting value of n is certainly large enough and possibly larger than necessary.

An interesting feature of problems like this one is that, contrary to the belief of most people, the accuracy of an estimate of a proportion p does not depend upon the size of the population but only upon the size of the sample. Thus a sample of 2500 voters out of 50,000,000 voters is sufficient, theoretically, to determine their voting preferences with high accuracy.

For obvious economic reasons, professional pollsters do not take simple random samples. They usually combine a type of cluster sampling with stratified sampling.

Unfortunately, voters do not always behave like trials in a game of chance, so that the binomial distribution model is not strictly applicable to voting problems. For example, a voter when interviewed may favor one candidate and yet a week later he may vote for another candidate, or he may not bother to vote at all. He may also misinterpret a pollster's question and therefore respond incorrectly. Experience has shown that because of uncontrolled human factors the accuracy of an estimate of p for voters does not increase appreciably after a sample of 10,000 has been taken. It is necessary to use good sense in applying mathematical models to real life, particularly when it comes to human beings and some of their inconsistencies. Wild animals seem to be better subjects on which to apply statistical methods.

5. REVIEW EXERCISES

Two review exercises will be solved in this section, one is concerned with means and the other with proportions.

1. For the sampling experiment corresponding to Table 4 of Chapter 5, consider the entire experiment as one large sample of size 1000 from the population given by Fig. 5 of Chapter 5, for which it is known that $\mu = 2.75$ and $\sigma = 1.48$, and solve the following problems. (a) Determine the probability accuracy of $\bar{x}$ as an estimate of μ. What is the actual accuracy? Is the sample value compatible with what was to be expected by theory? (b) Find how large an experiment should have been conducted if one wanted to be certain with a probability of .80 that the estimate would not be in error by more than .05 units. (c) Find an 80 per cent confidence interval for μ. Does this interval actually contain μ? The solutions follow.

(a) Here $\mu = 2.75$, $\sigma = 1.48$, $n = 1000$, and $\bar{x} = 2.77$.

$$1.96\sigma_{\bar{x}} = 1.96\,\frac{1.48}{\sqrt{1000}} = .092.$$

The probability is .95 that the error won't exceed .092. The actual error is $|\bar{x} - \mu| = 2.77 - 2.75 = .02$; therefore the sample value is certainly compatible with theory.

(b) Since .80 corresponds to a z value of 1.28 and the maximum tolerable error is to be $e = .05$, n is given by

$$n = \frac{(1.28)^2(1.48)^2}{(.05)^2} = 1436.$$

An additional sample of 436 would suffice.

(c) The general formula for an 80 per cent interval is

$$\bar{x} - 1.28 \frac{\sigma}{\sqrt{n}} < \mu < \bar{x} + 1.28 \frac{\sigma}{\sqrt{n}}.$$

Hence, for this problem it becomes

$$2.77 - 1.28 \frac{1.48}{\sqrt{1000}} < \mu < 2.77 + 1.28 \frac{1.48}{\sqrt{1000}}.$$

Or,

$$2.71 < \mu < 2.83.$$

Since $\mu = 2.75$, it is contained inside this interval.

2. From the theory related to the sampling experiment corresponding to Table 4 of Chapter 5 it is known that the probability of a sample mean $\bar{x}$ exceeding the value 2.95 is approximately .34. Using Table 4, count the proportion, p', of the 100 experiments that yielded a value of $\bar{x} > 2.95$. (a) What is the probability accuracy of this estimate? What is the actual accuracy? Is the sample proportion compatible with what was to be expected here by theory? (b) Find how large an additional set of experiments would need to be performed if one wished to estimate p to within .03 units with a probability of .90 of being correct. Assume that p is not known here. (c) Work part (b) if the conservative value $p = \frac{1}{2}$ is used in place of the sample estimate of p. (d) Find a 90 per cent confidence interval for p, assuming that the value of p is unknown. Does this interval actually contain p? The solutions follow.

(a) There are 31 samples yielding $\bar{x} > 2.95$; hence $p' = .31$. Since $p = .34$ and $n = 100$,

$$1.96\sigma_{p'} = 1.96 \sqrt{\frac{(.34)(.66)}{100}} \doteq .093.$$

The probability is .95 that the error will not exceed .093. The actual error is $|p' - p| = |.31 - 34| = .03$; therefore the sample value is compatible with theory.

(b) Since .90 corresponds to a z value of 1.64 and the maximum tolerable error is to be $e = .03$, n is given by

$$n = \frac{(1.64)^2 pq}{(.03)^2} \doteq \frac{(1.64)^2(.31)(.69)}{(.03)^2} \doteq 639.$$

Thus, 539 additional experiments would be required.

(c) Using $p = \frac{1}{2}$,

$$n = \frac{(1.64)^2(.5)(.5)}{(.03)^2} \doteq 747.$$

Thus, 647 additional experiments will certainly suffice.

(d)
$$p' - 1.64\sqrt{\frac{pq}{100}} < p < p' + 1.64\sqrt{\frac{pq}{100}}.$$

This is approximated by

$$.31 - 1.64\sqrt{\frac{(.31)(.69)}{100}} < p < .31 + 1.64\sqrt{\frac{(.31)(.69)}{100}}.$$

Hence,

$$.234 < p < .386.$$

The value $p = .34$ is well inside this interval.

EXERCISES

1. Experience with workmen in a certain industry indicates that the time required for a randomly selected workman to complete a job is approximately normally distributed with a standard deviation of 12 minutes. (a) If each of a random sample of 25 workmen performed the job, how accurate is their sample mean as an estimate of the mean for all the workmen? (b) How much improvement would have resulted in the accuracy of this estimate if 100 workmen had been selected?

2. From past experience the standard deviation of the height of fifth-grade children in a school system is 2 inches. (a) If a random sample of 36 such children is taken, how accurate would their sample mean be as an estimate of the mean for all such children? (b) What would happen to the accuracy of this estimate if the sample were made 9 times as large?

3. (a) In problem 1(a) how large a sample would one need to take if one wished to estimate the population mean to within 2 minutes, with a probability of .95 of being correct? (b) What size sample would be needed if the maximum error of estimate were to be 1 minute?

4. Work problem 3 for the case in which one is satisfied to have a probability of .90 of being correct.

5. (a) In problem 2 how large a sample would one need to take if one wished to estimate the population mean to within $\frac{1}{2}$ inch, with a probability of .95 of being correct? (b) What size sample would be needed if the maximum error of estimate were to be $\frac{1}{6}$ inch?

6. Work problem 5(a) for the case in which one is satisfied to have a probability of .90 of being correct.

7. If the results of the experiment in problem 1(a) yielded $\bar{x} = 140$ minutes, find (a) 95 per cent confidence limits for μ, (b) 90 per cent confidence limits for μ.

8. If the results of the experiment in problem 2(a) yielded $\bar{x} = 54$ inches, find (a) 95 per cent confidence limits for μ, (b) 90 per cent confidence limits for μ.

9. A set of 50 experimental animals is fed a certain kind of rations for a 2-week period. Their gains in weight yielded the values $\bar{x} = 42$ ounces and $s = 5$ ounces. (a) How accurate is 42 as an estimate of the population mean? (b) How large a sample would you take if you wished $\bar{x}$ to differ from μ by less than 1 ounce, with a probability of .95 of being correct? (c) Find 95 per cent confidence limits for μ.

10. Given that $\bar{x} = 20$, $s = 4$, $n = 10$, with x normally distributed, use Student's t distribution to find (a) 95 per cent confidence limits for μ, (b) 99 per cent confidence limits for μ.

11. A sample of 15 cigarettes of a certain brand was tested for nicotine content and gave $\bar{x} = 22$ and $s = 4$ milligrams. Use Student's t distribution to find 95 per cent confidence limits for μ.

12. Work problem 11 by large sample methods and compare the results of the two methods.

13. A set of 12 experimental animals was fed a special diet for 3 weeks and produced the following gains in weight: 30, 22, 32, 26, 24, 40, 34, 36, 32, 33, 28, 30. Find 90 per cent confidence limits for μ.

14. Have each member of the class find a 75 per cent confidence interval for μ for a sample of size 25 from a table of one-digit random numbers (Table II in the appendix). Use the fact that σ for this distribution is given by $\sigma = 2.87$ and that $\bar{x}$ may be treated as a normal variable. Check to see what percentage of the student's confidence intervals contain the true mean $\mu = 4.5$. About 75 per cent should do so.

15. Work problem 14, but this time use a sample of size 10 and assume that the value of σ is not known. That is, use Student's t distribution to find the desired confidence interval. Check to see what percentage of the students' intervals contain μ.

16. A campus organization wishes to estimate the percentage of students who favor a new student-body constitution. It proposes to select a random sample of 200 students. If the results of this poll yield $p' = .60$, how accurate is this estimate of the true proportion likely to be?

17. A sample of 80 motorists showed that 20 per cent had lapsed driver's licenses. How accurate is this estimate of the true percentage likely to be?

18. If an estimate, accurate to within .04 units, is desired of p in problem 16, how large a sample should the organization plan to take? Assume that a probability of .95 of being correct will suffice and use $p' = .60$.

19. A manufacturer of parts believes that approximately 5 per cent of his product contains flaws. If he wishes to estimate the true percentage to within $\frac{1}{2}$ per cent and to be certain with a probability of .99 of being correct, how large a sample should he take?

20. If the campus organization in problem 18 had no experience to give it the estimate $p' = .60$, how large a sample should it plan on taking?

21. A random sample of 400 citizens in a community showed that 240 favored having their water fluoridated. Use these data to find 95 per cent confidence limits for the proportion of the population favoring fluoridation.

22. A campus organization wished to estimate the percentage of the student body favoring their candidate in a forthcoming election. They proceeded to do so by asking the first 200 students whom they met going to 8 o'clock classes for their views. They found that 30 per cent favored their candidate. (a) Criticize the validity of this estimate. (b) If the estimate were valid, what would 96 per cent confidence limits be for p?

23. Suppose the mean and standard deviation of the English Achievement scores for a sample of 20 students from a class of 100 were $\bar{x} = 150$ and $s = 20$. Calculate 95 per cent confidence limits for μ (a) by using the regular small sample method, ▶(b) by using the small population correction on s and small sample methods.

24. If a sample of 100 has been taken and $\bar{x} = 40$, $s = 8$ resulted, with what probability can one be assured that $\bar{x}$ is not more than 1 unit away from the true mean?

25. Work review exercise 1 of section 5 as it applies to the sampling experiment corresponding to Table 2 of Chapter 5. Assume that $\mu = 0$, $\sigma = 1$, and $n = 200$.

26. Work review exercise 2 of section 5 as it applies to the sampling experiment corresponding to Table 2 of Chapter 5. Here, count the proportion of experiments for which $\bar{x}$ exceeds the value $\frac{1}{8}$. From theory the probability that $\bar{x} > \frac{1}{8}$ is approximately .4.

▶27. Suggest how you might proceed to determine the sample size needed for estimating μ with a certain accuracy when σ is unknown by taking samples in small groups and re-estimating σ as additional groups are taken.

▶28. Obtain 80 per cent confidence limits for the number of accident claims that will be paid by an insurance company during the next year if this year's experience showed that 5 per cent of those carrying insurance collected claims and the company has 6000 policies.

▶29. Solve each of the inequalities in the double inequality $p' - z_0\sqrt{pq/n} < p < p' + z_0\sqrt{pq/n}$ for the variable p. This will involve the solution of a quadratic equation. Use your results to obtain a confidence interval for p that does not contain p in its limits.

CHAPTER 7

Testing Hypotheses

1. TWO TYPES OF ERROR

As indicated in Chapter 1, a second fundamental problem of statistics is the testing of hypotheses about populations. From the discussion on estimation in Chapter 6, it follows that the testing of hypotheses about binomial populations can usually be reduced to testing some hypothesis about the parameter p. Similarly, the testing of hypotheses about normal populations can usually be reduced to testing hypotheses about the parameters μ and σ.

Examples, which are essentially hypothesis-testing problems related to binomial or normal distributions, have already been discussed. For example, the problem of determining by means of a sample of 400 voters whether a politician's claim of 60 per cent backing was valid is a problem of testing the hypothesis that $p = .6$ for a binomial distribution for which $n = 400$. The problem of comparing weights of dormitory and nondormitory students, introduced in Chapter 2, can be treated as a problem of testing the hypothesis that the means and standard deviations of two normal distributions are equal.

For the purpose of explaining the methods used to test a hypothesis about a population parameter, consider a particular problem.

During the last fifty years or more, archaeologists in a certain country have been attempting to classify skulls found in excavations into one of two racial groups, partly by the pottery and other utensils found with the skulls and partly by differences in skull dimensions. In particular, they have found that the mean length of all the skulls found thus far from race A is 190 millimeters, whereas the mean length of those from race B is 196 millimeters. The standard deviation of such measurements of length was found to be about the same for the two groups and approximately equal to 8 millimeters. A new excavation produced 12 skulls, which there is reason to believe belong to race A. The mean length of these skulls is $\bar{x} = 194$ millimeters. The problem is to test the hypothesis that the skulls belong to race A rather than to race B.

Since the test is to be based on the value of $\bar{x}$, it is formulated as a test of the hypothesis, denoted by H_0, that the population mean for the 12 skulls is 190, as contrasted to the alternative hypothesis, denoted by H_1, that the population mean is 196. This can be condensed as follows:

$$H_0 : \mu = 190$$

(1)

$$H_1 : \mu = 196.$$

There are two possibilities for making the wrong decision here. If the skulls really belong to race A and on the basis of the value of $\bar{x}$ one

TABLE 1

	H_0 True	H_1 True
H_0 accepted	correct decision	type II error
H_1 accepted	type I error	correct decision

decides to accept H_1, an incorrect decision will be made. If, however, the skulls really belong to race B and one decides to accept H_0, an incorrect decision will also be made. The first type of wrong decision is usually called the type I error, whereas the second type of wrong decision is called the type II error. These two possibilities of incorrect decisions, together with the two possibilities for correct decisions, are listed in Table 1.

Now most people would use good sense in this particular problem and decide in favor of H_0 if $\bar{x}$ were closer to 190 than to 196 and in favor of H_1 if the reverse were true. Thus most people would accept H_1 in this problem. However, archaeologists who have other reasons for believing that the skulls belong to race A, such as pieces of pottery found with the skulls, would not be willing to use the halfway point between the two means as the borderline value for making decisions based on $\bar{x}$. They would undoubtedly insist that $\bar{x}$ be fairly close to the mean corresponding to H_1 before they would be willing to give up the hypothesis H_0 in favor of H_1. To study the reasonableness of using the halfway point, and other points to the right of it, for making decisions, the probabilities of making the two types of error are calculated.

For the purpose of calculating these probabilities, it is assumed that x, the length of a skull, is approximately normally distributed with standard deviation $\sigma = 8$ and with mean $\mu = 190$, if the skull is from race A, and with mean $\mu = 196$, if the skull is from race B. Then $\bar{x}$ may be assumed to be normally distributed with standard deviation

$$\sigma_{\bar{x}} = \frac{\sigma}{\sqrt{n}} = \frac{8}{\sqrt{12}} = 2.31$$

and with mean 190 if the skulls are from race A and with mean 196 if they are from race B. The graphs of the two normal curves for $\bar{x}$ corresponding to H_0 and H_1 are shown in Fig. 1.

If the halfway point, 193, is used for the borderline of decisions, then the probability of making a type I error, that is, the probability of accepting H_1 when H_0 is true, is the probability that $\bar{x} > 193$ when H_0 is true. This probability is equal to the shaded area *under the H_0 curve* to the right of $\bar{x} = 193$. Its value, which is denoted by α, was found by the methods explained in Chapter 4 to be .10. The probability of making a type II error, that is, the probability of accepting H_0 when H_1 is true, is the probability that $\bar{x} < 193$ when H_1 is true. This probability is equal to the shaded area *under the H_1 curve* to the left of $\bar{x} = 193$. Its value, which is denoted by β, is, by symmetry, the same as that for α; hence $\alpha = .10$ and $\beta = .10$.

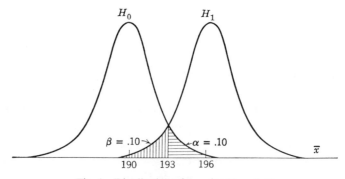

Fig. 1   Distribution of $\bar{x}$ under H_0 and H_1.

If an archaeologist is fairly confident, through other sources of information, that the hypothesis H_0 is true, he will wish to make the probability of rejecting H_0 when it is actually true considerably smaller than the probability of rejecting H_1 when it is actually true. Thus he will want α to be considerably smaller than β. Now it is clear from Fig. 1 that if a point to the right of 193 were chosen for the borderline of decisions the value of α would become smaller than .10 and the value of β would become larger than .10. Since it is not possible to decrease α without increasing β, the archaeologist will need to show some constraint in decreasing α or he will be faced with an unbearably large value of β. Suppose he decides that a value of $\alpha = .05$ will be small enough to give him the protection he desires against incorrectly rejecting H_0. This means that in only about one experiment in twenty will he incorrectly reject H_0 when it is true. With this choice agreed upon, it becomes necessary to select a value of $\bar{x}$ to the right of the halfway point such that the probability of making a type I error will be equal to $\alpha = .05$. Now, from Table IV in the appendix, it is known that 5 per cent of the area of the standard normal curve lies to the right of $z = 1.64$. Since $\mu = 190$ and $\sigma_{\bar{x}} = 2.31$ here and

$$z = \frac{\bar{x} - \mu}{\sigma_{\bar{x}}},$$

it follows that the value of $\bar{x}$ that cuts off a 5 per cent right tail of the $\bar{x}$ curve is obtained by solving for $\bar{x}$ in the equation

$$1.64 = \frac{\bar{x} - 190}{2.31}.$$

The solution of this equation, which is denoted by $\bar{x}_0$, is given by $\bar{x}_0 = 193.8$. Another manner of arriving at this value is to argue that it is necessary to go 1.64 standard deviations to the right of the mean of a normal distribution to obtain a value such that 5 per cent of the area under the curve will be to the right of it. Thus, $\bar{x}_0$ must be given by

$$\bar{x}_0 = 190 + 1.64(2.31) = 193.8$$

Thus it follows that H_1 should be accepted here because the sample value $\bar{x} = 194$ is to the right of $\bar{x}_0 = 193.8$.

With this choice of $\bar{x}$ as the borderline value for making decisions, the value of β becomes the area under the H_1 curve to the left of $\bar{x} = 193.8$. By the methods explained in Chapter 4, the value of β will be found to

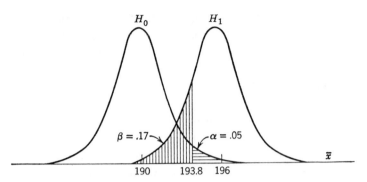

Fig. 2   Distribution of $\bar{x}$ under H_0 and H_1, with selected critical region.

be .17. Figure 2 displays these results geometrically. Although the value of β is considerably larger than the value of α here, as contrasted to using the halfway point which made $\beta = \alpha = .10$, the archaeologist may consider the relative sizes of α and β to be satisfactory because he was much more concerned about making a type I error than about making a type II error. If the archaeologist should feel that the value of β is too large in relation to the value of α, all he would need to do is to decrease the value of $\bar{x}_0$ until he obtained a pair of values that were satisfactory to him in a relative sense.

The part of the $\bar{x}$-axis to the right of $\bar{x}_0$ is called the *critical region* of the test. It consists of those values of $\bar{x}$ that correspond to the rejection of H_0. The method for testing the hypothesis H_0 by means of $\bar{x}$ can be expressed very simply in terms of its critical region by stating that the hypothesis H_0 will be rejected if the sample value of $\bar{x}$ falls in the critical region of the test; otherwise H_0 will be accepted.

This method for testing the hypothesis H_0 is the method that will be used in this book for testing various hypotheses. It consists essentially of selecting a critical region for the variable being used to test the hypothesis such that the probability of the variable falling in the critical region is a fixed value α, and then agreeing to reject the hypothesis if, and only if, the sample value of the variable falls in the critical region. The experimental value of $\bar{x}$ is used only to make a decision after the critical region has been selected and is never permitted to influence the selection of the critical region.

In the foregoing problem α had the value .10 when the critical region was $\bar{x} > 193$ and the value .05 when the critical region was $\bar{x} > 193.8$.

For problems of this type, the proper procedure is to choose the critical region so that the relative sizes of α and β are satisfactory; however, in many of the problems to come, this procedure would require lengthy computations and discussions of the relative importance of the two types of error involved. In order to avoid such lengthy discussions, a uniform procedure will be adopted of always choosing a critical region for which the value of α is .05. The value of $\alpha = .05$ is quite arbitrary here and some other value could have been agreed upon; however, it is the value of α most commonly used by applied statisticians. In any applied problem one can calculate the value of β and then adjust the value of α if the value of β is unsatisfactory when $\alpha = .05$. This works both ways, of course. For a very large experiment, with α fixed at .05, it might turn out that β is considerably smaller than .05. If the type I error were considered more serious than a type II error, then one would need to adjust the test to make α smaller than β, which would, of course, then make α smaller than .05.

This method of testing hypotheses requires one to choose a critical region for which $\alpha = .05$, but otherwise it does not determine how the critical region is to be chosen. Since it is desirable to make the probabilities of the two types of error as small as possible and since α is being fixed, one should choose a critical region that makes β as small as possible. Although the choice of the critical region in Fig. 2 was based on good sense, with the restriction that $\alpha = .05$, it can be shown that no other critical region with $\alpha = .05$ will have as small a value of β as the value $\beta = .17$.

Fortunately, in most simple problems an individual's good sense, or intuition, will lead him to a choice of a critical region that is the best possible in the sense that it will minimize the value of β. For more difficult problems in testing hypotheses, there is a mathematical theory that enables statisticians to find best critical regions. The critical regions that have been chosen in the problems to be solved in this and later chapters are the ones obtained by using this theory whenever it applies.

2. TESTING A MEAN

The problem discussed in section 1 is an illustration of the general problem of testing the hypothesis that the mean of a particular normal population has a certain value. That problem was rather unusual in that there was only one alternative value for the mean. In most practical problems one has no specific information about the possible alternative values of the mean in case the value being tested is not the true value. The commonest situation is one in which all other values are possible. For such problems, the formulation corresponding to (1) assumes the form

$$H_0: \mu = \mu_0$$

(2)

$$H_1: \mu \neq \mu_0.$$

Here μ_0 denotes the particular value being tested. There are many practical problems, however, in which one is quite certain that if the mean is not equal to the value postulated under H_0 then its value must be larger than the postulated value. For such problems (2) would be replaced by

$$H_0: \mu = \mu_0$$

(3)

$$H_1: \mu > \mu_0.$$

For problems in which one is quite certain that if the mean is not equal to μ_0 then its value must be smaller than μ_0, one would, of course, replace $\mu > \mu_0$ by $\mu < \mu_0$ in (3).

As an illustration, suppose that a city has been purchasing brand A light bulbs for several years but is contemplating switching to brand B because of a better price. Salesmen for brand B claim that their product is just as good as brand A. Experience over several years has shown that brand A bulbs have a mean life of 1180 hours, with a standard deviation of 90 hours. To test the claim of the salesmen for brand B, 100 of their bulbs, purchased from regular retail sources, were tested. This sample yielded the values $\bar{x} = 1140$ and $s = 80$. Since mean burning time is a good measure of quality, the problem now is to test the hypothesis that the mean of brand B is equal to the brand A value against the alternative hypothesis that it has a smaller value. If the mean of brand B is denoted by μ, this test will assume the form of (3), namely,

$$H_0: \mu = 1180$$
$$H_1: \mu < 1180.$$

This alternative was chosen because it was felt that if the quality of brand B bulbs were not the same as that of brand A bulbs then the brand B quality would undoubtedly be lower than the brand A quality. Salesmen are not likely to underrate their own products. Therefore, if these salesmen are telling the truth, H_0 will be true. If they are not telling the truth, their brand will be of lower quality because no salesman would be so stupid as to claim only equality when he could actually claim superiority for his product.

Now, good sense would suggest that the further $\bar{x}$ is to the left of the postulated mean of 1180 the less faith one should have in the truth of H_0 and the more faith one should have in some smaller value of μ being the true mean. Thus it is clear that the critical region should consist of small values of $\bar{x}$ and therefore of that part of the $\bar{x}$ axis to the left of some point $\bar{x}_0$. The problem therefore is to determine the point $\bar{x}_0$ so that the value of α will be .05. The technique for doing this is the same as that employed in solving the archaeologists' problem.

Since $n = 100$ here, it follows that

$$\sigma_{\bar{x}} = \frac{\sigma}{\sqrt{100}} = \frac{\sigma}{10}.$$

If the hypothesis being tested here were the hypothesis of equal quality with respect to variability as well as mean burning time, rather than merely equal mean burning time, then it would be proper to use $\sigma = 90$ in this expression for $\sigma_{\bar{x}}$. However, since only the means are being assumed equal, the sample estimate $s = 80$ is used instead; consequently

$$\sigma_{\bar{x}} \doteq \frac{80}{10} = 8.$$

Since the 5 per cent left tail area of a standard normal curve lies to the left of the point $z = -1.64$, it follows that $\bar{x}_0$ is a point 1.64 standard deviations to the left of the mean $\mu = 1180$. Since the standard deviation here is $\sigma_{\bar{x}} \doteq 8$, the desired critical region is that part of the $\bar{x}$ axis to the left of

$$1180 - 1.64(8) \doteq 1167.$$

These results are displayed in Fig. 3. If you prefer to use algebra to obtain the value of $\bar{x}_0$, you should proceed as in the archaeologists' problem and write down the equation

$$-1.64 = \frac{\bar{x} - 1180}{8}.$$

Solving for $\bar{x}$ will, of course, yield the solution $\bar{x}_0 = 1167$.

Now that the critical region has been selected, one can proceed to test the hypothesis H_0. Since the sample value $\bar{x} = 1140$ falls in the

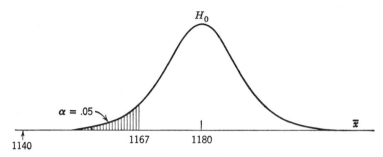

Fig. 3   Critical region for testing H_0.

critical region, the hypothesis H_0 will be rejected. It seems quite certain that a sample mean as low as 1140 could not have been obtained from a random sample of size 100 taken from a population with mean 1180. This implies that the salesmen of brand B bulbs are not justified in their claim of the same quality as brand A. Since it is quite certain that μ is less than 1180, one should consider next the question of how much less. If a point estimate of μ were desired, then, of course, $\bar{x} = 1140$ would be selected as the estimate. One could also find a confidence interval for μ and then determine the maximum and minimum differences that are likely to exist between the two population means. Such considerations would be necessary before one could decide whether the lower price for brand B would compensate for the lower quality. Since the object of this section is to explain how to test hypotheses, these practical matters are not discussed here; however, the solutions of actual problems by statistical methods usually require such considerations.

As an illustration for which formulation (2) would be preferred to (3), consider the following problem. Records for the last several years of freshmen admitted to a certain college showed that their mean score on an aptitude test was 115. An administrator who is interested in knowing whether the new freshman class is a typical class with respect to aptitude proposes to test the hypothesis that the new freshman class mean is the same as that of former classes. Since he has no reason for believing that the new class is any better or any worse than former classes, he should use formulation (2). This becomes

$$H_0 : \mu = 115$$

$$H_1 : \mu \neq 115.$$

For the purpose of testing this hypothesis, the aptitude-test score of every tenth student is obtained from the admissions office. Suppose this yielded a sample of size $n = 50$ and that for this sample the mean and standard deviation turned out to be $\bar{x} = 118$ and $s = 20$.

Since the further $\bar{x}$ is from the hypothetical mean value of 115, whether to the right or the left, the less faith one would have in the truth of H_0, it is clear that the critical region here should consist of values of $\bar{x}$ out in the two tails of the $\bar{x}$ curve centered at 115. Now, for a sample as large as 50, $\bar{x}$ may be assumed to be normally distributed. Furthermore, since $s = 20$, the standard deviation of $\bar{x}$ may be approximated as follows:

$$\sigma_{\bar{x}} = \frac{\sigma}{\sqrt{50}} \doteq \frac{20}{\sqrt{50}} \doteq 2.8.$$

Since the probability is .05 that $\bar{x}$ will assume a value more than 1.96 standard deviations away from the mean, it follows that the desired critical region of size $\alpha = .05$ should consist of the values of $\bar{x}$ out in the two tails of the $\bar{x}$ curve determined by the two values $115 - 1.96(2.8)$ and $115 + 1.96(2.8)$. These results are displayed in Fig. 4.

Since $\bar{x} = 118$ yields a point, indicated on Fig. 4 by an arrow, that does not fall in the critical region, the hypothesis H_0 will be accepted. The college administration may relax in the knowledge that the new freshman class is at about the same level of aptitude as former classes.

The acceptance of a hypothesis in this manner is a practical decision matter. It does not imply that one believes that the hypothesis is precisely correct, and it certainly is not a proof of the truth of the hypothesis. Rather, it implies that the sample data are compatible with the postulated value of the mean. From a practical point of view, it makes little difference

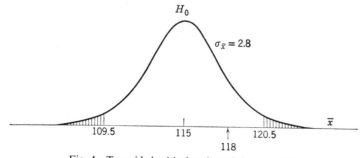

Fig. 4   Two-sided critical region of size $\alpha = .05$.

whether the true mean has the postulated value or whether it has a value close to the postulated value. How close the true value of the mean must be to the postulated value in order that the hypothesis be accepted can be determined by the confidence-interval methods explained in Chapter 6. In view of these remarks, accepting a hypothesis is to be construed as admitting that the hypothesis is reasonably close to the true situation and that, from a practical point of view, one may therefore treat it as representing the true situation.

After the administrator notices that the sample mean is higher than the old mean, he will undoubtedly wish to claim that the new class is better than the former classes. In view of this fact, there would be the temptation to treat this problem as one of testing $H_0:\mu = 115$ against $H_1:\mu > 115$ and to use a one-sided critical region as in the earlier problems; however, this would be illegal because the decision as to the possible alternative values must be based on knowledge other than that given by the sample. A simple way of deciding whether to use a one-sided or two-sided test is to ask oneself what the alternative values of interest are before the sample has been taken or, what is equivalent, before the sample results have been observed.

The sizes of the type II errors in these problems have not been calculated because that would require considerably more discussion of the problems. This matter is considered in section 4 for the benefit of those who are interested in knowing how large such errors are in problems such as these.

A useful application of the idea of testing a mean arises in industrial quality-control work. Suppose that a machine is turning out a large number of parts that are used in some manufactured article and that it is important for the diameter of such a part to be very accurate. It is customary for an inspector to sample periodically from the production line to see whether the diameters are behaving properly. If 5 parts are measured every hour and their sample mean recorded, a large number of $\bar{x}$ values will be obtained after a few weeks of inspection. The mean of all these $\bar{x}$'s may be treated as the true mean of the population of diameters of parts and the standard deviation of these $\bar{x}$'s as the true value of $\sigma_{\bar{x}}$.

By treating the preceding values as true values, one can calculate the values $\mu - 3\sigma_{\bar{x}}$ and $\mu + 3\sigma_{\bar{x}}$. From normal-curve properties, the probability is .997 that a sample value of $\bar{x}$ will fall between these two limits; therefore, if an $\bar{x}$ value falls outside this interval, there is good reason to believe that something has gone wrong with the machine turning out the parts. Experience has shown that a machine that is operating properly will behave very much like a random-number machine in the sense that successive parts turned out behave very much like random samples from a population of parts. A three-standard deviation interval is used instead of, say, a two-standard deviation interval because about 5 per cent of the $\bar{x}$ values would fall outside a two-standard deviation interval, even though the machine is operating satisfactorily, and therefore the inspector would be looking for trouble too often when there is none. Furthermore, an industrial machine is only an approximation of an ideal random number machine. Experience indicates that a three-standard deviation interval is about right from a practical point of view.

After data have been gathered for a few weeks so that the limits $\mu - 3\sigma_{\bar{x}}$ and $\mu + 3\sigma_{\bar{x}}$ can be obtained, the control chart is ready to be constructed. It merely consists of a horizontal band with the horizontal axis marked off with sample numbers. A control chart of this type is shown in Fig. 5.

Each point corresponds to a sample value of $\bar{x}$ obtained from the five parts selected each hour, after the initial data-gathering period. It will be observed that the process appears to be under control. The striking advantage of a control chart is that it warns the inspector by means of probability of trouble with a machine before it has turned out a large number of bad parts, which otherwise might not be discovered until some time later when the parts were being used in assembling the article being manufactured.

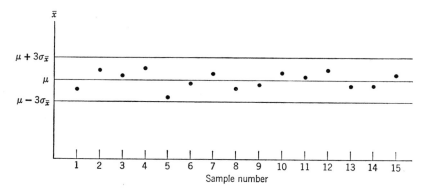

Fig. 5   Control chart for the mean.

2.1   Small-Sample Method

In the problem of testing the mean aptitude score of freshmen, discussed in section 2, the sample size was large enough to justify the approximation used there. If the sample size had been considerably smaller than 50, the replacement of σ by s might have introduced a serious error. For such small-sample problems, one can use Student's t distribution in the same manner that normal z is used for large samples. For example, suppose n had been equal to 20 in the aptitude problem. Then one would have calculated the value of t given by formula (4) in Chapter 6. For this problem,

$$t = \frac{\bar{x} - \mu}{s} \sqrt{n} = \frac{118 - 115}{20} \sqrt{20} = .67.$$

From Table V in the appendix, it will be found that for $\nu = 19$ degrees of freedom the .05 value of t is 2.093. Since a two-sided critical region is being used here, it follows that it should consist of those values of t numerically larger than 2.093. Since $t = .67$ does not fall in the critical region, H_0 is accepted. Of course, if $\bar{x} = 118$ were compatible with H_0 when based on a sample of size 50, it would necessarily be compatible with H_0 when based on a smaller sample, since in general the smaller the sample size, the greater the variation of $\bar{x}$ about μ. The purpose of carrying out the test is merely to explain how one proceeds when using Student's t distribution on such problems. Since the derivation of Student's t distribution requires the assumption that the basic variable x is normally distributed, one must be a little careful when applying it to small samples to make certain that x possesses an approximate normal distribution. The large-sample method does not require this precaution, since $\bar{x}$ is likely to be very nearly normally distributed, even for fairly small samples; however, the large-sample method has the more serious fault of requiring a knowledge of σ or a good estimate of it, and this is not likely to be available in small-sample practical problems.

3.   TESTING THE DIFFERENCE OF TWO MEANS

The problem of the light bulbs that was solved in section 2 can be modified slightly to produce a problem that is typical of many in real life. Suppose the city buying light bulbs had no experience with either brand A or brand B bulbs and wished to decide which brand to purchase, the prices being the same. It would then be necessary to test a sample of each brand, rather than just a sample of brand B, as in the earlier problem. Suppose a sample of 100 bulbs from each of the two brands is tested and that the samples yield the values $\bar{x}_1 = 1160$, $s_1 = 90$, $\bar{x}_2 = 1140$, and $s_2 = 80$, in which the subscripts 1 and 2 refer to brands A and B, respectively.

Now since brand A yields a larger mean burning time than brand B, it would appear that brand A is superior to brand B; however, it might be that the reverse is true, but some bad luck with a few of the bulbs of brand B produced an unusually low sample mean. A second set of samples of 100 each might conceivably produce different results. The problem therefore reduces to determining whether this difference of sample means, namely $\bar{x}_1 - \bar{x}_2$, is large enough to justify the belief that brand A is superior to brand B.

In order to solve this problem, it is necessary to know how $\bar{x}_1 - \bar{x}_2$ varies if repeated sampling experiments of the same kind are performed. Each sampling experiment consists of taking a sample of 100 bulbs from brands A and B, testing the 200 bulbs, determining the values of $\bar{x}_1$ and $\bar{x}_2$, and recording the value of the variable $\bar{x}_1 - \bar{x}_2$. If a large number of such sampling experiments were carried out, a large number of values of the variable $\bar{x}_1 - \bar{x}_2$ would be obtained. These values could be classified into a frequency table, and a histogram drawn, to give one a good idea of the limiting, or theoretical, distribution of $\bar{x}_1 - \bar{x}_2$. As in the case of a single mean, $\bar{x}$, it is not necessary to carry out these sampling experiments because the form of the limiting distribution can be worked out mathematically. It can be shown that $\bar{x}_1 - \bar{x}_2$ will possess a normal distribution, if x_1 and x_2 do, with a mean equal to the difference of the population means of x_1 and x_2, namely $\mu_1 - \mu_2$, and with a variance (square of standard deviation) equal to the sum of the variances of $\bar{x}_1$ and $\bar{x}_2$. This result is expressed in the form of a theorem:

(4)   **Theorem.** *If x_1 and x_2 possess independent normal distributions with means μ_1 and μ_2 and standard deviations σ_1 and σ_2, then the variable $\bar{x}_1 - \bar{x}_2$ will possess a normal distribution with mean $\mu_1 - \mu_2$ and standard deviation given by the formula*

$$\sigma_{\bar{x}_1 - \bar{x}_2} = \sqrt{\sigma_{\bar{x}_1}{}^2 + \sigma_{\bar{x}_2}{}^2} = \sqrt{\frac{\sigma_1{}^2}{n_1} + \frac{\sigma_2{}^2}{n_2}}.$$

Here n_1 and n_2 are the sample sizes on which $\bar{x}_1$ and $\bar{x}_2$ are based. It should be noted that the theorem requires that the two populations being sampled be normal; however, if n_1 and n_2 are as large as 25, say, then $\bar{x}_1$ and $\bar{x}_2$ may be assumed to be normally distributed, in which case $\bar{x}_1 - \bar{x}_2$ will also be normally distributed. It should also be noted that x_1 and x_2 are required to be independent variables. For example, if the problem had been to test the hypothesis that there is no difference between the mean length of people's right feet and left feet, it would not be correct to let x_1 represent the length of an individual's right foot and x_2 the length of his left foot because a large value of x_1 would certainly increase the probability of a large value of x_2. If, however, the x_2 values were obtained from a different set of individuals, rather than those for x_1, then x_1 and x_2 would be independent variables. The proper way to treat paired data, such as would arise in measuring both feet of each individual, would be to take the difference of each pair and then use the earlier methods for testing whether the mean of the variable $x_1 - x_2$ is zero. The test would then be based on a sample of size $n = n_1 = n_2$.

Problems such as the selection of light bulbs can be solved by means of the theorem in (4), provided they are treated as problems of testing the appropriate hypothesis. From a practical point of view, it should make little difference whether one rejects the hypothesis that the brands are equally good or accepts the hypothesis that they differ in quality. From a theoretical point of view, however, it is more convenient to test the hypothesis that the brands are equally good than the hypothesis that they differ in quality. As a result, one sets up the hypothesis

$$(5) \qquad\qquad H_0 : \mu_1 - \mu_2 = 0.$$

An equivalent way of writing this is

$$H_0 : \mu_1 = \mu_2.$$

This type of hypothesis is known as a *null* hypothesis because it assumes that there is no difference. Very often, however, the experimenter believes that there is an appreciable difference and hopes that the sample evidence will reject the hypothesis. If the sample does reject the hypothesis, then one can claim with justification that a real difference in population means exist. If the sample does not reject the hypothesis, then there is a fair probability that the sample difference is caused by sampling variation, under the assumption that the population means are equal.

In the light of the theorem in (4) and the preceding discussion, testing the hypothesis given by (5) is equivalent to testing the hypothesis that the mean of the normal variable $\bar{x}_1 - \bar{x}_2$ is 0. But this type of problem was solved in section 2. Since the alternative hypothesis would ordinarily be chosen as

$$H_1: \mu_1 \neq \mu_2,$$

it follows that the same methods should be applied here as in the solution of the aptitude-test problem which used the formulation in (2). Now, from the theory in (4) the variable $\bar{x}_1 - \bar{x}_2$ may be assumed to be normally distributed with mean 0, because $\mu_1 = \mu_2$ under H_0, and with standard deviation given by

$$\sigma_{\bar{x}_1 - \bar{x}_2} = \sqrt{\frac{\sigma_1^2}{n_1} + \frac{\sigma_2^2}{n_2}}.$$

Unfortunately, the population values σ_1^2 and σ_2^2 are unknown; consequently, they must be approximated by their sample estimates, namely $s_1^2 = (90)^2$ and $s_2^2 = (80)^2$. Since $n_1 = n_2 = 100$ here, the approximate value of the standard deviation becomes

$$\sigma_{\bar{x}_1 - \bar{x}_2} \doteq \sqrt{\frac{8100}{100} + \frac{6400}{100}} \doteq 12.$$

A critical region based on equal tail areas under the normal curve for $\bar{x}_1 - \bar{x}_2$ is chosen for which $\alpha = .05$. This means that the critical region consists of that part of the horizontal axis lying more than $1.96\sigma_{\bar{x}_1 - \bar{x}_2} = 24$ units away from 0. Figure 6 shows geometrically the distribution of $\bar{x}_1 - \bar{x}_2$ and the selected critical region.

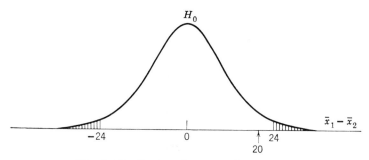

Fig. 6   Distribution of $\bar{x}_1 - \bar{x}_2$ when $\mu_1 = \mu_2$.

Since the two samples of 100 each yielded the value $\bar{x}_1 - \bar{x}_2 = 1160 - 1140 = 20$ and since 20 does not fall in the critical region for this test, the hypothesis is accepted.

Just as in the earlier problem of testing a single mean, the acceptance of a hypothesis in this manner does not imply that one believes that the hypothesis is true. It does imply, however, that one is not convinced by the sample evidence that there is an appreciable difference and that, unless further evidence is presented to the contrary, one is willing to assume that for all practical purposes there is no appreciable difference in the population means. It is a mathematical convenience to formulate a hypothesis in this manner. It would be more realistic to test whether the means differed by less than a specified amount, but the resulting theory would be much more complicated. A student should not deceive himself into believing that he has proved the hypothesis to be true just because he has agreed to accept it.

In view of the fact that sample estimates were needed as approximations for population variances, the methods used here are large-sample methods.

There are several words and phrases used in connection with testing hypotheses that should be brought to the attention of students. When a test of a hypothesis produces a sample value falling in the critical region of the test, the result is said to be *significant;* otherwise one says that the result is *not significant.* This word arises from the fact that such a sample value is not compatible with the hypothesis and therefore signifies that some other hypothesis is necessary. The probability of committing a type I error, which is denoted by α, is called the *significance level* of the test. For problems being solved routinely in this book, the significance level has been chosen equal to .05.

If one analyzes the technique that has been used to test the various hypotheses that have been treated thus far he will observe that it is merely a rule for making a decision. This rule is usually based on the sample value of some random variable and consists in dividing all the possible values of the random variable into two groups, those associated with the rejection of H_0 and which form what is called the critical region of the test, and those associated with the acceptance of H_0. From this general point of view, a test of a hypothesis is merely a systematic way of making a practical decision and there is no implication made concerning the truth or falsity of the hypothesis being treated.

▶3.1 Small-Sample Method

If the sample sizes are too small to justify replacing σ_1 and σ_2 by their sample estimates in the preceding test, then the appropriate Student t test may be used. For testing the difference of two means, the theory of Student's t distribution requires one to assume that the two basic variables x_1 and x_2 possess independent normal distributions with equal standard deviations. These assumptions are considerably more restrictive than those needed for the large-sample method. If these assumptions are reasonably satisfied, then one may treat the variable

$$t = \frac{\bar{x}_1 - \bar{x}_2 - (\mu_1 - \mu_2)}{\sqrt{(n_1 - 1)s_1{}^2 + (n_2 - 1)s_2{}^2}} \sqrt{\frac{n_1 n_2 (n_1 + n_2 - 2)}{n_1 + n_2}}$$

as a Student t variable with $\nu = n_1 + n_2 - 2$ degrees of freedom. The solution is now carried out in the same manner as for testing a single mean. For example, if the problem just solved is altered to make the sample sizes 10 each, then the value of t will become

$$t = \frac{1160 - 1140}{\sqrt{9(90)^2 + 9(80)^2}} \sqrt{\frac{100(18)}{20}} = .53.$$

From Table V in the appendix it will be found that the 5 per cent critical value of t corresponding to $\nu = 18$ degrees of freedom is 2.10. Since the value $t = .53$ falls inside the noncritical interval, which extends from -2.10 to $+2.10$, the hypothesis is accepted. Since the hypothesis was accepted before for a much larger sample, it would obviously be accepted here as well.

Modifications of the foregoing t test exist for problems in which it is unreasonable to assume that the two variances are equal; however, they are not considered here.

▶4. OPERATING CHARACTERISTIC

Because of the seemingly large interval of values corresponding to the acceptance of H_0, as shown in Fig. 6 for the problem in section 3, one might be disturbed by the possibility that brand A is really better than brand B, but this fact is not being discovered by the test. In order to check on this possibility, it is necessary to study the size of the type II error.

In any practical situation like this it should be possible for the individual concerned to specify the smallest difference in the population means that would be considered of practical importance to him. In the preceding problem, for example, the purchasing agent might state that a difference smaller than 25 is too small to be important but that any larger difference is of economic importance. Now, consider the alternative hypothesis based upon this smallest important difference, namely,

$$H_1: \mu_1 - \mu_2 = 25.$$

The value of β can be calculated for this H_1 in the manner of the archaeologists' problem. The distribution of $\bar{x}_1 - \bar{x}_2$ under H_1 will be the same as under H_0, except that the mean will be 25 instead of 0. The graphs of these two distributions are shown in Fig. 7. The value of β is given by the area under the H_1 curve from -24 to $+24$ because this interval is the noncritical region of the test; however, this area is practically equivalent to the area under the H_1 curve to the left of 24. Since the standard deviation here is 12 and the mean is 25, the z value corresponding to 24 is

$$z = \frac{24 - 25}{12} = -.08.$$

From Table IV in the appendix it will be found that the probability that z will lie to the left of $-.08$ is $.47$; consequently $\beta = .47$ here. This means that about half the time a difference of 25 in the population means will not be detected by this test.

If the difference in the population means is actually greater than 25, then, of course, the value of β will be smaller than $.47$. For example, if

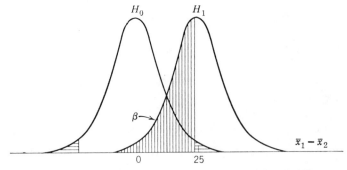

Fig. 7   The distribution of $\bar{x}_1 - \bar{x}_2$ under H_0 and under H_1.

the true difference is 50, then similar calculations with the H_1 curve now centered over 50 will show that β assumes the value .015. Thus one is almost certain to detect a difference as large as 50 with this test, that is, with a sample of this size. If different values of $\mu_1 - \mu_2$ are postulated, starting with 0 and increasing in regular steps, and the value of β is calculated for each such alternative, then these values when plotted against the value of $\mu_1 - \mu_2$ will show how good the test is for detecting true differences when they exist. The values of β were calculated for this problem for steps of 10 in the value of $\mu_1 - \mu_2$. These values were graphed and a smooth curve was drawn through the resulting points, as shown in Fig. 8. The curve is symmetric; however, only the positive axis half is shown here. This curve is called the *operating characteristic* of the test. It enables one to determine how good the test is for various values of $\mu_1 - \mu_2$. For example, it is clear from this graph that a difference of 10 in the population means will seldom be detected because β is very large for this value of $\mu_1 - \mu_2$. This is not a serious matter, however, if the purchasing agent is not interested in differences less than 25. A more serious matter is the relatively large value of β for $\mu_1 - \mu_2$ having a value between 25 and 35.

If the value of β for values of $\mu_1 - \mu_2$ between 25 and 35 is larger than desired, then two methods for decreasing the value of β are possible. The first method consists in choosing a larger critical region. Thus, instead of using the two $2\frac{1}{2}$ per cent tails of the distribution for determining the critical region, one might choose the two 5 per cent tails. This larger critical region will, of course, increase the value of α from .05 to .10. Calculations will show that the value of β for $\mu_1 - \mu_2 = 25$ will now decrease from .47 to .33. The relative importance of the two

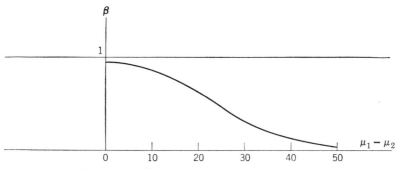

Fig. 8   Operating characteristic for a two-sided test.

types of error here would determine how much α should be allowed to increase in order to decrease β. The second method of decreasing β consists in taking a larger sample. If α is to be fixed at a value such as .05, then the only way to decrease β is to take a larger sample. As an illustration, suppose the sample size in the problem being discussed is increased from 200 to 400. Then the estimate of the standard deviation will be found to decrease from 12 to 8.5. The two-sided critical region is now determined by -17 and $+17$. Calculations of the same type as those used earlier will show that the value of β for $\mu_1 - \mu_2 = 25$ now becomes .17.

It should be clear from the foregoing discussion of this problem that anyone who intends to take a sample for the purpose of testing some hypothesis about a mean or any other parameter should concern himself with the operating characteristic of his proposed test so that he will be able to tell whether his sample is large enough to give him the protection he desires against making various type I and type II errors. The size sample needed to make β reasonably small for $\alpha = .05$ is often much larger than anticipated by those who apply significance tests.

5. TESTING A PROPORTION

The large-sample normal-curve methods employed to solve estimation problems for binomial p can be employed also to test hypotheses about p. As a result, the techniques for testing the hypothesis that p has a fixed value or that two proportions are equal are much the same as those explained in the last two sections for means. As an illustration, consider the following genetics problem. According to Mendelian inheritance theory, certain crosses of peas should give yellow and green peas in a ratio of $3:1$. In an experiment 176 yellow and 48 green peas were obtained. Are these numbers compatible with Mendelian theory?

This problem may be considered as a problem of testing the hypothesis

$$H_0: p = \frac{3}{4}$$

in which p denotes the probability that a pea selected at random will be yellow. The 224 peas may be treated as 224 trials of an experiment for which $p = \frac{3}{4}$ is the probability of success in a single trial. From formula (11), Chapter 4, it follows that $p' = x/n$ may be treated as a normal variable with mean $p = \frac{3}{4}$ and standard deviation given by

$$\sigma_{p'} = \sqrt{\frac{pq}{n}} = \sqrt{\frac{\frac{3}{4} \cdot \frac{1}{4}}{224}} = .029.$$

The problem now is much the same as the problem of testing a normal mean. The critical region here is chosen as those values of p' in the two tails of the normal curve for p'. For $\alpha = .05$, the critical region will then consist of those values of p' lying outside the interval given by

$$p - 1.96\sqrt{\frac{pq}{n}} \quad \text{and} \quad p + 1.96\sqrt{\frac{pq}{n}}.$$

Since $n = 224$ and $p = \frac{3}{4}$ here, computations will yield the interval (.693, .807). Figure 9 shows the approximate normal distribution for p' and the critical region just determined. Since the sample value $p' = 176/224 = .79$ does not fall in the critical region, the hypothesis H_0 is accepted. Thus, on the basis of these data, there is no reason for doubting that Mendelian inheritance is operating here.

As a second illustration of how to use normal-curve methods to test a hypothesis about binomial p, consider the problem discussed briefly near the end of Chapter 4. A politician had claimed a 60 per cent backing on a piece of legislation and a sample of 400 voters had been taken to check this claim. The question then arose as to how small the sample percentage would need to be before the claim could be rightfully refuted. This problem can be considered as a problem of testing the hypothesis

$$H_0 : p = .6.$$

Since the interest in this problem centers on whether $p = .6$, as against the possibility that $p < .6$, this problem is somewhat like that of the

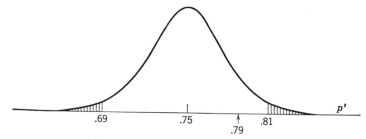

Fig. 9 Approximate normal distribution of p'.

light bulbs discussed in the first section of this chapter in that the alternatives are all on one side of the hypothetical value and therefore that the critical region should be under one tail of the proper normal curve. The natural alternative hypothesis here is

$$H_1 : p < .6.$$

The critical region of size $\alpha = .05$ for this problem should therefore be selected to be under the left 5 per cent tail of the normal curve whose mean is $p = .6$ and whose standard deviation is given by

$$\sigma_{p'} = \sqrt{\frac{pq}{n}} = \sqrt{\frac{(.6)(.4)}{400}} = .0245.$$

Since, from Table IV, 5 per cent of the area of a standard normal curve lies to the left of $z = -1.64$, this means that the critical region should consist of all those values of p' that are smaller than the value of p' which is 1.64 standard deviations to the left of the mean. For this problem, the critical region therefore consists of all those values of p' that are smaller than

$$p - 1.64 \sqrt{\frac{pq}{n}} = .6 - 1.64(.0245) = .56.$$

If the sample value of p' turned out to be less than .56, the politician's claim would be rejected.

Another useful application of testing a binomial p arises in industrial control charts for the percentage of defective parts in mass production of parts. This application is not confined to industrial problems; it may be used wherever one has repeated operations. The technique is precisely the same as for control charts for the mean. One uses accumulated experience to obtain a good estimate of p; then one constructs the control band given by $p - 3\sqrt{pq/n}$ and $p + 3\sqrt{pq/n}$. Here n is the size sample on which each plotted proportion is based.

As an illustration of how one would construct such a chart, consider the following problem. A record is kept for ten days of the number of words mistyped by students learning typing. During that period of time they typed a total of approximately 20,000 words, of which 800 were mistyped. The problem is to use these data to construct a control chart for the proportion of errors made per class hour by a student who types approximately 600 words per class hour. Assuming the given student is typical, a good estimate of p is given by dividing the total number of mistyped words by the total number of typed words. This estimate is

$$p \doteq \frac{800}{20,000} = .04.$$

Since the proportions to be plotted on the control chart are those for an hour's typing, it follows that $n = 600$ here. If these values are substituted in the formulas given in the preceding paragraph, the desired lower and upper boundaries for the control chart will become

$$.04 - 3\sqrt{\frac{(.04)(.96)}{600}} \quad \text{and} \quad .04 + 3\sqrt{\frac{(.04)(.96)}{600}}.$$

These simplify to .016 and .064. The chart can now be constructed in the same manner as for the mean, except that now one plots the proportion of mistyped words every hour rather than the sample mean.

6. TESTING THE DIFFERENCE OF TWO PROPORTIONS

A problem of much importance and frequent occurrence in statistical work is the problem of determining whether two populations differ with respect to a certain attribute. For example, is there any difference in the percentages of smokers and nonsmokers who have heart ailments?

Problems of this type can be treated as problems of testing the hypothesis

$$H_0 : p_1 = p_2,$$

in which p_1 and p_2 are the two population proportions of the attribute. If n_1 and n_2 denote the size samples taken and p_1' and p_2' the resulting sample proportions obtained, then the variable to use in solving this problem is $p_1' - p_2'$. This corresponds to using $\bar{x}_1 - \bar{x}_2$ in the problem of testing the hypothesis that $\mu_1 = \mu_2$. The methods used to solve that problem can be employed here as well because p_1' and p_2' may be treated as two independent normal variables. The theory in (4) can then be used to show that $p_1' - p_2'$ may be considered as being approximately normally distributed with mean $p_1 - p_2$ and with standard deviation given by

$$\sigma_{p_1' - p_2'} = \sqrt{\frac{p_1 q_1}{n_1} + \frac{p_2 q_2}{n_2}}.$$

When testing the hypothesis $H_0:p_1 = p_2$, the mean of the distribution of $p_1' - p_2'$ will, of course, be equal to 0.

As an illustration of how to use these formulas, consider the following problem. A sample of 400 sailors was split into two equal groups by random selection. One group was given brand A pills of a seasickness preventive, and the other brand B pills. The number in each group that refrained from becoming seasick during a heavy storm was 152 and 132. Can one conclude that there is no real difference in the effectiveness of these pills?

Calculations give

$$p_1' = \frac{152}{200} = .76, \qquad p_2' = \frac{132}{200} = .66,$$

$$\sigma_{p_1'-p_2'} = \sqrt{\frac{p_1 q_1}{200} + \frac{p_2 q_2}{200}}.$$

Since the values of p_1 and p_2 are unknown, they must be approximated by sample estimates. Although the values are unknown, they are assumed to be equal under the hypothesis $H_0:p_1 = p_2$. If this common value is denoted by p, then a good estimate of p is the value obtained from the sample proportion of the combined data. There were 284 of 400 sailors who were successes in this total experiment; hence p would be estimated by means of

$$p' = \frac{284}{400} = .71.$$

By replacing p_1 and p_2 by p in the formula for the standard deviation and then approximating p by p', one obtains

$$\sigma_{p_1'-p_2'} \doteq \sqrt{(.71)(.29)(\tfrac{1}{200} + \tfrac{1}{200})} = .045.$$

The use of a two-sided critical region of size .05 yields the critical region

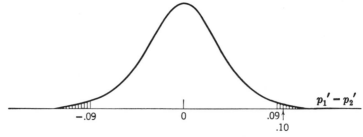

Fig. 10   Distribution and critical region for $p_1' - p_2'$.

displayed in Fig. 10. Since $p_1' - p_2' = .10$ here, it falls in the critical region and therefore the hypothesis is rejected. It would appear that brand A gives somewhat better protection against seasickness than brand B, at least for sailors in stormy weather.

7. REVIEW EXERCISES

The results of the sampling experiment that gave rise to Tables 4 and 5 of Chapter 5 will be used to solve the following review exercises. The 100 sample values of $\bar{x}$ in Table 4 should be treated as a sample of size 100 from a normal population for which $\mu = 2.75$ and $\sigma = .47$, and the fact that these values are sample means should be ignored. (a) Test the hypothesis that $\mu = 2.75$. (b) Divide the sample into two sets of 50 each by taking the first 50 for one group and the remaining 50 for the other group. Test the hypothesis that $\mu_1 = \mu_2$ using the fact that $\sigma_1 = \sigma_2 = .47$. (c) Work part (b) without assuming that the standard deviations are known. (d) Suppose one is interested only in whether the value of $\bar{x}$ exceeds 2.95. Using the data of Table 4, test the hypothesis that the probability of $\bar{x}$ exceeding 2.95 is .40. (e) Using the data of Table 4, test the hypothesis that the two groups of part (b) possess the same probability of having $\bar{x}$ exceed 2.95. Assume that this probability is not known. (f) Using the fact that the data of Table 4 are sample means based on 10 measurements each, construct a control chart for $\bar{x}$ using the fact that $\mu = 2.75$ and $\sigma = 1.48$ for the variable x and determine whether the samples seem to be under control. ▶(g) Work part (b) by means of the t distribution and compare your results with those of part (b). ▶(h) Calculate the value of β in part (a) if the alternative value of μ is chosen to be 2.85 and a one-sided test is used.

(a) $\mu = 2.75$, $\sigma = .47$, $n = 100$, $\bar{x} = 2.77$,

$$\sigma_{\bar{x}} = \frac{.47}{\sqrt{100}} = .047, \qquad z = \frac{2.77 - 2.75}{.047} = \frac{.02}{.047} \doteq .43;$$

hence accept $H_0 : \mu = 2.75$.

(b) $\bar{x}_1 = 2.78$, $\bar{x}_2 = 2.74$, $\sigma_{\bar{x}_1 - \bar{x}_2} = \sqrt{\frac{(.47)^2}{50} + \frac{(.47)^2}{50}} = .094$

$$z = \frac{\bar{x}_1 - \bar{x}_2}{\sigma_{\bar{x}_1 - \bar{x}_2}} = \frac{.04}{.094} \doteq .43; \text{ hence accept } H_0 : \mu_1 = \mu_2.$$

(c) Without classifying the data $s_1{}^2 = .20$ and $s_2{}^2 = .14$; hence

$$\sigma_{\bar{x}_1-\bar{x}_2} \doteq \sqrt{\frac{.20}{50} + \frac{.14}{50}} = .082$$

$$z = \frac{\bar{x}_1 - \bar{x}_2}{\sigma_{\bar{x}_1-\bar{x}_2}} = \frac{.04}{.082} \doteq .49; \text{ hence accept } H_0:\mu_1 = \mu_2.$$

(d) $p = .4$, $n = 100$, $p' = .31$, $\sigma_{p'} = \sqrt{\frac{(.4)(.6)}{100}} \doteq .049$

$$z = \frac{.31 - .40}{.049} = -1.84; \text{ hence accept } H_0:p = .4.$$

(e) $p_1' = .32$, $p_2' = .30$, $p \doteq .31$

$$\sigma_{p_1'-p_2'} = \sqrt{(.31)(.69)(\tfrac{1}{50} + \tfrac{1}{50})} = .092$$

$$z = \frac{.32 - .30}{.092} = \frac{.02}{.092} \doteq .22; \text{ hence accept } H_0:p_1 = p_2.$$

(f) $\mu \pm 3\sigma_{\bar{x}} = 2.75 \pm 3\frac{1.48}{\sqrt{10}} = 2.75 \pm 1.40$; hence the limits are 1.35

and 4.15. Without constructing the chart, it is obvious from Fig. 6 of Chapter 5 that none of the sample values will yield a point outside this control-band interval.

(g) $(n_1 - 1)s_1{}^2 + (n_2 - 1)s_2{}^2 = 49(.20) + 49(.14) = 16.7$

$$t = \frac{2.78 - 2.74}{\sqrt{16.7}} \sqrt{\frac{50 \cdot 50(98)}{100}} = .48; \text{ hence accept } H_0:\mu_1 = \mu_2.$$

The values of t and z are practically the same here, but this is to be expected because for such large samples the t distribution can hardly be distinguished from a standard normal distribution.

(h) The critical region to choose here should be under the right tail of the $\bar{x}$ distribution; it should consist of those values of $\bar{x}$ to the right of

$$\bar{x}_0 = 2.75 + 1.64\sigma_{\bar{x}} = 2.75 + 1.64\frac{.47}{\sqrt{100}} = 2.83.$$

As shown in the sketch, β is the area under the normal curve with mean 2.85 and standard deviation .047 to the left of 2.83. Now

$$z = \frac{\bar{x} - \mu}{\sigma_{\bar{x}}} = \frac{2.83 - 2.85}{.047} = -\frac{.02}{.047} = -.43.$$

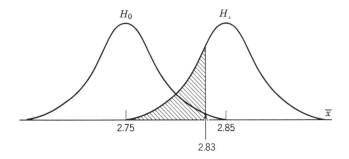

From Table IV the corresponding positive z value gives the probability .17; hence $\beta = .33$.

In all of the preceding problems involving the testing of some hypothesis, except for part (d), the hypothesis was true because of the knowledge available concerning the data used. The results are in good agreement with the assumption that random numbers produce random samples.

EXERCISES

1. In a court case in which an individual is being tried for theft, what are the two types of error? Which type of error is considered by society more important?

2. Give an illustration of a hypothesis for which the type II error would be considered much more serious than the type I error.

3. Suppose you agree to reject a hypothesis if two tosses of an honest coin produce two heads. What are the sizes of the two types of error?

√4. Given $\bar{x} = 82$, $\sigma = 15$, and $n = 100$, test the hypothesis that $\mu = 86$.

5. Given $\bar{x} = 82$, $\sigma = 15$, and $n = 25$, test the hypothesis that $\mu = 86$.

√6. A purchaser of bricks believes that the quality of the bricks is deteriorating. From past experience, the mean crushing strength of such bricks is 400 pounds, with a standard deviation of 20 pounds. A sample of 100 bricks yielded a mean of 390 pounds. Test the hypothesis that the mean quality has not changed against the alternative that it has deteriorated.

7. Many years of experience with a university entrance examination in English yielded a mean score of 64 with a standard deviation of 8. All the students from a certain city, of which there were 54, obtained a mean score of 68. Can one be quite certain that students from this city are superior in English?

8. A manufacturer of fishing line claims that his 5-pound test line will average 8 pounds test. Is he justified in his claim if a sample of size 50 yielded $\bar{x} = 8.8$ pounds and $s = 1.4$ pounds?

9. Construct a control chart for $\bar{x}$ for the following data on the blowing time of fuses, samples of 5 being taken every hour. Each set of 5 has been arranged in order of magnitude. Estimate μ by calculating the mean of all the data and estimate $\sigma_{\bar{x}}$ by first estimating σ by means of s calculated for all 60 values. State whether control seems to exist here.

42	42	19	36	42	51	60	18	15	69	64	61
65	45	24	54	51	74	60	20	30	109	91	78
75	68	80	69	57	75	72	27	39	113	93	94
78	72	81	77	59	78	95	42	62	118	109	109
87	90	81	84	78	132	138	60	84	153	112	136

10. Given that x is normally distributed and given the sample values $\bar{x} = 42$, $s = 5$, $n = 20$, test the hypothesis that $\mu = 44$, using the t distribution.

11. The following data give the corrosion effects in various soils for coated and uncoated steel pipe. Taking differences of pairs of values, test by means of the t distribution the hypothesis that the mean of such differences is zero.

Uncoated	42	37	61	74	55	57	44	55	37	70	52	55
Coated	39	43	43	52	52	59	40	45	47	62	40	27

12. Take a sample of size 25 from a table of one-digit random numbers (Table II in the appendix) and test the hypothesis that $\mu = 4.5$. Use the fact that $\sigma = 2.87$ for this distribution and that $\bar{x}$ may be treated as a normal variable. Bring your result to class. Approximately 95 per cent of the class should accept this hypothesis because it is true.

13. Work problem 12, choosing $\alpha = .20$, using a sample of size 10 and assuming that the value of σ is not known; that is, use Student's t test here. Compare the results of the students with expectation.

14. Given two random samples of size 100 each from two normal populations with sample values $\bar{x}_1 = 20$, $\bar{x}_2 = 22$, $s_1 = 5$, $s_2 = 6$, test the hypothesis that $\mu_1 = \mu_2$.

15. Two sets of 50 elementary-school children were taught to read by two different methods. After instruction was over, a reading test gave the following results: $\bar{x}_1 = 73.4$, $\bar{x}_2 = 70.3$, $s_1 = 8$, $s_2 = 10$. Test the hypothesis that $\mu_1 = \mu_2$.

16. In an industrial experiment a job was performed by 40 workmen according to method I and by 50 workmen according to method II. The results of the experiment yielded the following data on the length of time required to complete the job: $\bar{x}_1 = 54$ minutes, $\bar{x}_2 = 57$ minutes, $s_1 = 6$ minutes, $s_2 = 8$ minutes. Test the hypothesis that $\mu_1 = \mu_2$.

17. A coin is tossed twice. Let x denote the number of heads obtained. Consider the hypothesis $H_0 : p = .5$ and the alternative $H_1 : p = .7$, in which p is the probability of obtaining a head, and assume that one is goint to test this hypothesis by means of the value of x. The distributions of x under H_0 and H_1 can be

obtained by means of the binomial distribution formula (1) in Chapter 4. Suppose one chooses $x = 2$ as the critical region for the test. Calculate the sizes of the two types of error.

18. In problem 17 suppose $x = 0$ had been chosen as the critical region for the test. Now calculate the sizes of the two types of error and compare your results with those of problem 17. Comment about these two choices of critical region.

19. Have each member of the class draw 10 pairs of one-digit random numbers (Table II in the appendix). The second number should be subtracted from the first number for each pair. Each student should bring to class the sum of the squares of these differences as well as the sum of the differences. By combining the class results, an estimate of σ_z^2, in which $z = x - y$, can be obtained and compared to the value expected from (4), namely $\sigma_{x-y}^2 = \sigma_x^2 + \sigma_y^2 = (2.87)^2 + (2.87)^2 = 16.5$. Here x and y denote, respectively, the first and second random digits of each pair. From earlier work it was found that $\mu_x = 4.5$ and $\sigma_x = 2.87$.

20. If you rolled a die 240 times and obtained 50 sixes, would you decide that the die favored sixes?

21. Past experience has shown that 40 per cent of students fail a university entrance examination in English. If 50 out of 110 students from a certain city failed, would one be justified in concluding that the students from this city are inferior in English?

22. A biologist has mixed a spray designed to kill 50 per cent of a certain type of insect. If a spraying of 200 such insects killed 120 of them, would you conclude his mixture was satisfactory?

23. What is the difference between saying that a coin is honest for all practical purposes and saying that it is honest in a mathematical sense?

24. Explain why you might hesitate from practical considerations to reject the hypothesis that a coin is honest if you tossed the coin 1000 times and obtained 535 heads.

25. The following data were obtained for a daily percentage defective of parts for a production averaging 1000 parts a day. Construct a control chart and indicate whether control seems to exist here. The data are for the percentage (not proportion) of defectives and are to be read a row at a time. Estimate p by calculating the mean of these sample values.

2.2	2.3	2.1	1.7	3.8	2.5	2.0	1.6	1.4	2.6	1.5	2.8	2.9	2.6	2.5
2.6	3.2	4.6	3.3	3.0	3.1	4.3	1.8	2.6	2.1	2.2	1.8	2.4	2.4	1.6
1.7	1.6	2.8	3.2	1.8	2.6	3.6	4.2							

26. In a poll taken among college students 46 of 200 fraternity men favored a certain proposition, whereas 51 of 300 nonfraternity men favored it. Is there a real difference of opinion on this proposition?

27. In a poll of the television audience in a city 60 out of 200 men disliked a certain program, whereas 75 out of 300 women disliked it. Is there a real difference of opinion here?

28. In one section of a city 64 out of 480 taxpayers were delinquent with their tax payments, whereas in another section 42 out of 500 were delinquent. Test to see if the delinquency rate is the same for those two sections of the city.

29. A test of 100 youths and 200 adults showed that 50 of the youths and 60 of the adults were careless drivers. Use these data to test the claim that the youth percentage of careless drivers is larger than the adult percentage by 10 percentage points against the alternative that it exeeeds this amount.

30. Two classes of the same size are taught by the same instructor. One class is a regular class, whereas the other one is in an adjoining class room and receives the instructor's lecture by closed circuit television. Discuss possible factors that might prevent a valid statistical comparison to be made of the two learning methods.

31. As a review exercise use the results of the sampling experiment that produced Table 2 of Chapter 5 to work the review exercise of section 7, replacing the numbers there in both the information given and the questions asked by the corresponding numbers $\mu = 0$ and $\sigma = \frac{1}{2}$, and divide the data into two groups of 25 each. In parts (d) and (e) replace 2.95 by $\frac{1}{8}$ and test the hypothesis that the probability of $\bar{x}$ exceeding $\frac{1}{8}$ is .5. In part (f) use the fact that the data are sample means based on 4 measurements each of a variable with $\mu = 0$ and $\sigma = 1$. In part (k) calculate β for $\mu = \frac{1}{8}$.

▶32. Given two random samples of sizes 10 and 12 from two independent normal populations with $\bar{x}_1 = 20$, $\bar{x}_2 = 24$, $s_1 = 5$, $s_2 = 6$, test by means of the t distribution the hypothesis that $\mu_1 = \mu_2$, assuming that $\sigma_1 = \sigma_2$.

▶33. The following data give the gains of 20 rats, of which half received their protein from raw peanuts and the other half received their protein from roasted peanuts. Test by means of the t distribution to see whether roasting the peanuts had an effect on their protein value.

Raw	61	60	56	63	56	63	59	56	44	61
Roasted	55	54	47	59	51	61	57	54	62	58

▶34. Select two sets of 20 one-digit random numbers and test the hypothesis (which is true here) that the two population means are equal. Work first by large-sample methods, using the fact that $\sigma = 2.87$; then work by means of Student's t distribution.

▶35. Calculate the values of β when $p = 0, .1, .3, .5, .7, .9,$ and 1 for the test of problem 17. Graph these values of β against p and draw a smooth curve through them to obtain the operating characteristic for that test. Discuss how good this test is for discovering alternative values of p when they exist.

►36. A coin is to be tossed eight times. The number of heads, x, is to be used to test the hypothesis $H_0 : p = .5$ against the alternative hypothesis $H_1 : p = .7$. The critical region for the test is to be chosen as the values of x that exceed 5, that is, the values 6, 7, and 8. Calculate the distribution of x under both hypotheses and represent their distributions as line charts on the same graph. Use your results to calculate the values of α and β for this test.

►37. For the test of problem 36, calculate the value of β for $p = 0, .5, .6,$ and 1 and sketch a characteristic curve for the test based on these four values and the value found previously for $p = .7$. Comment on the usefulness of this test.

CHAPTER 8

Correlation

1. LINEAR CORRELATION

The statistical methods presented thus far have all been concerned with a single variable x and its frequency distribution. In particular, the preceding two chapters have been concerned with the estimation of, and the testing of hypotheses about, the parameters of binomial and normal variable frequency distributions. Many of the problems in statistical work, however, involve several variables. This chapter is devoted to explaining one of the techniques for dealing with data associated with two or more variables. The emphasis is on two variables, but the methods can be extended to deal with more than two.

In some problems the several variables are studied simultaneously to see how they are interrelated; in others there is one particular variable of interest, and the remaining variables are studied for their possible aid in throwing light on this particular variable. These two classes of problems are usually associated with the names of *correlation* and *regression*, respectively. Correlation methods are discussed in this chapter and regression methods in Chapter 9.

A correlation problem arises when an individual asks himself whether there is any relationship between a pair of variables that interests him. For example, is there any relationship between smoking and heart ailments, between music appreciation and scientific aptitude, between radio reception and sun-spot activity, between beauty and brains?

For the purpose of illustrating how one proceeds to study the relationship between two variables, consider the data of Table 1, which consist of the scores of 30 students on a language test and a science test. The language test score is denoted by x, and the science test score by y. The maximum possible score on each of these tests was 50 points. The choice of which variable to call x and which to call y is arbitrary here.

TABLE 1

x	y	x	y	x	y
34	37	28	30	39	36
37	37	30	34	33	29
36	34	32	30	30	29
32	34	41	37	33	40
32	33	38	40	43	42
36	40	36	42	31	29
35	39	37	40	38	40
34	37	33	36	34	31
29	36	32	31	36	38
35	35	33	31	34	32

The investigation of the relationship of two variables such as these usually begins with an attempt to discover the approximate form of the relationship by graphing the data as points in the x, y plane. Such a graph is called a *scatter diagram*. By means of it, one can quickly discern whether there is any pronounced relationship and, if so, whether the relationship may be treated as approximately linear. The scatter diagram for the 30 points obtained from the data of Table 1 is shown in Fig. 1.

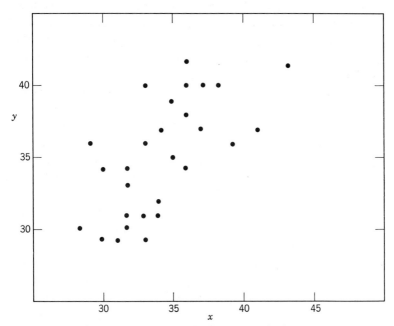

Fig. 1 Scatter diagram for language and science scores.

An inspection of this scatter diagram shows that there is a tendency for small values of x to be associated with small values of y and for large values of x to be associated with large values of y. Furthermore, roughly speaking, the general trend of the scatter is that of a straight line. In determining the nature of a trend, one looks to see whether there is any pronounced tendency for the points to be scattered on both sides of some smooth curve with a few waves or whether they appear to be scattered on both sides of a straight line. It would appear here that a straight line would do about as well as some mildly undulating curve. For variables such as these, it would be desirable to be able to measure in some sense the degree to which the variables are linearly related. For the purpose of devising such a measure, consider the properties that would be desirable.

A measure of relationship should certainly be independent of the choice of origin for the variables. The fact that the scatter diagram of Fig. 1 was plotted with the axes conveniently chosen to pass through the point (25, 25) implies that the relationship was admitted to be independent of the choice of origin. This property can be realized by using the deviations of the variables from their mean rather than the variables themselves. This was done in defining the standard deviation in Chapter 2. Thus one uses the variables $x_i - \bar{x}$ and $y_i - \bar{y}$ in place of the variables x_i and y_i in constructing the desired measure of relationship. The notation x_i, y_i denotes the ith pair of numbers in Table 1.

A measure of relationship should also be independent of the scale of measurement used for x and y. Thus, if the x and y scores of Table 1 were doubled in order to make them look like conventional test scores, with a maximum of 100 rather than 50, the relationship between the variables should be unaffected thereby. Similarly, if one were interested in studying the relationship between stature of husbands and wives, one would not want the measure of the relationship to depend upon whether stature were measured in centimeters or inches. This property can be realized by dividing x and y by quantities that possess the same units as x and y. For reasons that will be appreciated presently, the quantities that will be chosen here are s_x and s_y, the two sample standard deviations. Both properties are therefore realized if the measure of relationship is constructed by using the variables x_i and y_i in the forms $u_i = (x_i - \bar{x})/s_x$ and $v_i = (y_i - \bar{y})/s_y$. This merely means that the x's and y's should be measured in sample standard units. This correspond‹

to doing for samples what was done in (8), Chapter 4, to measure a variable in theoretical standard units.

The scatter diagram of the points (u_i, v_i) for the data of Table 1 is shown in Fig. 2. It will be observed that most of the points are located in the first and third quadrants and that the points in those quadrants tend to have larger coordinates, in magnitude, than those in the second and fourth quadrants. A simple measure of this property of the scatter is the sum $\sum_{i=1}^{n} u_i v_i$. The terms of the sum contributed by points in the first and third quadrants will be positive, but those corresponding to points in the second and fourth quadrants will be negative. A large positive value of this sum would therefore seem to indicate a strong linear trend in the scatter diagram. This is not strictly true, however, for if the number of points were doubled without changing the nature of the scatter the value of the sum would be approximately doubled. It is therefore necessary to divide the sum by n, the number of points, before using it as a measure of relationship. There are theoretical reasons for preferring to divide by $n - 1$ rather than n here, just as in the case of defining the sample standard deviation. The resulting sum $\sum u_i v_i / (n - 1)$ is the desired measure of relationship. It is called the *correlation coefficient*

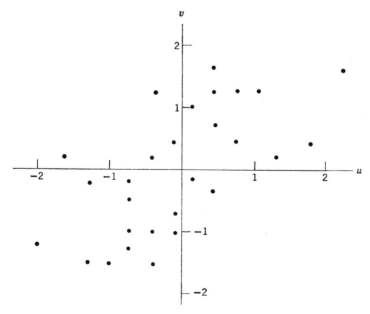

Fig. 2   Scatter diagram for standardized scores.

and is denoted by the letter r; hence, in terms of the original measurements, r is defined by the following formula:

(1)   ***Correlation Coefficient.*** $r = \dfrac{\sum\limits_{i=1}^{n} (x_i - \bar{x})(y_i - \bar{y})}{(n-1)s_x s_y}$.

Calculations with the data of Table 1 will show that $r = .66$ for those data. In order to interpret this value of r and to discover what values of r are likely to be obtained for various types of relationships between x and y, a number of different scatter diagrams have been plotted and the corresponding values of r computed in Fig. 3. The first four diagrams

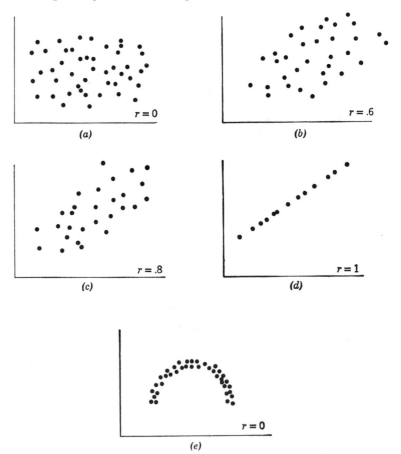

Fig. 3   Scatter diagrams and their associated values of r.

correspond to increasing degrees, or strength, of linear relationship. The fifth diagram illustrates a scatter in which x and y are closely related but in which the relationship is not linear. This illustration points out the fact that r is a useful measure of the strength of the relationship between two variables only when the variables are linearly related.

If these diagrams could be viewed from the reverse side of the page, the scatters would tend to go downhill instead of uphill. Calculations of r for the resulting scatters would show that the new values of r would be the negatives of the old values. Thus the strength of the relationship is given by the magnitude of r, whereas the sign of r merely tells one whether the values of y tend to increase or decrease with x, with the positive value indicating that y tends to increase with x.

The diagrams of Fig. 3, together with the associated values of r, make plausible two properties of r, namely that the value of r must satisfy the inequalities

$$-1 \leq r \leq 1$$

and that the value of r will be equal to plus 1 or minus 1 if, and only if, all the points of the scatter lie on a straight line. These properties of r can be demonstrated to be correct by mathematical methods.

2. INTERPRETATION OF r

The interpretation of a correlation coefficient as a measure of the strength of the linear relationship between two variables is a purely mathematical interpretation and is completely devoid of any cause or effect implications. The fact that two variables tend to increase or decrease together does not imply that one has any direct or indirect effect on the other. Both may be influenced by other variables in such a manner as to give rise to a strong mathematical relationship. For example, over a period of years the correlation coefficient between teachers' salaries and the consumption of liquor turned out to be .98. During this period of time there was a steady rise in wages and salaries of all types and a general upward trend of good times. Under such conditions, teachers' salaries would also increase. Moreover, the general upward trend in wages and buying power, together with the increase in population, would be reflected in increased total purchases of liquor. Thus the high correlation merely reflects the common effect of the upward trend on the two variables. Correlation coefficients must be handled with care if they are to give sensible information concerning relationships between pairs of variables. Success with them requires familiarity with the field of application as well as with their mathematical properties.

Correlation coefficients have proved very useful, for example, in studying the abilities of students. Thus, by their calculation, it has been found that as much information concerning a student's success in college is sometimes given by a few aptitude tests as by his unmodified high-school record. The correlation between college grade-point averages and high-school grade-point averages for certain colleges has been found to be around .5 or lower. One reason for such an apparently low value of r is the large variation in the quality and grading of the high schools in a state system.

▶3. CALCULATION OF r

The formula given in (1) to define r is not always convenient for computational purposes. A better form is obtained by multiplying out factors, inserting values for s_x and s_y, and doing some algebra, with the following results:

$$r = \frac{\sum xy - n\bar{x}\bar{y}}{\sqrt{[\sum x^2 - n\bar{x}^2][\sum y^2 - n\bar{y}^2]}}$$

(2)

$$= \frac{n \sum xy - \sum x \sum y}{\sqrt{[n \sum x^2 - (\sum x)^2][n \sum y^2 - (\sum y)^2]}}.$$

This last form is probably the most convenient, provided the values of $\bar{x}$ and $\bar{y}$ are not needed. It requires the sums of x, y, x^2, y^2, and xy, all of which are readily calculated with modern electric calculators.

If the data are so numerous that these computations would become unduly lengthy, even with a calculating machine, and larger calculating equipment is not available, then it may be worthwhile to classify the data with respect to both variables, just as was done for one variable in Chapter 2 in calculating $\bar{x}$. When the data have been so classified, the short method of computation based on coding and used for finding $\bar{x}$ may be employed to advantage in computing r. Let

$$x_i = c_x u_i + x_0$$

and

$$y_i = c_y v_i + y_0$$

in which c_x and c_y are the class intervals for x and y and u and v are the new integer coding variables. Then, because of the property of being independent of the choice of origin and choice of scale for x and y, the value of r calculated for the integer variables u and v will be the same as for x and y. This fact may also be verified directly by substituting these changes of variables in (1) and simplifying. In terms of these coding variables, the second of the computational formulas given in (2) is

$$(3) \qquad r = \frac{n \sum uv - \sum u \sum v}{\sqrt{[n \sum u^2 - (\sum u)^2][n \sum v^2 - (\sum v)^2]}} .$$

The technique of computing r by means of coding variables is illustrated in Table 2. These classified data represent the relationship between the percentage of trend values for high-grade bond yields, x, and stock sales, y, at the New York Stock Exchange. Since formula (3) was derived from formula (2), which is for nonclassified data, it is assumed in (3) that the sums displayed there are over all n pairs of values. If the sums are to be taken over the class marks only, then it is necessary to multiply

TABLE 2

y \ x	94.5	96.5	98.5	100.5	102.5	104.5	106.5	108.5	110.5	f_y	v	vf_y	v^2f_y	uv
29.5			4	3		4	1		1	13	−3	−39	117	−36
59.5	1	3	6	18	6	9	2	3	1	49	−2	−98	196	−64
89.5	7	3	16	16	4	4	1		1	52	−1	−52	52	23
119.5	5	9	10	9	2		1	2		38	0			
149.5	3	5	8	1		1				18	1	18	18	−25
179.5	4	2	3	1						10	2	20	40	−38
209.5	4	4		1						9	3	27	81	−60
239.5	1	1								2	4	8	32	−20
f_x	25	27	47	49	12	18	5	5	3	191		−116	536	−220
u	−3	−2	−1	0	1	2	3	4	5					
uf_x	−75	−54	−47		12	36	15	20	15	−78				
u^2f_x	225	108	47		12	72	45	80	75	664				
vu	−54	−32	26		−16	−66	−24	−24	−30	−220				

the variables in these sums by the frequencies with which they occurred. This accounts for the column headings vf_y and v^2f_y and the row headings uf_x and u^2f_x, since the frequency for any v is the same as that for the corresponding y and the frequency for any u is the same as that for the corresponding x. The only new feature of these computations, beyond that done earlier for the mean and standard deviation, is the method of computing the products of u and v in the last row and column. The sum of these products is computed two ways to provide a check. In computing the entries in the uv column, for example, it is convenient to start with the first row and compute the uv terms for it first. Since all uv terms in this row have the same value of v, namely -3, it is necessary merely to compute the sum of the u values in this row and then multiply by the common v value. Thus the third cell in the first row contains a frequency of 4 corresponding to $u = -1$; hence -4 is recorded, mentally or otherwise. Next, the frequency of 3 corresponds to $u = 0$; hence it contributes nothing to the sum. Next, the frequency of 4 corresponds to $u = 2$; hence 8 is added to the previous sum of -4 to give 4. Then the frequency of 1 corresponding to $u = 3$ brings the sum to 7, and finally the frequency of 1 corresponding to $u = 5$ brings the total to 12. This value is then multiplied by the common v value of -3 to give -36, which is then recorded. This procedure is followed for each row to give the last column entries and similarly for each column to give the last row entries. The substitution of the values obtained from Table 2 in formula (3) gives

$$r = \frac{(191)(-220) - (-116)(-78)}{\sqrt{[(191)(536) - (-116)^2][(191)(664) - (-78)^2]}} = -.49.$$

▶ **4. RELIABILITY OF r**

The value of r obtained for Table 1 may be thought of as the first sample value of a sequence of sample values, $r_1, r_2, r_3, \ldots$, that would be obtained if repeated sets of similar data were obtained. Such sets of data are thought of as having been obtained from drawing random samples of size $n = 30$ from a population of students. If the values of r were classified into a frequency table and the resulting histogram sketched, a good approximation would be obtained to the limiting, or theoretical, frequency distribution of r. As in the case of other variables, such as $\bar{x}$ and $\bar{x}_1 - \bar{x}_2$, the limiting distribution can be derived by mathematical methods. The theory behind this derivation requires that the population being sampled possess what is known as a two-dimensional normal distribution. This implies, among other things, that both x and y possess normal distributions. With this requirement satisfied, the derivation then shows that the desired sampling distribution of r depends only upon n and ρ, where ρ is the value that r would be expected to approach if n were made increasingly large. For the problem being discussed, $n = 30$, but the value of ρ is unknown. The value of r is a sample estimate of ρ based on a random sample of size 30, just as $\bar{x}$ is a sample estimate of μ, and s is a sample estimate of σ.

Since the frequency distribution of r depends upon both n and ρ and changes its form rapidly with changes in ρ, it is not possible to show what this distribution is like, except in a few special cases. Figure 4 shows graphs of the frequency distribution of r for $\rho = 0$ and $n = 9$ and for $\rho = .8$ and $n = 9$. It is clear from Fig. 4 that the distribution of r is decidedly nonnormal in appearance for large values of ρ and small values of n. Fortunately, a simple change of variable exists, which transforms the complicated distribution of r into an approximately normal distribution. The resulting normal distribution may then be used to determine the accuracy of r as an estimate of ρ in the same way that the normal distribution of $\bar{x}$ was used to determine the accuracy of $\bar{x}$ as an estimate of μ. This means that instead of working with r and its complicated distribution, one takes a certain function of r as a new

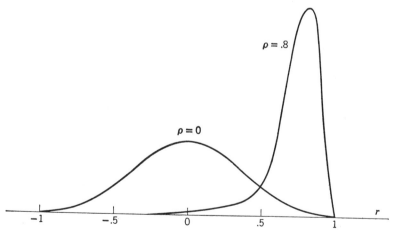

Fig. 4   Distribution of r for $\rho = 0$ and $\rho = .8$ when $n = 9$.

random variable and works with it and its distribution. If the proper function is chosen, the resulting random variable will have a simple distribution compared to the original distribution. The particular function of r, which will be denoted by w, that has been found to be very useful here is the function

(4) $$w = \frac{1}{2} \log_e \frac{1 + r}{1 - r}.$$

The symbol $\log_e N$ denotes what is known as the "natural logarithm" of the number N. Ordinary tables of logarithms use the base 10, whereas natural logarithms use the base e, where e is a number approximately equal to 2.7. It is not necessary to look up such logarithms, however, because Table VI in the appendix has done this for you. By means of it, any value of r can be converted to the corresponding value of w.

Now if one took the sequence of sample values of r that were considered at the beginning of this section, and calculated the corresponding values of w, say $w_1, w_2, w_3, \ldots$, and if those values of w were classified into a frequency table and the resulting histogram drawn, it would be found that the histogram could be fitted very well by a normal curve. Thus the effect of taking this particular function of r as the random variable with which to work, instead of using r itself, is to obtain a random variable that possesses an approximate normal distribution. The advantage of this procedure is that one can then use all the familiar normal distribution methods for solving correlation-coefficient problems.

The theory behind this change of variable shows that the mean value of the distribution of w is given by

$$\mu_w = \frac{1}{2} \log \frac{1 + \rho}{1 - \rho}.$$

and that the standard deviation of w is given by

(5) $$\sigma_w = \frac{1}{\sqrt{n - 3}}.$$

The relationship between the distributions of r and w for the case in which $\rho = .8$ and $n = 9$ is seen by comparing the sketch of the distribution of r given in Fig. 4 and a sketch of the distribution of w shown in Fig. 5. The value of $r = .6$ on Fig. 4, for example, corresponds to the value $w = .69$ on Fig. 5, and the value $r = .8$ on Fig. 4 corresponds to the value

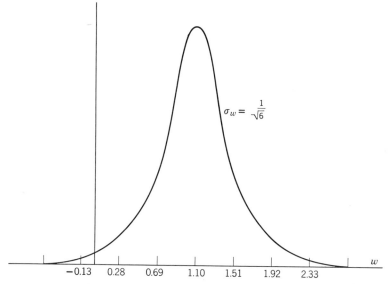

Fig. 5   Distribution of w for $\rho = .8$ when $n = 9$.

$w = 1.10$ on Fig. 5. By using the correspondence between these two distributions one can solve statistical problems concerning r by means of w, which possesses the approximate normal distribution shown in Fig. 5 for this special case.

As an illustration of the use of these formulas and of Table VI, consider the following problem. Is a correlation of $r = .20$ between the face index (x) and the cephalic index (y) of 50 members of a certain race significant? This may be treated as a problem of testing the hypothesis

$$H_0 : \rho = 0.$$

From Table VI, $\rho = 0$ corresponds to $w = 0$; therefore, this hypothesis is equivalent to the hypothesis

$$H_0 : \mu_w = 0.$$

Since $n = 50$ here, formula (5) gives

$$\sigma_w = \frac{1}{\sqrt{47}} = .15.$$

If w is treated as a normal variable, with mean 0 and standard deviation .15, and if a two-sided critical region of size .05 is used, the critical region will consist of those values of w outside the interval $-.29$ to $.29$. From

Table VI, the sample value of $r = .2$ corresponds to $w = .2$. Since this value of w does not fall in the critical region, the hypothesis is accepted. Thus $r = .2$ is not significant. This is the language, mentioned in the preceding chapter, that is frequently used in connection with statistical tests. It really means that the hypothesis being tested here is accepted rather than rejected. It implies that the sample value of r is compatible in a probability sense with the parameter value postulated by the test.

As a second illustration, consider the problem of how to find a 95 per cent confidence interval for ρ if a sample of size 28 gave the value $r = .6$. This is accomplished by first finding a 95 per cent confidence interval for μ_w and then using the relationship between r and w to find the corresponding interval for ρ. Working with the variable w once more, formula (5) gives

$$\sigma_w = \frac{1}{\sqrt{25}} = .2.$$

From Table VI, the value of w corresponding to the sample value $r = .6$ is $w = .69$. By the methods of Chapter 6 on finding confidence limits for the true mean of a normal distribution, approximate 95 per cent confidence limits for μ_w are therefore given by

$$w - 1.96\sigma_w = .69 - 1.96(.2) = .30$$
and
$$w + 1.96\sigma_w = .69 + 1.96(.2) = 1.08.$$

It is now necessary to convert these w values to the corresponding r values. From Table VI it will be seen that the corresponding r values are .29 and .79, respectively. Since the mean μ_w will lie inside an interval on the w-axis if, and only if, ρ lies inside the corresponding interval on the r-axis, the desired 95 per cent confidence interval for ρ is therefore given by

$$.29 < \rho < .79.$$

It should be noticed that this confidence interval does not have the sample estimate $r = .6$ as the middle point of the interval, as was the case with means and proportions. This is because of the skewed nature of the distribution of r for $\rho \neq 0$.

The last illustration shows the danger of placing too much reliability on a sample value of r as an estimate of the true correlation ρ when the sample is small. Because of the large variation in r for samples of even moderate size, correlation methods are usually not very useful unless a fairly large sample is available.

5. REVIEW EXERCISES

The following pairs of numbers were obtained by choosing three random digits from Table II and then adding the third digit to each of the first two to yield a pair labeled x and y. (a) Plot the scatter diagram. Does the relationship appear to be linear? (b) Calculate the value of r using formula (2). ▶(c) Test the hypothesis that $\rho = 0$. ▶(d) Find a 90 per cent confidence interval for ρ. ▶(e) Test the hypothesis that $\rho = .5$. ▶(f) How large a sample of the preceding type would it take to be certain with a probability of .90 that the maximum error of estimate of ρ by r would not exceed .1 if you have reason to believe that the true value of ρ is close to $\frac{1}{2}$?

x	8	8	4	10	11	1	13	12	6	14	7	8	6	13	8	4	7	8	5	14	5	10	8	13	17
y	7	8	11	14	13	3	8	8	3	8	3	11	5	11	5	10	11	3	14	13	2	10	17	10	15
x	14	9	7	10	13	9	5	13	12	5	9	6	12	14	0	10	10	17	9	13	12	9	1	12	12
y	7	11	10	1	12	2	5	13	14	14	15	11	10	15	5	13	3	8	11	9	10	14	5	14	12

(a)

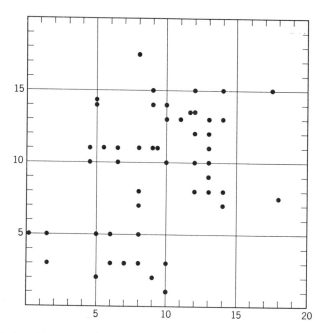

The relationship appears to be a fairly weak linear one.

(b) Calculations give $\Sigma x = 463$, $\Sigma y = 467$, $\Sigma x^2 = 5039$, $\Sigma y^2 = 5229$, $\Sigma xy = 4615$; hence (2) gives

$$r = \frac{(50)(4615) - (463)(467)}{\sqrt{[(50)(5039) - (463)^2][(50)(5229) - (467)^2]}} = .36.$$

(c) $\rho = 0$ corresponds to $\mu_w = 0$, $r = .36$ corresponds to $w = .377$. $\sigma_w = 1/\sqrt{47} = .146$; hence

$$z = \frac{w - \mu_w}{\sigma_w} = \frac{.377}{.146} = 2.58.$$

Since $|z| > 1.96$, the hypothesis $H_0: \rho = 0$ is rejected.

(d) A 90 per cent confidence interval for μ_w is given by

$$.377 - 1.64(.146) < \mu_w < .377 + 1.64(.146) \quad \text{or} \quad .138 < \mu_w < .616.$$

The corresponding r values give the desired interval for ρ, namely,

$$.14 < \rho < .55.$$

(e) $\rho = .5$ corresponds to $\mu_w = .549$; hence

$$z = \frac{.377 - .549}{.146} = -1.18$$

The hypothesis $H_0: \rho = .5$ is therefore accepted.

(f) If the error of estimate shall not exceed .1 and $\rho = .5$, this implies that r must satisfy $.4 < r < .6$. These inequalities correspond to $.424 < w < .693$. Since $\rho = .5$ corresponds to $\mu_w = .549$, the maximum error in estimating μ_w is given by $.693 - .549 = .144$. This maximum error will be exceeded only 10 per cent of the time if n is sufficiently large to satisfy the equation

$$1.64\sigma_w = .144, \quad \text{or} \quad \frac{1.64}{\sqrt{n - 3}} = .144.$$

The solution of this equation is $n = 133$.

Comment: It can be shown that $\rho = \frac{1}{2}$ for pairs of variables that have been constructed in this manner. Although $r = .36$ is not a good estimate of $\rho = .5$, it is a satisfactory estimate in a probability sense. For example, in part (e) it will be seen that it is just slightly more than one standard deviation below the true value on the w scale.

EXERCISES

1. For the following data on the heights (x) and weights (y) of 12 college students, (a) plot the scatter diagram, (b) guess the value of r, (c) calculate the value of r.

x	65	73	70	68	66	69	75	70	64	72	65	71
y	124	184	161	164	140	154	210	164	126	172	133	150

2. Calculate the value of r for the following data on intelligence-test scores and grade-point averages, after first plotting the scatter diagram and guessing the value of r.

I.T.	295	152	214	171	131	178	225	141	116	173	230
G.P.A.	3.4	1.6	1.2	1.0	2.0	1.6	2.0	1.4	1.0	3.6	3.6

	195	174	236	198	217	143	135	146	227
	1.0	2.8	2.8	1.8	2.0	1.2	2.4	2.2	2.4

3. What would you guess the value of r to be for the following pairs of variables: (a) the number of man-hours of work and the number of units of a product produced in a given industry, (b) the size of a city and the crime rate, (c) the cost per unit of producing an article and the number of units produced?

4. Guess the value of r for the following pairs of variables: (a) mathematics and foreign-language grades, (b) consumption of butter and the price of butter, (c) amount of rain in the spring and the mean temperature.

5. What interpretation would you give if told that the correlation between the number of automobile accidents per year and the age of the driver is $r = -.60$ if only drivers with at least one accident are considered?

6. What explanation would you give if told that the correlation between fertilizer added and profit made in raising vegetables on a certain experimental farm was only .20?

7. Explain why it would not be surprising to find a fairly high correlation between the density of traffic on Wall Street and the height of the tide in Maine if observations were taken every hour from 6:00 A.M. to 10:00 P.M. and high tide occurred at 7:00 A.M. Plot a scatter diagram of relative values of these two variables for each hour of the day to assist you in the explanation.

8. Why is the value of the correlation coefficient unaffected if the variables x and y are interchanged?

9. For the data of problem 2, delete those items for which the intelligence-test score is less than 150 and more than 225. Now calculate the value of r and compare with the value obtained for problem 2. What does this comparison seem to indicate?

10. What would be the effect on the value of r for the correlation between height and weight of males of all ages if only males in the 20–25 age group were sampled? In answering this question, it is helpful to observe the effect this restriction would have on the type of scatter diagram expected for these two variables.

11. Form 30 pairs of numbers by choosing four random digits from Table II and adding the last two to each of the first two to yield a pair labeled x and y. Work the problems of the review exercise in section 5. Do you believe that the value of ρ here is close to $\frac{1}{2}$? If not what would you guess its value to be?

▶12. The following table gives the results of classifying 330 students on the basis of their scores on an entrance examination in English (x) and their final examination scores in English I (y). Calculate the value of r.

x / y	110	120	130	140	150
45	3	4		1	
55	6	35	30	5	1
65	3	42	58	30	
75	1	18	52	16	1
85		2	6	8	3
95		1	1	1	2

▶13. Test the hypothesis that $\rho = 0$ if a sample of size 25 gave $r = .35$.

▶14. Test the hypothesis that $\rho = .7$ if a sample of size 50 gave $r = .6$.

▶15. Find a 90 per cent confidence interval for ρ for problem 2.

▶16. Find a 95 per cent confidence interval for ρ if a sample of size 40 gave $r = .5$.

▶17. If it is known that $\rho < .5$, approximately how large a sample would you need to take if you wish to estimate ρ by means of r and you want the probability to be .95 that your estimate will not be in error by more than .20 units? Try different guesses for n to arrive at this approximation, after first working with w values.

CHAPTER 9

Regression

1. LINEAR REGRESSION

In the first section of Chapter 8 it was pointed out that correlation methods are used when one is interested in studying how two or more variables are interrelated. It often happens, however, that one studies the relationship between the variables in the hope that any relationship that is found can be used to assist in making estimates or predictions of a particular variable. Thus, if the two variables for Table 1, Chapter 8, had been scores representing college aptitude, x, and college success, y, rather than the variables listed there, the relationship between x and y would have been useful in predicting a student's college success from a knowledge of his score on a college aptitude test. The correlation coefficient is merely concerned with determining how strongly such variables are linearly related and is not capable of solving prediction problems. Methods that have been designed to handle these problems are known as regression methods. This chapter discusses the simplest of these methods.

For the purpose of explaining regression methods, consider the particular problem of predicting the yield of hay as a function of the amount of irrigation water applied. The data in Table 1 represent the amount of water applied in inches and the yield of alfalfa in tons per acre on an experimental farm. The graph of these data is given in Fig. 1. From this graph, it appears that x and y are approximately linearly related for this range of x values. A straight line will therefore be fitted to this set of

TABLE 1

Water (x)	12	18	24	30	36	42	48
Yield (y)	5.27	5.68	6.25	7.21	8.02	8.71	8.42

209

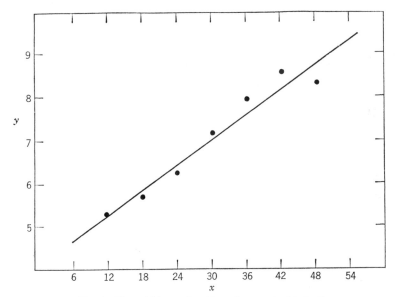

Fig. 1 Hay yield as a function of amount of irrigation.

points for the purpose of trying to predict the value of y from the value of x. Such a line has been fitted in Fig. 1. Now, for any given value of x, say $x = 30$, the predicted value of y is chosen as the distance up to the line directly above that value of x. Reading across on the y axis, it will be observed that the predicted value of y for $x = 30$ is slightly more than 7, as compared to the observed value of 7.21.

Suppose, now, that it is assumed that the relationship between mean yield and water is strictly linear over this range of x values. This means that if this experiment had been repeated a large number of times under the same growth conditions and if the y values corresponding to each of the seven x values had been averaged separately, then those averages would yield a set of points lying almost precisely on a straight line. The larger the number of such repetitions, the greater the expected precision. This assumption essentially says that there is a theoretical straight line that expresses the linear relationship between the theoretical mean value of y and the corresponding value of x.

If one accepts the linearity assumption, then one would expect the sample straight-line value of slightly more than 7 to be closer to the theoretical line value for $x = 30$ than the observed value of 7.21 because one would expect the sample straight line, which is based on all seven experimental points, to be more stable than a single observed point. In view of this reasoning, one would predict the theoretical line value corresponding to $x = 30$ to be the corresponding y value on the sample regression line. Similar predictions would be made for the six other x values. Furthermore, if one were interested in an intermediate value of x, he would use the sample straight-line value as the predicted value of y for this value of x also. Since it is being assumed that the relationship is linear only for this range of x values, it is not legitimate to use the sample straight line to predict y values beyond this range of x values.

2. LEAST SQUARES

In view of the preceding discussion, the problem of linear prediction reduces to the problem of fitting a straight line to a set of points. Now the equation of a straight line can be written in the form

$$(1) \qquad\qquad y = a + bx,$$

in which a and b are parameters determining the line. Thus the equations

$$y = 2 + 3x$$

and

$$y = 4 - 2x$$

determine the two straight lines graphed in Fig. 2. The parameter a determines where the line cuts the y axis. Thus the two lines in Fig. 2 cut the y axis at 2 and 4, respectively. The parameter b determines the slope of the line. The slope 3 for the first line means that the line rises 3 units vertically for every positive horizontal unit change. A negative value such as -2 means that the line drops 2 units for every positive horizontal change of 1 unit. Since only two points are needed to graph a line, these lines are readily graphed by assigning two different values to x and calculating the corresponding values of y to give the coordinates of two points on the line. To graph the two lines of Fig. 2, the following pairs of points were computed:

$y = 2 + 3x$			$x = 4 - 2x$		
x	0	1	x	0	2
y	2	5	y	4	0

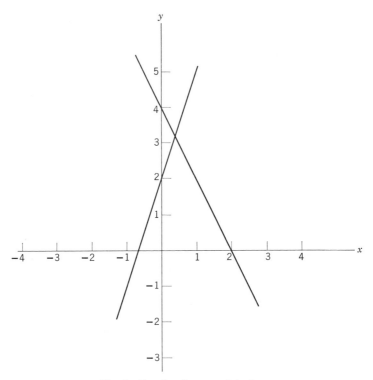

Fig. 2   Graphs of two straight lines.

Since the problem is to determine the values of the parameters *a* and *b* so that the line will fit a set of points well, the problem is essentially one of estimating the parameters *a* and *b* in some efficient manner. Although there are numerous methods for performing the estimation of such parameters, the best known for regression problems is the *method of least squares*.

Since the desired line is to be used for predicting purposes, it is reasonable to require that the line be such that it will make the errors of prediction small. By an error of prediction is meant the difference between an observed value of *y* and the corresponding straight-line value of *y*. For example, the error of prediction in Fig. 1 for $x = 30$ is approximately equal to $7.21 - 7 = .21$. If a different straight line had been used for prediction, this error of prediction ordinarily would have been different. Since the errors may be positive or negative and might add up to a small value for a poorly fitting line, it will not do to require merely that the sum of the errors be as small as possible. This difficulty can be avoided by requiring that the sum of the absolute values, that is, the magnitudes of the errors be as small as possible. However, sums of absolute values are not convenient to work with mathematically; consequently the difficulty is avoided by requiring that the sum of the squares of the errors be as small as possible. The values of the parameters that minimize the sum of the squares of the errors determine what is known as the best-fitting straight line in the sense of least squares. It is clear from inspecting Figs. 1 and 2 that by varying a and b properly one should be able to find the equation of a line that fits the points of Fig. 1 well. The problem, however, is one of finding a best-fitting line in some systematic rational way, and this is where the principle of least squares enters.

The problem of determining the least-squares values of a and b requires more mathematical background than that expected for this book; therefore, it is not considered here. The results of applying the proper mathematical methods, however, are written down. It turns out that they are somewhat simpler if the variable x is measured from the sample mean. Thus the equation of the line is written in the form

$$(2) \qquad y' = a + b(x - \bar{x}).$$

The prime is placed on y only to distinguish the straight-line value of y from the observed value of y for any x. When the equation of a straight line is written in form (2), b is still the slope of the line, but a is now the value of y when $x = \bar{x}$ rather than the value of y when $x = 0$. The least-squares estimates of a and b for the equation of the line expressed in form (2) turn out to be

$$a = \bar{y} \qquad \text{and} \qquad b = \frac{\sum (x_i - \bar{x}) y_i}{\sum (x_i - \bar{x})^2}.$$

In these formulas it is assumed that there are n pairs of values of x and y, such as those in Table 1, and that x_i and y_i denote the ith pair of values. Although the range of summation is not indicated on the Σ symbol, it is understood to be $i = 1$ to $i = n$. Thus, for Table 1, the summation would be $i = 1$ to $i = 7$. These values when substituted in (2) yield the desired least-squares line. This line is customarily called the *regression line of y on x*; hence the preceding results may be summarized:

(3) **_Regression Line._** $y' = \bar{y} + b(x - \bar{x})$, *where* $b = \dfrac{\sum (x_i - \bar{x}) y_i}{\sum (x_i - \bar{x})^2}$.

A pioneer in the field of applied statistics gave the least squares line this name in connection with some studies he was making on estimating the extent to which the stature of sons of tall parents reverts, or regresses, toward the mean stature of the population.

For computational purposes, it is convenient to change the form of b slightly. If one multiplies out the factors in the numerator and simplifies the denominator in the same manner that s^2 was simplified in Chapter 2, it is easily shown that b reduces to

$$(4) \qquad b = \frac{\sum x_i y_i - n\bar{x}\bar{y}}{\sum x_i^2 - n\bar{x}^2}.$$

Table 2 illustrates the computational procedure for the data of Table 1. Here (3) was used to calculate b instead of the suggested computing

TABLE 2

x	y	$x - \bar{x}$	$(x - \bar{x})y$	$(x - \bar{x})^2$
12	5.27	−18	−94.86	324
18	5.68	−12	−68.16	144
24	6.25	−6	−37.50	36
30	7.21	0	0	0
36	8.02	6	48.12	36
42	8.71	12	104.52	144
48	8.42	18	151.56	324
210	49.56		103.68	1008

formula (4) because $\bar{x}$ is an integer here. As a result of these computations, the equation of the regression line was found to be

$$y' = 7.08 + .103(x - 30).$$

Multiplying out the parenthesis and collecting terms will yield

$$(5) \qquad y' = 3.99 + .103x.$$

This is the equation of the regression line that was graphed in Fig. 1.

This problem illustrates very well the basic difference between correlation and regression methods for two variables. In the correlation problem studied in Chapter 8, corresponding to the scatter diagram of Fig. 1 in that chapter, the data consisted of a random sample of size 30 from a population of students. This means that both x and y are statistical variables whose values are determined only after the sample is obtained. In the preceding regression problem, however, the x values were chosen in advance, so that only the y values are determined by the sample. Now the least-squares technique of fitting a line to a set of points can be applied whether the x values are fixed in advance or were obtained from random samples; hence regression methods could have been applied to data of the type considered in the study of correlation. On the other hand, the interpretation of r as a measure of the strength of the linear relationship between two variables obviously does not apply if the values of x are selected as desired, because the value of r will usually depend heavily upon the choice of x values.

In addition to being more flexible, regression methods also possess the advantage of being the natural methods to use in many experimental situations. The experimenter often wishes to change x by uniform amounts over the range of interest for that variable rather than to take a random sample of x values. Thus, if he wished to study the effect of an amino acid on growth, he would wish to increase the amount of amino acid by a fixed amount, or factor, each time he ran the experiment.

Although a correlation coefficient is useful for describing how strongly two variables are linearly related, it is not very useful otherwise. If the correlation coefficient between aptitude in mathematics and aptitude in music is .4, whereas that between aptitude in mathematics and aptitude in art is .2, one can conclude that the first association is stronger than the second and that both relationships are rather weak, but not a great deal more can be said. Correlation coefficients do not lend themselves readily to quantitative statements unless they are associated with regression. Thus correlation is usually only a first phase in the study of the relationship of two variables, whereas regression is the basic technique in such a study.

3. THE REGRESSION FALLACY

The name of regression, which is commonly given to the least-squares line, is associated with an error frequently made in the interpretation of observations taken at two different periods of time. This error, which is called the regression fallacy, is best explained by means of illustrations.

Suppose a teacher studies the scores of his students in a given course on their first two hour tests. If he selects, say, the top five papers from the first test and calculates the mean score for those five students on both tests, he will very likely discover that their second test mean is lower than their first test mean. Similarly, if he calculates the mean score on both tests for the five students having the lowest scores on the first test, he will undoubtedly find that their mean has risen. Thus he might conclude that the good students are slipping, whereas the poor students are improving. The explanation lies partly in the reaction of students to test scores but also partly in the natural variability of students' test scores. Even if students did not vary from one test to another in their study habits and in their total relative knowledge of the subject, the inaccuracy of a test to measure this knowledge would cause considerable variation in a student's performance from test to test. As a result, some of the top five students on the first test may be there because of fortuitous circumstances; however, the second test is likely to bring them down to their natural level, thereby dragging the mean of this group of five students down with them. The same type of reasoning applies to the lowest five students on the first test to account for their improved mean.

There is undoubtedly a psychological factor operating here also to accentuate the "regression" of high and low scores toward the mean of the entire group. Students who did poorly on the first test would be expected to study considerably harder than before and thus raise their scores on the second test. Since early success often leads to overconfidence, the students making the highest scores on the first test might be expected to ease up slightly and thus lower their mean score on the second test. Nevertheless, the natural variation of test scores alone will suffice to produce a fair amount of regression toward the group mean.

The regression fallacy often occurs in the interpretation of business data. For example, in comparing the profits made by a group of similar business firms for two consecutive years, there might be a temptation to claim that the firms with high profits are becoming less efficient, whereas those with low profits are becoming more efficient because the mean profit for each of those two extreme groups would tend to shift toward the mean of the entire group. The firms with high profits the first year were high in the list either because they are normally highly efficient or because they were fortunate that year but are normally of lower efficiency. The latter group would be expected to show lower profits the second year and thus decrease the mean for the first year's high-profit group. The same type of reasoning would explain the apparent increased efficiency of the first year's low-profit group.

The original study of the relationship between the stature of fathers and sons, which gave rise to the name regression, is another illustration of this type of possible misinterpretation. It was found that the tallest group of the total group of men being studied had sons whose mean height was lower than that of the fathers. It was also found that the shortest group had sons whose mean height was higher than that of the fathers. As in the other illustrations, the explanation lies in the natural variation of subgroups of a population. Since many tall men come from families whose parents are of average size, such tall men are likely to have sons who are shorter than they are; consequently, when a group of tall men is selected, the sons of such men would not be expected to be quite so tall as the fathers. There are, of course, factors such as the tendency of tall men to marry taller-than-average women and the steady increase in stature from generation to generation to dampen the above regression tendency somewhat.

4. STANDARD ERROR OF ESTIMATE

After a regression line has been fitted to a set of points, it is usually possible to inspect its graph, such as the one in Fig. 1, and observe how accurately it predicts y values. An arithmetical procedure for doing this is to calculate the sizes of all the errors, $y_i - y_i'$, by reading them off the graph, if it is on graph paper, or by computing them by means of formula (3). A useful measure of the accuracy of prediction is obtained by calculating the standard deviation of the errors of prediction. If the error of prediction $y_i - y_i'$, corresponding to $x = x_i$, is denoted by e_i, then by definition the standard deviation of the errors is

$$\sqrt{\frac{\sum_{i=1}^{n}(e_i - \bar{e})^2}{n-1}}.$$

But it can be shown that $\bar{e} = 0$. This means that the positive errors corresponding to points above the regression line cancel the negative errors corresponding to points below the regression line. In view of this property, the standard deviation of those errors will reduce to

$$\sqrt{\frac{\sum_{i=1}^{n} e_i^2}{n-1}}.$$

For problems related to finding confidence limits for the parameters a and b, it turns out that it is better to divide the sum of squares of the errors by $n-2$ rather than by $n-1$, just as it was considered better to divide by $n-1$ rather than by n in defining the ordinary sample standard deviation. The same arguments apply here as applied there. If this is done, the resulting expression is denoted by s_e and is called the *standard error of estimate*. Thus, in terms of the original variables,

(6)   ***Standard Error of Estimate.*** $s_e = \sqrt{\dfrac{\sum_{i=1}^{n} (y_i - y_i')^2}{n-2}}.$

Table 3 gives the calculation of s_e for the data of Table 1 by means of formulas (5) and (6).

If one assumes, as before, that there is a theoretical regression line, of which the least-squares line is an estimate, and in addition one assumes that the values of $y_i - y_i'$, where y_i' is now the theoretical line value, are independently and normally distributed with zero means and the same standard deviation σ, then s_e given by (6) is an estimate of σ. Furthermore, the normal distribution assumption enables one to make approximate probability statements about the errors of prediction. For example,

TABLE 3

y	y'	$y - y'$	$(y - y')^2$
5.27	5.23	.04	.0016
5.68	5.84	−.16	.0256
6.25	6.46	−.21	.0441
7.21	7.08	.13	.0169
8.02	7.70	.32	.1024
8.71	8.32	.39	.1521
8.42	8.93	−.51	.2601
			.6028

$$s_e = \sqrt{\frac{.6028}{5}} = .35$$

one can state that approximately 95 per cent of the errors of prediction will be less than $1.96s_e$ in magnitude. The approximation arises because 1.96σ has been replaced by its sample estimate $1.96s_e$ and because only the sample regression line is available; therefore, this is a large-sample technique. Since most regression problems involve small samples, particularly the experimental kind like the one in Table 1, this technique is of somewhat limited use. A small-sample method for dealing with regression problems is discussed in the next section.

Even though the sample given by Table 1 is too small to justify the large-sample methods that have just been discussed, the results of the calculations that yielded equation (5) and the value .35 for (6) will be used to sketch the type of graph that one might legitimately construct if one had a larger sample. For this purpose it suffices to calculate the number $1.96s_e = 1.96(.35) = .7$ and then draw two lines parallel to the line (5) which is shown in Fig. 1, one being .7 unit above that line and the other being .7 unit below it. The two lines are shown in Fig. 3.

From Fig. 3 it will be seen that all seven points lie within the 95 per cent band, which of course was to be expected. In the long run of similar experiments one would expect approximately 95 per cent of such points to

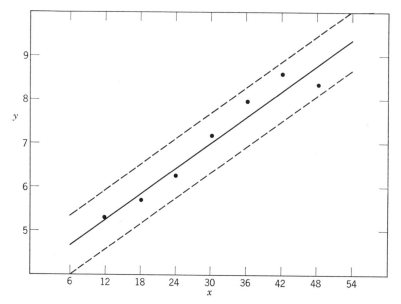

Fig. 3   An approximate 95 per cent prediction band.

lie inside the band constructed in this fashion, provided the normal distribution assumption is satisfied.

This geometrical manner of looking at the prediction problem is a useful one for giving the experimenter a rough idea of what y values he is likely to obtain if he performs experiments at other x values.

The problem of predicting a y value for an x value beyond the range of observed x values is a considerably more difficult problem than that of predicting for a value of x inside the interval of observations. Prediction beyond the range of observations is called extrapolation, whereas prediction inside the range is called interpolation. The difficulty with extrapolation is that the assumptions necessary to justify it are seldom realized in real-life situations. Thus, it is highly unlikely that the relationship between the amount of irrigation water applied and the yield of hay will continue to be linear beyond the range of x values given in Fig. 1. It certainly will not be if x is chosen sufficiently large. Furthermore, in most realistic regression problems it is unreasonable to expect the prediction errors to be normally distributed about the regression line with the standard deviation of those errors remaining constant as x goes beyond the interval of observations. Extrapolation is a legitimate technique only when the experimenter has valid reasons for believing that his model holds beyond the range of the available observations. Stock market prices (y) as a function of time (x), for example, are an excellent illustration of a regression problem for which no satisfactory extrapolation model has yet been constructed.

A kind word needs to be said for the usefulness of straight-line regression models in realistic situations. If the scatter diagram for a set of data indicates that the relationship between x and y is not linear, it may still be possible to use the linear model if one can find a function of x and also a function of y such that the relationship between those two functional values is linear. There are many known relationships in science that are not linear but which can be made linear by taking the proper functions of x and y. This technique of considering the relationship between functions of x and y rather than between x and y extends the range of applicability of linear methods considerably.

▶ 5. SMALL-SAMPLE METHOD

As indicated in the preceding paragraph, in order to be able to make probability statements about errors of prediction, it is necessary to assume that there exists a theoretical regression line, of which the least-squares line is a sample estimate, and then make some distribution assumptions. This postulated line is written in the form

$$y' = \alpha + \beta(x - \bar{x}).$$

Here α and β play the same role for this theoretical line as a and b do for the line determined by the sample points and given by (2). Thus the values of a and b given by (3) are the estimates of α and β obtained by least squares. There are no new problems of estimation or hypothesis testing in connection with the parameter α because, from (3), its estimate is $\bar{y}$ and therefore the small sample methods for treating a normal mean, explained in earlier chapters, may be applied here. The slope parameter β, however, does require new formulas. Fortunately, it can be shown that Student's t distribution can be applied to problems related to β. In particular, it can be shown that the quantity

(7)
$$t = \frac{b - \beta}{s_e}\sqrt{\sum(x_i - \bar{x})^2}$$

possesses a Student's t distribution with $\nu = n - 2$ degrees of freedom, provided the $y_i - y_i'$ are independently and normally distributed with zero means and equal standard deviations.

For the purpose of illustrating how to use formula (7) consider the problem of finding a 95 per cent confidence interval for β for the problem of section 3. Since $\nu = 5$ for that problem, the .05 critical value of t in Table V in the appendix is $t = 2.57$. Therefore, the probability is .95 that t will satisfy the inequalities

$$-2.57 < t < 2.57.$$

From (7), this is equivalent to

$$-2.57 < \frac{b - \beta}{s_e}\sqrt{\sum(x_i - \bar{x})^2} < 2.57.$$

When these inequalities are solved for β, it will be found that they are equivalent to

(8)
$$b - 2.57\frac{s_e}{\sqrt{\sum(x_i - \bar{x})^2}} < \beta < b + 2.57\frac{s_e}{\sqrt{\sum(x_i - \bar{x})^2}}.$$

If 2.57 is replaced by the proper t value, these inequalities may serve as a formula for finding confidence limits for β for any size sample and any desired percentage limits. Earlier calculations yielded the values $b = .103$ and $s_e = .35$. The last column of Table 2 yields the value $\Sigma (x_i - \bar{x})^2 = 1008$; hence $\sqrt{\Sigma (x_i - \bar{x})^2} = 31.7$. If these values are substituted in (8), it will reduce to

$$.103 - 2.57 \frac{.35}{31.7} < \beta < .103 + 2.57 \frac{.35}{31.7}$$

or

$$.075 < \beta < .131.$$

As a result, the desired 95 per cent confidence interval for β is the interval from .075 to .131.

Tests of hypotheses about β can be made by means of formula (7) in the usual manner.

6. MULTIPLE LINEAR REGRESSION

Methods for dealing with problems of predicting one variable by means of several other variables, rather than by means of just one other variable, are similar to those for one variable. For example, if one were to predict the variable y in terms of the two variables x_1 and x_2, the problem would become one of finding the best-fitting plane, in the sense of least squares, to a scatter diagram of points in three dimensions. The geometry of such a problem is illustrated in Fig. 4.

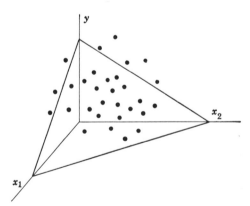

Fig. 4   Regression plane in three dimensions.

Since the equation of any plane can be written in the form

(9)
$$y' = a_0 + a_1x_1 + a_2x_2,$$

the problem is one of estimating the three parameters a_0, a_1, and a_2 by the method of least squares. This is done by mathematical methods in the same manner as for simple linear regression. It turns out that the least squares values of a_0, a_1, and a_2 are obtained by solving the following set of three linear equations:

(10)
$$a_0 n + a_1 \sum x_1 + a_2 \sum x_2 = \sum y$$
$$a_0 \sum x_1 + a_1 \sum x_1^2 + a_2 \sum x_1 x_2 = \sum x_1 y$$
$$a_0 \sum x_2 + a_1 \sum x_1 x_2 + a_2 \sum x_2^2 = \sum x_2 y.$$

This result generalizes for additional variables. Thus, if one had four variables, x_1, x_2, x_3, and x_4, by means of which to predict y, there would be five equations in the five unknowns a_0, a_1, a_2, a_3, and a_4 to solve.

One of the attractive features of the least-squares approach in regression problems is the simple manner of writing down the equations that need to be solved to obtain estimates of the regression equation parameters. Thus, equations (10) can be written down by carrying out the following operations. Remove the prime on y in the multiple-regression equation so that it will represent an observed value of y rather than a regression value, then sum both sides of the resulting equation to obtain the first least-squares equation. Next, multiply both sides of this modified regression equation by x_1 and sum both sides to obtain the second least-squares equation. Finally, multiply both sides by x_2 and sum to obtain the third equation.

If there had been five x variables instead of two in the regression equation, one would have continued this procedure by multiplying by x_3 and summing, then by x_4 and summing, and finally by x_5 and summing to obtain three more least-squares equations. There would then be six least-squares equations to be solved for estimates of the six unknown regression parameters.

Since the reader is not expected to be familiar with methods for solving sets of equations, the details of multiple linear regression methods are omitted. The purpose of this section is to point out that methods are available for the more general problem and that these methods are very similar to those discussed in the preceding sections.

▶7. NONLINEAR REGRESSION

The discussion in section 4 pointed out the possibility of reducing many nonlinear relationships between two variables x and y to linear ones by choosing the proper functions of x and y. Although this is always possible theoretically, the proper functions may be exceedingly complicated or one may not be able to determine what the proper functions are. It is then often more satisfactory to work with nonlinear relationships between x and y. The simplest curve to use as a regression model if a straight line will not suffice is a parabola. Its equation can be written in the form

$$(11) \qquad\qquad y' = a_0 + a_1 x + a_2 x^2.$$

The problem of fitting a curve of this type to a set of points in the x, y plane by least squares is similar to that of fitting a multiple-regression equation to a set of points in three dimensions. As a matter of fact, the results that were obtained in the preceding section can be applied directly to this problem. It is merely necessary to choose $x_1 = x$ and $x_2 = x^2$ in equation (9) to obtain equation (11). As a result the least-squares equations for (11) are obtained by making these same substitutions in the least-squares equations given in (10). Thus, the equations whose solutions give the desired estimates for a_0, a_1, and a_2 in fitting the parabola (11) to a set of points are the following:

$$
\begin{aligned}
a_0 n + a_1 \sum x \;\; + a_2 \sum x^2 &= \sum y \\
a_0 \sum x \;\; + a_1 \sum x^2 + a_2 \sum x^3 &= \sum xy \\
a_0 \sum x^2 + a_1 \sum x^3 + a_2 \sum x^4 &= \sum x^2 y.
\end{aligned}
$$

(12)

For the purpose of observing to what extent a parabola fits a set of points better than a straight line, it suffices to calculate the errors of prediction for both fitted curves and compare them. The standard error of estimate given by (6) may also be calculated for both curves and compared; however, the standard error of estimate for a parabola uses the divisor $n - 3$ in place of $n - 2$ in formula (6). If there is very little difference between the two calculated standard errors of estimate, not much is gained by using a parabola rather than a straight line for the regression curve.

These methods can be extended to polynomial curves of higher degree. All that one needs to do is to replace x_3 by x^3, x_4 by x^4, etc., in the more general forms of (9) and (10) to obtain the desired degree polynomial regression-curve equation and its corresponding least-squares equations for estimating the coefficients. Formula (6) for the standard error of estimate is modified by dividing by $n - s$, where s denotes the number of unknown parameters in (9) that are being estimated.

8. REVIEW EXERCISES

1. Given the following data, (a) plot the points, (b) find the equation of the least squares line, (c) graph the line on the graph containing the plotted points, (d) calculate the errors of prediction, (e) predict the value of y for $x = 16.5$, (f) calculate the standard error of estimate, (g) draw two lines parallel to the least-squares line forming a band within which 68 per cent of the points might be expected to lie under a normal distribution assumption and comment, ▶(h) test the hypothesis that $\beta = .5$, (i) find 90 per cent confidence limits for β, ▶(j) fit a parabola to the points, ▶(k) calculate the standard error of estimate for the fitted parabola and compare with the result in (f).

x	5	6	7	8	9	10	11	12	13	14	15	16	17
y	7.6	9.5	9.3	10.3	11.1	12.1	13.3	12.7	13.0	13.8	14.6	14.6	14.7

(a), (c), and (g)

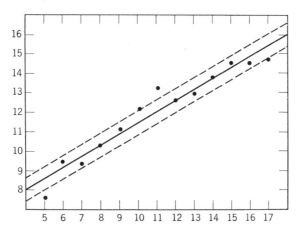

(b)

x	y	x^2	xy
5	7.6	25	38.0
6	9.5	36	57.0
7	9.3	49	65.1
8	10.3	64	82.4
9	11.1	81	99.9
10	12.1	100	121.0
11	13.3	121	146.3
12	12.7	144	152.4
13	13.0	169	169.0
14	13.8	196	193.2
15	14.6	225	219.0
16	14.6	256	233.6
17	14.7	289	249.9
143	156.6	1755	1826.8

$$\bar{x} = \frac{143}{13} = 11$$

$$\bar{y} = \frac{156.6}{13} = 12.05$$

$$b = \frac{1826.8 - 143(12.05)}{1755 - 143(11)} = .570$$

$$y' = 12.05 + .570(x - 11), \text{ or}$$

$$y' = 5.78 + .570x$$

The calculating formulas were used here even though it would have been easier to take advantage of the fact that $\bar{x} = 11$.

(d)

y	7.6	9.5	9.3	10.3	11.1	12.1	13.3	12.7	13.0	13.8	14.6	14.6	14.7
y'	8.6	9.2	9.8	10.3	10.9	11.5	12.0	12.6	13.2	13.8	14.3	14.9	15.5
e	−1.0	.3	−.5	.0	.2	.6	1.3	.1	−.2	.0	.3	−.3	−.8

Each value of y' was obtained from the preceding one by adding .57 to it. The first value was obtained by substituting $x = 5$ in the equation.

(e) $y' = 15.2$ for $x = 16.5$.

(*f*) From part (*d*), $\Sigma e^2 = 4.30$; hence $s_e = \sqrt{4.30/11} = .63$.

(*g*) There are four points lying outside this band, which is about what is to be expected.

(*h*) Using the fact that $\bar{x} = 11$, $\Sigma(x_i - \bar{x})^2 = 182$,

$$t = \frac{.57 - .50}{.63}\sqrt{182} = 1.50; \quad \text{hence accept } H : \beta = .5.$$

(*i*)
$$.57 - 1.796\frac{.63}{\sqrt{182}} < \beta < .57 + 1.796\frac{.63}{\sqrt{182}}, \text{ or}$$

$$.57 - .084 < \beta < .57 + .084, \text{ or}$$

$$.49 < \beta < .65.$$

x	y	x^3	x^4	x^2y
5	7.6	125	625	1,900
6	9.5	216	1,296	3,420
7	9.3	343	2,401	4,557
8	10.3	512	4,096	6,592
9	11.1	729	6,561	8,991
10	12.1	1,000	10,000	12,100
11	13.3	1,331	14,641	16,093
12	12.7	1,728	20,736	18,288
13	13.0	2,197	28,561	21,970
14	13.8	2,744	38,416	27,048
15	14.6	3,375	50,625	32,850
16	14.6	4,096	65,536	37,376
17	14.7	4,913	83,521	42,483
		23,309	327,015	233,668

$$a_0 13 + a_1 143 \quad + a_2 1,755 \quad = 156.6$$
$$a_0 143 + a_1 1,755 \quad + a_2 23,309 \quad = 1,826.8$$
$$a_0 1,755 + a_1 23,309 + a_2 327,015 = 23,366.8$$

or

$$a_0 + a_1 11 \quad + a_2 135 \quad = 12.046$$
$$a_0 + a_1 12.273 + a_2 163 \quad = 12.775$$
$$a_0 + a_1 13.281 + a_2 186.33 = 13.314$$

or

$$a_1 1.273 + a_2 28 = .729, \quad a_1 2.281 + a_2 51.33 = 1.268$$

or
$$a_1 + a_2 21.995 = .573, \; a_1 + a_2 22.505 = .556$$

or
$$a_2 = -.033, \; a_1 = 1.299, \; a_0 = 2.212$$

Hence
$$y' = 2.21 + 1.30x - .033x^2.$$

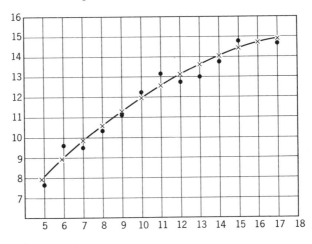

(k)

y	7.6	9.5	9.3	10.3	11.1	12.1	13.3	12.7	13.0	13.8	14.6	14.6	14.7
y'	7.9	8.8	9.7	10.5	11.2	11.9	12.5	13.1	13.5	13.9	14.3	14.6	14.8
e	−.3	.7	−.4	−.2	−.1	.2	.8	−.4	−.5	−.1	.3	.0	−.1

$s_e = \sqrt{\Sigma e^2 / 10} = .45$. Since $s_e = .63$ for the straight line, the parabola gives a better fit. The standard error has been decreased about $\frac{1}{3}$.

2. Given the following data, (a) find the equation of its least-squares plane, (b) calculate the errors of prediction, (c) calculate the standard error of estimate, (d) omit the variable x_2 and then find the equation of the least-squares line, (e) calculate the standard error of estimate for the line obtained in (d) and compare with the value obtained in (c). Was much gained by introducing the variable x_2 in addition to x_1?

x_1	1	7	6	2	5	2	8	3	7	6
x_2	4	6	8	0	1	5	8	8	3	0
y	11	21	23	7	13	18	30	18	21	20

(a) Calculations give $\Sigma x_1 = 47$, $\Sigma x_2 = 43$, $\Sigma y = 182$, $\Sigma x_1^2 = 277$, $\Sigma x_2^2 = 279$, $\Sigma x_1 x_2 = 218$, $\Sigma x_1 y = 972$, $\Sigma x_2 y = 904$; hence the following equations need to be solved

$$a_0 10 + a_1 47 + a_2 43 = 182$$
$$a_0 47 + a_1 277 + a_2 218 = 972$$
$$a_0 43 + a_1 218 + a_2 279 = 904$$

The solutions of these equations are $a_0 = 5.48$, $a_1 = 1.81$, $a_2 = .98$; hence the equation of the regression plane is

$$y' = 5.48 + 1.81 x_1 + .98 x_2.$$

(b)

y	11	21	23	7	13	18	30	18	21	20
y'	11.2	24.0	24.2	9.1	15.5	14.0	27.8	18.8	21.1	16.3
e	−.2	−3.0	−1.2	−2.1	−2.5	4.0	2.2	−.8	−.1	3.7

(c) $\Sigma e_i^2 = 56.32$; hence $s_e = 2.84$.

(d) From (a), $\bar{y} = 18.2$, $b = 2.08$; hence $y' = 8.42 + 2.08x$.

y	11	21	23	7	13	18	30	18	21	20
y'	10.5	23.0	20.9	12.6	18.8	12.6	25.1	14.7	23.0	20.9
e	.5	−2.0	2.1	−5.6	−5.8	5.4	4.9	3.3	−2.0	−.9

Hence $\Sigma e^2 = 142.5$, $s_e = \sqrt{142.5/8} = 4.22$. Hence it follows from (c) where $s_e = 2.84$ that x_2 was very useful because it reduced the value of s_e by about $\frac{1}{3}$.

EXERCISES

1. Graph the line whose equation is $y = .3x - 1$ for values of x between 0 and 5.

2. Graph the line whose equation is $y = -.5x + 1.5$ for values of x between −2 and 4.

3. The regression line for estimating the yearly family expenditure on food by means of yearly income, in dollars, is given by $y = 200 + .20x$. (a) What is the average expenditure for families with incomes of 2000 dollars, 5000 dollars? (b) Why would you hesitate to use this formula for incomes of 0 dollars?

4. Find the equation of the regression line for the following data. Graph the line on the scatter diagram.

x	1	2	3	4	5
y	2	5	3	8	7

5. The following data are for tensile strength and hardness of die-cast aluminum. Find the equation of the regression line for estimating tensile strength from hardness and graph it on the scatter diagram.

T.S. (y)	293	349	368	301	340	308	354	313	322	334	377	247
H (x)	53	70	84	55	78	64	71	53	82	67	70	56

6. The following data are the scores made by students on an entrance examination (x) and a final examination (y). (a) Find the equation of the regression line. (b) Graph the line on the scatter diagram.

x	129	179	347	328	286	256	477	430	327	245	286	326
y	370	361	405	302	496	323	374	332	435	165	375	466

7. Calculate the standard error of estimate in problem 4.

8. Calculate the standard error of estimate in problem 5 and find what percentage of the errors exceed it. What percentage of the errors exceed twice the standard error of estimate?

9. Explain why the standard error of estimate calculated in problem 7 and also in problem 8 would not be reliable for predicting the sizes of future errors of estimate.

10. Explain the regression fallacy in the statement that track stars seem to go down hill after establishing a record.

11. Give an illustration of data for which the regression fallacy might easily be made.

12. Give examples of pairs of variables for which the regression line would be expected to have a negative slope.

13. Given the following data, work parts (a) through (g) for the first of the two review exercises of section 8.

x	1	9	6	4	5	7	7	1	2	8	6	3
y	15	75	55	42	33	45	55	17	32	80	48	45

▶14. Given $n = 8$, $b = 2$, $s_e = .2$, and $\Sigma(x_i - \bar{x})^2 = 50$, find 95 per cent confidence limits for β.

▶15. Find 95 per cent confidence limits for β in problem 5.

▶16. Test the hypothesis that $\beta = 1.0$ in problem 4.

▶17. Test the hypothesis that $\beta = 2.5$ in problem 5.

▶18. By inspecting formula (8), determine how you would choose ten values of x between $x = 0$ and $x = 10$ at which to take observations on y so as to make the confidence interval for β as short as possible.

▶19. Given the following data, work the problems in the second of the two review exercises of section 8.

x_1	2	1	5	8	7	2	1	3	0	9	4	6
x_2	6	5	5	7	3	1	8	2	6	7	7	9
y	13	9	15	16	21	9	15	11	12	30	19	22

►Special Topics

CHAPTER 10

The Chi-Square
Distribution

1. INTRODUCTION

In the preceding chapters problems of estimation and hypothesis testing were solved by means of the binomial, normal, or Student t distribution. However, such problems for the normal distribution parameter σ had to be postponed because they were not capable of being solved satisfactorily by means of any of those distributions. Problems of the counting type, in which an experimental outcome cannot be classified as either a success or a failure but instead requires more than two categories of classification, also had to be postponed because the binomial distribution does not suffice to treat them. Now it turns out that there is a distribution, called the chi-square distribution, which is capable of solving these two classes of problems. The second type is considered first.

The problem of testing the equality of two population proportions, which was solved in Chapter 7, is a special case of the more general problems of this type. Such problems can be described in the following manner.

There is a finite number, denoted by k, of possible outcomes of an experiment. These possible outcomes are represented by k cells or boxes. The experiment is performed n times, and the results are expressed by recording the observed frequencies of outcomes in the corresponding cells. The problem then is to determine whether the frequencies are compatible with those expected from some postulated theory.

As an illustration, if the experiment consists of rolling a single die, there will be 6 cells. The results of performing such an experiment sixty times are recorded in the first row of cells in Table 1. If the die is "honest," each face will have the probability $\frac{1}{6}$ of appearing in a single roll. Each face would therefore be expected to appear ten times, on the average, in an experiment of this kind. These mean frequencies are usually called expected frequencies. The problem then is to decide whether the observed frequencies in Table 1 are compatible with the expected frequencies listed there.

TABLE 1

	1	2	3	4	5	6
o	15	7	4	11	6	17
e	10	10	10	10	10	10

The general method for testing compatibility is based on a measure of the extent to which the observed and expected frequencies agree. This measure, called chi-square, is defined by the formula

(1)
$$\chi^2 = \sum_{i=1}^{k} \frac{(o_i - e_i)^2}{e_i}.$$

Here o_i and e_i denote the observed and expected frequencies, respectively, for the ith cell, and k denotes the number of cells.

For Table 1 the value of χ^2 is given by

$$\chi^2 = \frac{(15 - 10)^2}{10} + \frac{(7 - 10)^2}{10} + \frac{(4 - 10)^2}{10} + \frac{(11 - 10)^2}{10}$$
$$+ \frac{(6 - 10)^2}{10} + \frac{(17 - 10)^2}{10}$$
$$= 13.6.$$

Now, it is clear from inspecting formula (1) that the value of χ^2 will be 0 if there is perfect agreement with expectation, whereas its value will be large if the differences from expectation are large. Thus increasingly large values of χ^2 may be thought of as corresponding to increasingly poor experimental agreement. If an honest die were available and if the experiment of rolling the die sixty times were repeated a large number of times and each time the value of χ^2 were computed, a set of χ^2's would be obtained which could be classified into a relative frequency table and histogram of χ^2's. The histogram would tell approximately in what percentage of such experiments various ranges of values of χ^2 could be expected to be obtained. Then one would be able to judge whether the value of $\chi^2 = 13.6$ was unusually large, as compared to the run of χ^2's that are obtained in experiments with an honest die. If the percentage of experiments for which $\chi^2 > 13.6$ was very small, say less than 5 per cent, one would judge that the observed frequencies were not compatible with the frequencies expected for an honest die; hence one would conclude that the die was not honest.

2. THE CHI-SQUARE DISTRIBUTION

Just as in the case of other sampling distributions, it is possible to use mathematical methods to arrive at the desired theoretical frequency distribution. Since there is only a limited number of possible values for the cell frequencies in Table 1, there is only a limited number of values of χ^2 possible. Thus the theoretical distribution of χ^2 must be a discrete distribution. Since a discrete distribution with many possible values requires the application of lengthy computations, practical considerations demand a simple continuous approximation to the discrete χ^2 distribution, very much like the normal approximation to the binomial distribution. Such a continuous distribution is available in what is known as the chi-square distribution. It is unfortunate that the continuous distribution approximating the discrete chi-square distribution should also be called the chi-square distribution; however, there will be no confusion because the continuous distribution is the only one ever used.

The graph of the continuous chi-square distribution for the die problem is shown in Fig. 1. The experimental value of $\chi^2 = 13.6$ has been located

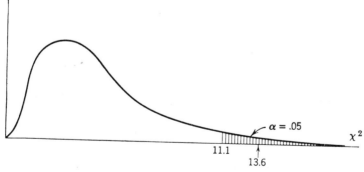

Fig. 1   Distribution of χ^2 for die problem.

on this graph, together with the value of $\chi^2 = 11.1$, which cuts off the 5 per cent right tail of the distribution. Since large values of χ^2 correspond to poor experimental agreement, the values of χ^2 exceeding 11.1 are chosen as the critical region of the test. The experimental value $\chi^2 = 13.6$ falls in the critical region; therefore, the hypothesis that the die is honest is rejected.

As a second illustration of the χ^2 test, consider the following genetics problem. In experiments on the breeding of flowers of a certain species, an experimenter obtained 120 magenta flowers with a green stigma, 48 magenta flowers with a red stigma, 36 red flowers with a green stigma, and 13 red flowers with a red stigma. Mendelian theory predicts that flowers of these types should be obtained in the ratios $9:3:3:1$. Are these experimental results compatible with the theory?

For this problem, $n = 217$ and $k = 4$. The theoretical ratios $9:3:3:1$ imply that the probabilities are $\frac{9}{16}$, $\frac{3}{16}$, $\frac{3}{16}$, and $\frac{1}{16}$ that a flower will be of the corresponding type. The expected frequencies for the four cells are therefore obtained by multiplying 217 by each of these probabilities. The observed frequencies, together with the expected frequencies, correct to the nearest integer, are shown in Table 2.

Calculations give

$$\chi^2 = \frac{(120 - 122)^2}{122} + \frac{(48 - 41)^2}{41} + \frac{(36 - 41)^2}{41} + \frac{(13 - 14)^2}{14} = 1.9.$$

Now, the theory of the χ^2 distribution for problems such as these shows that the χ^2 curve in Fig. 1 does not apply to the present problem because the number of cells in this problem is not the same as before. A remarkable feature of the χ^2 distribution is that its form depends only upon the number of cells. Figure 2 gives the graphs of six such χ^2 curves corresponding to the number of cells ranging from 2 to 7. It is customary to label a χ^2 distribution by means of a parameter $\nu = k - 1$, called the number of degrees of freedom, rather than by the number of cells. The phrase degrees of freedom refers to the number of independent cell frequencies. Since the sum of the four observed frequencies in Table 2 must equal 217, the fourth cell frequency is determined as soon as the first three cell frequencies are specified. Thus there are $\nu = 3$ degrees of

TABLE 2

o_i	120	48	36	13
e_i	122	41	41	14

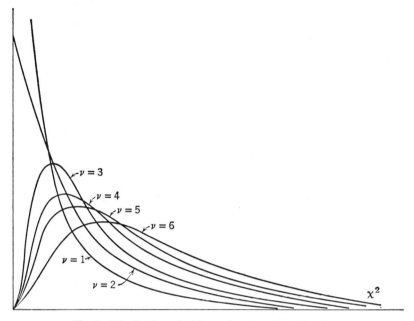

Fig. 2   Distribution of χ^2 for various degrees of freedom.

freedom for this problem, just as there were $\nu = 5$ degrees of freedom in the earlier problem of the die. The value of χ^2 cutting off the 5 per cent right tail of the χ^2 distribution for $\nu = 3$ turns out to be 7.8. Since the value of χ^2 for Table 2, namely 1.9, does not fall in the critical region, the result is not significant. There is no reason on the basis of this test for doubting that Mendelian theory is applicable to the data of Table 2.

The values of χ^2 that determined the 5 per cent critical regions in the two preceding illustrations were obtained from Table VII in the appendix. The 5 per cent critical value is found in the column headed .05 and in the row corresponding to the appropriate number of degrees of freedom, $\nu = k - 1$.

3. LIMITATIONS ON THE χ^2 TEST

Since a χ^2 curve, such as those in Fig. 2, is only an approximation to the true discrete distribution of χ^2, the χ^2 test should be used only when the approximation is good. Experience and theory indicate that the approximation is usually satisfactory provided that the expected frequencies in all

TABLE 3

	15–16	17–18	19–20	21–22	23–24
o	5	12	10	8	5
e	4	8	8	10	10

the cells are at least as large as 5. This limitation is similar to that placed on the use of the normal-curve approximation to the binomial distribution in which np for $p \leq \frac{1}{2}$ was required to exceed 5.

If the expected frequency of a cell is not as large as 5, this cell can be combined with one or more other cells until the condition is satisfied. As an illustration, consider the data of Table 3 on the classification of automobile accidents in a certain community according to the age of the driver for drivers below 25 years of age. The percentages of drivers in these age groups in this community are approximately 10 per cent, 20 per cent, 20 per cent, 25 per cent, and 25 per cent, respectively. The problem here is to test whether the accident rate among drivers under 25 years of age is independent of age. Since the total number of observations here is $n = 40$, the expected frequencies are obtained by multiplying 40 by these percentages treated as decimals. They have been recorded in Table 3 in the row labeled e. Since the expected frequency in the first cell is less than 5, the first two cells are combined to give Table 4.

The value of χ^2 for Table 4 is 5.5. Since $v = 3$ here and Table VII yields the 5 per cent critical value of 7.8, this result is not significant.

TABLE 4

15–18	19–20	21–22	23–24
17	10	8	5
12	8	10	10

4. CONTINGENCY TABLES

A very useful application of the χ^2 test occurs in connection with testing the compatibility of observed and expected frequencies in two-way tables, known as *contingency tables*. Table 5, in which the frequencies corresponding to the indicated classifications for a sample of 400 are recorded, is an illustration of a contingency table.

TABLE 5

Marriage Adjustment

		Very Low	Low	High	Very High	Totals
Education	College	18(27)	29(39)	70(64)	115(102)	232
	High school	17(13)	28(19)	30(32)	41(51)	116
	Grade school	11(6)	10(9)	11(14)	20(23)	52
	Totals	46	67	111	176	400

A contingency table is usually constructed for the purpose of studying the relationship between the two variables of classification. In particular, one may wish to know whether the two variables are at all related. By means of the χ^2 test it is possible to test the hypothesis that the two variables are independent. Thus, in connection with Table 5, the χ^2 test can be used to test the hypothesis that there is no relationship between an individual's educational level and his adjustment to marriage.

This problem differs from the preceding problems in that the probabilities of an observation falling in the various cells are not known. As a result, it is not possible to write down the expected frequencies for the various cells, as was the case in the other problems. This difficulty can be overcome in the following manner.

Consider repeated sampling experiments of this kind in which 400 people are classified in their proper categories. If only those experiments that produce the same marginal totals are considered, then expected frequencies can be obtained. Since the margins are now fixed, the proportion of college graduates in such samples of 400 is always $232/400 = .58$. Therefore, if there is no relationship between education and marriage adjustment, 58 per cent of the 46 individuals in the very low adjustment category would be expected to be college graduates. Since 58 per cent of 46 is 27, to the nearest unit, this is the expected frequency for the first cell in Table 5 on the basis of independence. The expected frequencies in the remaining three cells of the first row are obtained in a similar manner by taking 58 per cent of the column totals. The second- and third-row cell frequencies are obtained by using 29 per cent and 13 per cent, respectively, corresponding to the proportions $116/400$ and $52/400$. These expected frequencies are the frequencies recorded in parentheses in Table 5.

The value of χ^2 for Table 5, using the numbers in parentheses as expected frequencies, is 20.7. Although there are twelve cells in this table, one does not choose $v = 11$ degrees of freedom in looking up the critical value of χ^2, as was the procedure in earlier problems. The correct value of v to choose here is quite different and is determined by strictly mathematical arguments; however, it is possible to acquire a feeling for the plausibility of the correct value by the following type of argument. Assume that n is large but fixed in value. Then χ^2 will be expected to decrease in variability if the number of cells is decreased, because there will be fewer possibilities for large differences between observed and expected frequencies. This is observed in Fig. 2 in the shifting of the distribution to the left as v decreases. Furthermore, if the number of cells is fixed but restrictions are placed on the frequencies that occur in the cells, the variability of χ^2 will also be expected to decrease. Now in repeated experiments of the preceding type the cell frequencies have been rather severely restricted by requiring them to possess the proper row sums and the proper column sums. In the first row of Table 5, for example, the observed frequencies must sum to 232. This essentially says that the frequencies in the first three cells of that row are free to assume any values they please, as long as they do not sum to more than 232, but that then the fourth cell frequency is completely determined. Thus, if the χ^2 test were to be applied to the first row only it would employ $v = 3$ degrees of freedom. The phrase "degrees of freedom" aptly describes what corresponds to the number of cell frequencies that are free to vary. The same argument would apply to the second row, thus giving a total of six degrees of freedom for the two rows. However, when one looks at the third row, the picture changes because now it is necessary to realize that what applies to rows must also apply to columns; therefore the frequency found in the last cell of the first column is determined when the first two cell frequencies in that column have been specified. As a result, the third-row frequencies as well as the fourth-column frequencies are determined when the remaining cell frequencies have been specified. Thus, it seems reasonable that the experiment should behave like one in which there are six cells in which the frequencies are free to vary, subject only to the restriction that their sums are not excessive. In view of arguments of this type it should come as no surprise to learn that mathematical theory has demonstrated that one should choose $v = 6$ here.

From Table VII, the 5 per cent critical value of χ^2 with $v = 6$ degrees of freedom is 12.6. Since $\chi^2 = 20.7$ here, this result is significant and the hypothesis of independence is rejected. An inspection of Table 5 shows that individuals with some college education appear to adjust themselves to marriage more readily than those with less education.

In the foregoing solution, since only experiments with the same marginal totals are being considered, it is tacitly assumed that any relationship, or lack of it, that exists for restricted sampling experiments will also hold for unrestricted sampling experiments. This seems to be a reasonable assumption here because there appears to be no reason for believing that fixing the marginal totals in this way will influence the relationship.

This problem illustrates very well the reason why Table VII for χ^2 lists the number of degrees of freedom ν rather than the number of cells to determine which χ^2 curve to use. For a contingency table having r rows and c columns, the number of degrees of freedom is given by the formula

$$\nu = (r - 1)(c - 1).$$

This follows from the earlier arguments that the frequencies in the last row and in the last column are determined by the marginal totals as soon as the other cell frequencies are given. Thus the number of independent cell frequencies is obtained by counting the number of cells after the last row and the last column have been deleted. After the deletion there will be $r - 1$ rows and $c - 1$ columns and therefore $(r - 1)(c - 1)$ cells.

5. DISTRIBUTION OF s^2

As indicated in section 1, the chi-square distribution can also be used to solve problems of estimation and hypothesis testing about the normal distribution parameter σ. For the purpose of explaining how it can be used to solve such problems, consider the following estimation problem.

A market analyst took a sample of 20 markets in a large city in an attempt to determine how much variation there is in meat prices. The 20 prices that were quoted him for the same cut of meat yielded the sample values $\bar{x} = 92$ and $s = 8$. The problem now is to find a 95 per cent confidence interval for the standard deviation of all the market prices.

Suppose a large number of experiments of the same kind was carried out. This means that each time a random sample of 20 markets would be taken and the value of s computed for the 20 quoted prices. The values of $\bar{x}$ are of no interest here, and they are therefore ignored. Suppose, further, that meat prices for this cut are normally distributed and, for the time being, assume that the value of σ^2 is known for this population. Then each experiment would yield a value of the variable

$$v = \frac{(n-1)s^2}{\sigma^2}.$$

If these values of v were classified into a frequency table, one would obtain a good estimate of the limiting, or theoretical, distribution of v. As usual, mathematical methods yield the exact distribution and show that the distribution of v depends only upon the value of n. Surprising as it may seem, the distribution of v turns out to be the χ^2 distribution, with $v = n - 1$ degrees of freedom. Since Table VII gives the necessary probabilities for the χ^2 distribution, problems of estimation and hypothesis testing for σ can be solved by methods similar to those used for μ.

For the problem under consideration, since $v = n - 1 = 19$, the variable v will possess a χ^2 distribution with 19 degrees of freedom. From Table VII it will be found that $\chi_1^2 = 8.91$ and $\chi_2^2 = 32.85$ are the two values of χ^2 cutting off $2\frac{1}{2}$ per cent tail areas of the χ^2 curve for 19 degrees of freedom. Hence the probability is .95 that v will satisfy the inequalities

$$\chi_1^2 < v < \chi_2^2.$$

If the value of v is substituted, these inequalities will become

$$\chi_1^2 < \frac{(n-1)s^2}{\sigma^2} < \chi_2^2.$$

Each of these inequalities may be solved for σ^2 to yield the equivalent inequalities

$$\frac{(n-1)s^2}{\chi_2^2} < \sigma^2 < \frac{(n-1)s^2}{\chi_1^2}.$$

When the proper numerical values are inserted, this expression will yield a 95 per cent confidence interval for σ^2. For this problem, such numerical substitutions yield

$$\frac{19(8)^2}{32.85} < \sigma^2 < \frac{19(8)^2}{8.91}.$$

This simplifies to

$$37 < \sigma^2 < 136.$$

If the square roots of these numbers are found, the desired 95 per cent confidence interval for σ will be obtained, namely

$$6.1 < \sigma < 11.7.$$

It is clear from this result that one cannot estimate σ with much precision when the sample is as small as 20. It should also be noted that the sample point estimate $s = 8$ is not in the middle of this interval. This is because the χ^2 curve for small degrees of freedom is heavily skewed to the right.

As a second illustration of the use of the χ^2 distribution for standard-deviation problems, consider once more the problem discussed in section 2, Chapter 7, on testing a mean. There a sample of 100 brand B light bulbs yielded a standard deviation of 80 hours burning time, whereas long experience with brand A bulbs showed a standard deviation of 90 hours. If one assumes that there is no difference between the two brands, then the two brands should possess the same standard deviations as well as the same means. Consider, therefore, the problem of testing the hypothesis that the population standard deviation of brand B bulbs is equal to that of brand A bulbs. Since the value 90 is based on long experience, it may be treated as the population value for brand A. The hypothesis to be tested then is that the standard deviation of the brand B bulbs is 90. This is written in the form

$$H_0: \sigma = 90.$$

A two-sided test is used here because before the sample was taken there was no reason to believe that the standard deviation of brand B bulbs would be larger, or smaller, than the standard deviation for brand A bulbs.

Since the sample size here is 100, there will be 99 degrees of freedom for this problem. To eliminate the necessity for interpolating in Table VII, assume that the sample size is 101 rather than 100. From Table VII it will be found that the two $2\frac{1}{2}$ per cent tail areas of the χ^2 curve for 100 degrees of freedom are cut off by the two χ^2 values given by

$$\chi_1^2 = 74 \quad \text{and} \quad \chi_2^2 = 130.$$

As a result, the 5 per cent two-sided critical region for the test is chosen as the values of χ^2 lying outside the interval determined by those two values of χ^2. Since, for this problem, the value

$$v = \frac{(n-1)s^2}{\sigma^2} = \frac{100(80)^2}{(90)^2} = 79$$

does not fall in the critical region, the hypothesis is accepted.

For degrees of freedom less than 100 but not listed in Table VII, it suffices to interpolate roughly between the two nearest listed values. For degrees of freedom larger than 100, one may treat the variable

$$z = \sqrt{2\chi^2} - \sqrt{2\nu - 1}$$

as an approximate normal variable with zero mean and unit standard deviation. For example, in the preceding problem with $n = 101$ one would obtain

$$z = \sqrt{2(79)} - \sqrt{2(100) - 1}$$

$$= \sqrt{158} - \sqrt{199}$$

$$= 12.57 - 14.11$$

$$= -1.54.$$

Since z is a standard normal variable, a two-sided critical region of size .05 consists of the z values outside the interval from -1.96 to 1.96. As was to be expected, $z = -1.54$ does not lie in the critical region.

EXERCISES

1. The number of automobile accidents per week in a certain community were as follows: 12, 8, 20, 2, 14, 10, 15, 6, 9, 4. Are these frequencies in agreement with the belief that accident conditions were the same over this 10-week period?

2. According to Mendelian inheritance, offspring of a certain crossing should be colored red, black, or white in the ratios 9:3:4. If an experiment gave 72, 34, and 38 offspring in those categories, is the theory substantiated?

3. The number of individuals of a certain race possessing the four blood types should be in the proportions .16, .48, .20, .16. Given the observed frequencies 180, 360, 132, 98 for another race, test to see whether it possesses the same distribution of blood types.

4. The following data represent the results of an investigation of the sex distribution of the children of 32 families containing 4 children each. Use the binomial distribution with $n = 4$ and $p = \frac{1}{2}$ to calculate expected frequencies. Then apply the χ^2 test to see whether this binomial distribution model is satisfactory here.

No. of sons	0	1	2	3	4
No. of families	4	9	8	8	3

5. Test to see whether the two variables of classification in the following contingency table are independent.

20	10	10
10	20	30

6. A certain drug is claimed to be effective in curing colds. In an experiment on 164 people with colds, half of them were given the drug and half of them were given sugar pills. The patients' reactions to the treatment are recorded in the following table. Test the hypothesis that the drug and the sugar pills yield similar reactions.

	Helped	Harmed	No Effect
Drug	52	10	20
Sugar	44	12	26

7. A market analyst is concerned whether housewives who are not at home when interviewers call differ in their opinions of a certain product. To check this possibility, interviewers returned to "not-at-home" houses until an interview was obtained. The results of this study are given in the following table. Test to see whether the "not-at-home" housewives have the same opinion as the "at-home" housewives.

Opinion of Product	Number of Housewives Interviewed	
	First Call	Later Call
Excellent	62	36
Satisfactory	84	42
Unsatisfactory	24	22

8. In an epidemic of a certain disease 927 children contracted the disease. Of these, 408 received no treatment and 104 of them suffered aftereffects. Of the remainder who did receive treatment, 166 suffered aftereffects. Test the hypothesis that the treatment was not effective and comment about the conclusion.

9. Work problem 8 by the method explained in Chapter 7 for testing the difference of two proportions. It can be shown that the two methods are equivalent for problems such as this.

10. Given that x is normally distributed and given the sample values $n = 15$ and $s = 7$, test the hypothesis that $\sigma = 5$.

11. Test the hypothesis that $\sigma = 8$, given that $s = 10$ for a sample of size (a) 20, (b) 51.

12. Using the data of problem 10, find (a) 95 per cent, (b) 99 per cent confidence limits for σ.

13. Find 95 per cent confidence limits for σ if $s = 10$ for a sample of size (a) 20, (b) 51.

14. Test the hypothesis that $\sigma = 20$, given that $s = 10$ for a sample of 25.

15. Work problem 13 for a sample of size (a) 76, (b) 120.

16. The following data represent the amounts of a certain chemical compound obtained in daily analyses of a chemical product. Long-run experience has yielded a standard deviation value of .5. (a) Test the hypothesis that $\sigma = .5$ for these analyses. (b) Find 95 per cent confidence limits for the σ of these analyses: 12.7, 12.3, 13.2, 12.8, 13.6, 13.1, 12.6, 12.4, 14.1, 13.3, 13.4, 13.1, 12.6, 12.9, 13.0, 12.4, 14.6, 13.8, 13.4, 12.7, 13.5, 12.5.

17. Take a sample of 500 random digits from Table II and list the observed frequencies in 10 cells. (a) Apply the χ^2 test to see whether the sample is compatible with theory here. (b) Combine the odd-digit cells and the even-digit cells to obtain only two cells and test to see whether odd and even digits possess the same probability of occurrence. (c) Could you have worked part (b) by an earlier technique? If you can, do so and compare your two results.

18. Take a sample of 20 random digits and (a) calculate the value of s^2, (b) test the hypothesis that $\sigma^2 = 8$, (c) find a 95 per cent confidence interval for σ. Does it include the true value, which is known to be $\sigma = 2.87$?

CHAPTER 11

Nonparametric Tests

1. INTRODUCTION

With one exception, all the methods that have been presented thus far for testing hypotheses have assumed that the form of the population distribution was known and that a test of some assumption about a parameter of the distribution was to be made. For example, methods were derived for testing values of μ and σ for a normal distribution and for testing values of p for a binomial distribution. The one exception occurred in Chapter 10 where the χ^2 distribution was employed to test the compatibility of a set of observed frequencies with a set of expected frequencies. Now, expected frequencies are often obtained without a knowledge of the distribution of the basic underlying variable. For example, in the contingency table problem it was not necessary to know how the two basic variables were distributed in order to test whether those variables were independent.

Situations often arise in which one has no knowledge of the distribution of the variable being studied or in which one knows definitely that it is not of the required type for applying the desired theory. For example, one may know that the variable possesses a distribution far different from a normal distribution, yet one would like to test whether the mean of the distribution has a specified value. Since small-sample methods require a normality assumption, the standard method would not be applicable to such a problem when only a small sample is available.

Methods have been designed to take the place of standard tests when the assumptions required by those tests are not satisfied. They are called nonparametric methods because they do not test parameter values of known population types, as in the case of the standard tests in the preceding chapters. Since nonparametric methods are more general than those requiring additional assumptions, it is to be expected that they will not be quite so good as the standard methods when both are applicable. These new methods should therefore be used only when a standard method is not appropriate.

The nonparametric methods that are presented in this chapter were chosen to solve some of the same types of problems solved earlier by parametric methods. There are quite a few other nonparametric tests available for these same problems and for other types of problems as well.

2. TESTING A MEDIAN

For nonparametric problems related to continuous variables the median is a more natural measure of location for a distribution than the mean. The median has the desirable property that the probability is $\frac{1}{2}$ that a sample value will exceed the population median, regardless of the nature of the distribution. As a result, it is possible to design tests for testing hypothetical values of the median without knowing what the underlying distribution is like. The simplest is the *sign test*. For the purpose of describing this test, consider the following data obtained from a city license bureau on the ages of bridegrooms applying for marriage licenses:

$$20, 42, 18, 21, 22, 35, 19, 18, 26, 20, 21, 32, 22, 20, 24.$$

Suppose that past experience in this section of the country has shown that the median age of bridegrooms is 25 years. Then a natural hypothesis to test here is that the median age for this particular community is also 25. If the median of the distribution is denoted by ξ, this hypothesis may be written in the form

$$H_0: \xi = 25.$$

It may be recalled from Chapter 2 that the distribution of ages of bridegrooms is heavily skewed to the right, and therefore it would be unreasonable to assume that a normal distribution exists here.

The first step in applying the sign test is to subtract the postulated median from each observed measurement and then record the sign of the corresponding difference. If 25 is subtracted from each of the foregoing observed values, the following signs will be obtained:

$$- + - - - + - - + - - + - - -$$

The next step is to count the number of + signs, denoted by x, and the total number of signs, denoted by n. Here, $x = 4$ and $n = 15$. If the hypothesis H_0 is true, the probability is $\frac{1}{2}$ that a + sign will be obtained when an observation is taken; consequently, the variable x represents the number of successes in n trials of an experiment for which the probability of success in a single trial is $p = \frac{1}{2}$. The problem has now been reduced to a binomial distribution problem of the type treated in Chapter 7.

Since popular opinion seems to indicate that "people are marrying earlier these days," the natural alternative hypothesis here is

$$H_1 : \xi < 25.$$

If the median of a distribution is smaller than the postulated value, then subtracting the postulated value from a set of observed measurements is likely to produce more negative than positive differences, hence a value of x that is smaller than expected under the hypothesis. Since small values of x favor the alternative hypothesis, the critical region of the test should be in the left tail of the binomial distribution.

Calculations by means of the binomial distribution formula given by (1), Chapter 4, with $n = 15$ and $p = \frac{1}{2}$, yielded the following probabilities:

$$P\{0\} = .000, \qquad P\{3\} = .014,$$
$$P\{1\} = .000, \qquad P\{4\} = .042.$$
$$P\{2\} = .003,$$

When these probabilities are summed, it follows that $P\{x \leq 4\} = .059$. Thus the observed value of $x = 4$ would be in the critical region if a critical region of size $\alpha = .059$ were selected, but it would not be in the critical region if a smaller value of α were selected.

If the normal approximation to the binomial distribution had been used here, one would have calculated

$$z = \frac{x - np}{\sqrt{npq}} = \frac{4.5 - 7.5}{\sqrt{15 \cdot \frac{1}{2} \cdot \frac{1}{2}}} = -1.55.$$

From Table IV in the appendix, $P\{z < -1.55\} = .06$, which agrees very well with the result obtained by calculating the necessary binomial probabilities.

The practical conclusions to be drawn here depend upon one's point of view. An individual who is convinced that people are marrying earlier these days will undoubtedly be satisfied with the choice of $\alpha = .059$ and thereby be justified in accepting the alternative hypothesis, which in the layman's language means that males are being caught earlier these days.

The problem that was just solved by nonparametric methods corresponds to the first hypothesis-testing problem considered in Chapter 7, which consisted of testing whether the mean of a normal distribution had a particular value. The next section considers a nonparametric analogue of the problem of testing whether the means of two normal distributions are equal.

3. TESTING THE DIFFERENCE OF TWO MEDIANS

Since the median is being used as a substitute for the mean as a location parameter in nonparametric problems, it is natural to test the difference of two medians rather than the difference of two means in nonparametric situations. This hypothesis may be written in the form

$$H_0 : \xi_1 = \xi_2,$$

in which ξ_1 and ξ_2 denote the medians of the two populations of interest. The nonparametric test that is introduced to solve this type of problem is called the *rank-sum test*. To illustrate how the test is applied, consider the following data on the number of trials required by rats to learn a certain task for a group of eight treated rats and a group of ten untreated rats:

T	24	28	15	47	23	25	53	20		
U	22	12	30	16	26	14	18	21	16	18

The two samples are first arranged together in order of increasing size. For the foregoing data this yields the following ordering, in which the entries from the treated group have been underlined:

12, 14, 15, 16, 16, 18, 18, 20, 21,

22, 23, 24, 25, 26, 28, 30, 47, 53.

These values are then replaced by their proper ranks to give

1, 2, 3, 4, 5, 6, 7, 8, 9,

10, 11, 12, 13, 14, 15, 16, 17, 18.

The next step is to sum the ranks of the smaller group (here the treated group). If this sum is denoted by R, it follows that the value of R will be given by summing the underlined ranks. For this problem, $R = 97$. The final step is to determine whether the value of R lies in the critical region of the test.

The sampling distribution of R, under the assumption that the two population distributions are identical, has been worked out by mathematical methods. The distribution of R depends, of course, upon the sizes of the two samples, which are denoted by n_1 and n_2. Here n_1 denotes the smaller of the two sample sizes. Table VIII in the appendix gives the desired critical values corresponding to various sample sizes for $n_2 \leq 10$. For larger sample sizes, the distribution of R can be approximated satisfactorily by the proper normal distribution. This is the normal distribution with mean and standard deviation given by the formulas

$$\mu_R = \frac{n_1(n_1 + n_2 + 1)}{2},$$

$$\sigma_R = \sqrt{\frac{n_1 n_2(n_1 + n_2 + 1)}{12}}.$$

For the problem being discussed it was expected that the treated rats would require a longer learning period than the untreated rats; therefore, the natural alternative hypothesis here is

$$H_1 : \xi_1 > \xi_2.$$

Under this alternative, R would tend to be larger than under H_0 because R is the sum of the ranks of the ξ_1 group of measurements; consequently, one should choose the critical region under the right tail of the distribution. From Table VIII it will be found that for $n_1 = 8$ and $n_2 = 10$ the probability is .051 that $R \geq 95$. Since $R = 97$ lies in the critical region, the hypothesis is rejected.

If the normal approximation had been used, one would have calculated

$$\mu_R = \frac{8(8 + 10 + 1)}{2} = 76$$

and

$$\sigma_R = \sqrt{\frac{8 \cdot 10(8 + 10 + 1)}{12}} = 11.3.$$

Then one would have calculated

$$z = \frac{R - \mu_R}{\sigma_R} = \frac{97 - 76}{11.3} = 1.86.$$

From Table IV in the appendix it will be found that $P\{z > 1.86\} = .03$. This result is in good agreement with that obtained by using Table VIII.

When $n_1 = n_2$, one may choose either group as the smaller for which R is to be computed. When the two groups of observations contain one or more common values, ties in ranking will occur. In such situations it suffices to give each set of equal observed values the rank that is the mean of the ranks occupied by them. This modification is not necessary for ties that occur in the same group.

Since the distribution of R was obtained on the assumption that the two population distributions were identical, one should really be testing the hypothesis that the two distributions are identical against the alternative that one of them has been shifted to the right. Two populations may have identical medians and yet differ in such a manner as to produce sample values of R that would regularly fall in the critical region of the preceding test. Thus it is not strictly correct to reject the hypothesis $H_0: \xi_1 = \xi_2$ when R falls in the critical region unless one is prepared to assume that the two distributions are identical except possibly for their locations. The foregoing test is often called a slippage test because it determines whether two distributions are identical against the possibility that one of them may have slipped relative to the other.

It is interesting to compare the rank-sum test for this problem with the corresponding parametric test that would be applied here if the two basic variables could be assumed to possess independent normal distributions. Since the sample sizes are rather small this comparison will be made by employing Student's t test as explained in section 3.1 of Chapter 7. This requires the assumption of equal variances for the variables in addition to the normality assumption. Calculations based on the formula of section 3.1 of Chapter 7 yielded the value $t = 2.18$. Since there are $v = 16$ degrees of freedom here, Table V shows that this value is very close to the .05 listed value, which means that it is close to the .025 value if one uses only the right tail of the t distribution for the critical region. This is very close to the probability value of .03 that was obtained by applying the normal distribution approximation to R for this problem.

The rank-sum test is known to be excellent for testing slippage. Even when there is justification in assuming that the two variables are independently normally distributed with the same variances, the rank-sum test does nearly as well as the Student t test, which was designed for this type of problem, in the sense of producing small type II errors. This property of being nearly as good as the t test when the latter is justified and being a valid test under all conditions makes the rank-sum test a very attractive test.

4. RANK CORRELATION COEFFICIENT

The problem of measuring the extent to which two variables are linearly related was considered in Chapter 8. There it was assumed that both variables were measured on a continuous scale. Furthermore, when testing whether the sample correlation coefficient was compatible with a postulated theoretical value, it was necessary to assume that the two variables were normally distributed. This assumption is a rather restrictive one; therefore, it would be desirable to have a test that requires no such assumption.

The problem of testing whether there is zero correlation between two variables is considerably easier to formulate and solve by nonparametric methods than the more general problem of testing whether the population correlation has any given postulated value; therefore, only the simpler problem is considered here.

A solution to the problem of testing for zero correlation between two variables has already been given in Chapter 10 in the section on contingency tables. There the χ^2 test was presented for testing whether the two variables of classification were independent variables. If two variables are independent, they are, of course, also uncorrelated. That method was very general in that it did not require the variables to be measurable on a continuous scale. It was merely necessary to be able to state categories, or groups, for the variables.

If the variables are capable of being measured on a continuous scale, as in correlation-coefficient problems, then it might be expected that the contingency table method of testing for independence could be improved upon, and this is the case.

The nonparametric analogue of the ordinary correlation coefficient is the *rank correlation coefficient*. As its name implies, it is merely the correlation coefficient calculated for the ranks of the variables rather than for the numerical values of the variables. Now, it can be shown by purely algebraic methods that when the x_i and y_i in the formula for r given by (1), Chapter 8, are treated as the ranks of the corresponding measurements then the formula reduces to

$$r = 1 - 6\frac{\sum_{i=1}^{n}(x_i - y_i)^2}{n(n^2 - 1)}.$$

Although the sample value of r obtained by means of this formula is usually close to the value obtained by means of the ordinary correlation coefficient based on measurements, the earlier theory about the distribution of r does not apply here. As a result, one cannot use the transformation $w = \frac{1}{2}\log_e(1 + r)/(1 - r)$ to test hypothetical values of r. However, under the assumption that the two variables are independent, the distribution of r can be obtained by mathematical methods without requiring a normality assumption. Table IX in the appendix gives 5 per cent and 1 per cent critical values of r for testing the hypothesis that the two variables are independent. This table is for one-sided tests; therefore, if it is used directly, one is testing the hypothesis of zero correlation against the alternative of a positive (or negative) correlation.

As in other tests based on ranks, it is customary to replace tied ranks by the mean rank of the ranks occupied by the equal measurements.

As an illustration of the use of the rank correlation coefficient for testing the indepencence of two variables, consider the following data on the ranking by two amateur judges of art of ten student paintings.

Judge A	7	4	5	8	2	10	1	9	6	3
Judge B	2	7	4	3	1	10	5	6	9	8

Taking the differences of these rankings, squaring, and summing will yield the value $\Sigma(x_i - y_i)^2 = 120$. As a result,

$$r = 1 - \frac{6(120)}{10(100 - 1)} = .27.$$

From Table IX, the 5 per cent critical value of r for $n = 10$ is .564. Since $r = .27$ is much too small to be significant, the hypothesis of independence is accepted. There is no evidence here that the two judges agree on what constitutes good painting. Since even professional art critics often disagree, it is not surprising to find two amateur judges disagreeing.

It should be noted that the nonparametric method applies only to testing whether there is zero correlation between the two variables, whereas the parametric method based on normality applies to testing any postulated correlation-coefficient value.

5. RUNS

In all the statistical methods of the preceding chapters it has been assumed that the data being used for estimation or hypothesis testing were obtained from drawing random samples from some stable population. If the sampled population changes with time and the samples are spread over time, it may be that the preceding assumptions are not justified. For example, if one were taking samples of the weights of chickens in a farming community every two weeks for six months, it is likely that one would tend to get heavier weights near the end of the sampling period because of the increase in weight of the younger growing chickens. As another illustration, stock-market prices over a period of time are obviously not capable of being treated as random samples from a stable population of prices.

When data have been taken over a period of time, and there is reason to believe that the observations may not be a random set of observations, it is advisable to apply a test that checks on the randomness assumption. One such test that is quite useful and easy to apply is based on runs. As an aid to explaining this test, consider the following set of measurements of the annual rainfall in inches for the last forty years in a certain western city:

20, 11, 16, 8, 9, 33, 14, 17, 12, 16, 23, 19, 12, 18,
21, 19, 11, 9, 15, 17, 15, 13, 22, 17, 38, 20, 14, 21,
16, 12, 25, 17, 20, 15, 23, 24, 14, 19, 13, 16.

The first step in applying the runs test to a set of measurements such as this is to find the median of the set. If these data are arranged in order of size, it will be found that there are twenty measurements less than or equal to 16 and twenty measurements greater than or equal to 17; hence the median is 16.5. Now each measurement in the set is replaced by the letter a if it is larger than the median and by the letter b if it is smaller than the median. Which two letters are used here is irrelevant; however, it is convenient to use a and b because a is associated with above the median and b with below the median. Since the median for the preceding set of measurements is 16.5, the replacement of the measurements by their appropriate letter yields the following set of letters:

$$a, b, b, b, b, a, b, a, b, b, a, a, b, a,$$
$$a, a, b, b, b, a, b, b, a, a, a, a, b, a,$$
$$b, b, a, a, a, b, a, a, b, a, b, b.$$

A sequence of identical letters that is preceded and followed by a different letter (or no letter if it is at the beginning or at the end of the entire sequence) is called a run. The length of the run is determined by the number of identical letters in the run. Thus, in the foregoing illustration, the first letter a is a run of length 1, and the next four letters (b's) constitute a run of length 4. The runs and their lengths for this illustration are

$$1, 4, 1, 1, 1, 2, 2, 1, 3, 3, 1, 2, 4, 1, 1, 2, 3, 1, 2, 1, 1, 2.$$

The test that is about to be presented depends only upon the total number of runs in the entire sequence, and therefore it is not concerned with the lengths of the runs. If the letter u is used to denote the total number of runs, then, if it is assumed that the sequence constitutes a random sample from some population, the distribution of the variable u can be obtained by fairly simple mathematical methods. This distribution will depend upon n_1 and n_2, which denote the number of a's and b's in the set. Since there is usually an equal number of a's and b's when they are obtained by determining whether measurements are above or below the median of the set, it would appear that either n_1 or n_2 alone would suffice. However, the test also applies to problems in which the a's and b's are obtained by different methods, and in some of these problems n_1 and n_2 may be quite different.

Table X in the appendix gives critical values of u corresponding to different values of n_1 and n_2. Since u is an integer, only integer values of u are listed in this table. The table entries consist of two integers. The smaller integer yields the left-tail critical value and the larger integer the right-tail critical value for a 5 per cent two-sided test. Each critical value is a $2\frac{1}{2}$ per cent critical value for a one-sided test. The critical region of the test therefore consists of those values of u equal to or smaller than the smaller integer and those values equal to or larger than the larger integer.

The value of α is usually slightly smaller than .05 because u assumes only integer values, with corresponding jumps in the probabilities.

For the problem being discussed, $n_1 = n_2 = 20$ and $u = 22$. From Table X it will be found that the 5 per cent critical values are given by $u = 14$ and $u = 28$. Since $u = 22$ does not fall in the critical region, the hypothesis of randomness is accepted. As far as the total number of runs is concerned, this sequence appears to behave like a typical random sequence.

Suppose annual rainfall had the tendency to run in fairly long cycles of dry and wet years. Since dry years would yield b's and wet years, a's, the annual rainfall data would then yield alternating sets of relatively long runs of a's and b's, with the result that the total number of runs would be considerably smaller than that expected under randomness. Thus the test based on total runs would be likely to discover this type of nonrandomness. As another possibility, suppose dry and wet years tended to alternate. Then the annual rainfall data would tend to yield a set of alternating a's and b's, with the result that the total number of runs would be excessively large, compared to that expected under randomness. The test based on total runs should be able to discover this type of nonrandomness also.

Neither of these types of nonrandomness appears to be present in the rainfall data just analyzed. This conclusion will, of course, disappoint amateur weather prophets. As far as the run test is concerned, the amount of rainfall during any year does not seem to depend upon the amounts of rainfall during the preceding years.

Although the runs test is effective in discovering certain types of non-randomness, there are many other types that go undetected when tested by means of total runs. For example, suppose one encountered a sequence of measurements that gave rise to the following sequence of a's and b's: *aabbaabbaabbaabbaabb*. Here $n_1 = n_2 = 10$ and $u = 10$. Table X gives the critical values (6, 16); therefore the value $u = 10$ must be fairly close to the mean of the u distribution and hence represents a very typical value to obtain under the randomness assumption. Most everyone meeting this sequence of a's and b's would, however, conclude that it was not a random sequence. The difficulty is that under randomness it can be shown that the average length of a run should be 2, and this is exactly the length of each run in the present sequence; therefore the total number of runs is certain to be about right. Any other type of nonrandomness in which the total number of runs is approximately half the total number of elements in the sequence will also fail to be detected by the runs test. Thus, it appears that this test is of somewhat limited value. There are other nonparametric tests available for testing randomness that are usually superior to the runs test; however, they are considerably more difficult to explain and apply, and therefore they are not studied here.

The foregoing nonparametric methods were selected to show how typical parametric problems can be solved by nonparametric methods. There are many other nonparametric techniques for these as well as for other types of problems.

EXERCISES

1. The following data represent the ages of burglars apprehended during the past year in a certain city. Test the hypothesis that the median age for burglars is 23 years, which is the age obtained from past experience, against the alternative that it is less than 23. In making the test, ignore the 23-year-old individuals. The ages are 24, 16, 18, 19, 18, 17, 26, 28, 23, 22, 19, 21, 21, 23, 17, 15, 21, 36, 18, 38, 19, 22, 23, 26, 21, 33, 21, 17, 26, 18.

2. In an elementary school seventeen pairs of first-grade children were formed on the basis of similarity of intelligence and background. One child of each pair was taught by reading method I and the other by method II. After a period of training, the children were given a reading test with the following results:

Method I	65 68 70 63 64 62 73 75 72 78 64 73 79 80 67 74 82
Method II	63 68 68 60 65 66 72 74 73 70 66 70 80 78 63 74 78

Taking differences of values and ignoring zero values, use the sign test to determine whether the two methods are equally effective.

3. The following data represent the number of red blood cells (million per cubic millimeter) for ten men and ten women. (a) Use the rank-sum test to see whether there is any difference between the sexes with respect to red blood cells. (b) Work the problem by using the normal approximation for this test.

Men	5.02 4.58 5.57 4.52 4.84 5.36 4.27 5.15 4.93 4.72
Women	4.15 4.56 3.89 4.40 4.38 4.20 4.31 4.73 4.26 3.95

4. Explain why the sign test applied to the differences of values in problem 3 would not be a satisfactory test to apply to such data.

5. These data represent the scores made on a grammar test by two groups of students. Group I students graduated from private schools, whereas Group II students are public-school graduates. Use the rank-sum test to test for equality of the medians.

I	25	30	28	34	24	25	13	32	24	30	31	36		
II	44	33	22	8	47	31	40	30	33	35	18	21	35	29	22

6. Work problem 2 by means of Student's t test, after taking differences, as explained in Chapter 7, and comment on the two outcomes.

7. Work problem 3 by means of Student's t test for the difference of two means, as explained in Chapter 7, and comment on the two outcomes.

8. At a county fair two judges ranked 12 jars of jam as follows:

Judge A	6	2	9	11	7	8	10	3	12	1	4	5
Judge B	5	7	4	10	2	11	8	6	9	3	12	1

Test to see whether there is any agreement between these judges by means of the rank correlation coefficient.

9. For the data of problem 2, replace the scores by their ranks and then use the rank correlation coefficient to test to see whether reading scores were affected by the method of pairing the children.

10. Work problem 1, Chapter 8, by changing the measurements to ranks and applying the rank correlation coefficient method.

11. How large a value of the rank correlation coefficient would be needed for a sample of size 20 before one would reject the hypothesis of no relationship? Compare this result with the corresponding result for the ordinary correlation coefficient based on normality and studied in Chapter 8. Assume $\alpha = .05$ for a one-sided test.

12. A row of snapdragon plants was inspected for rust. The sequence of healthy and infected plants was as follows: H H H H I H I I I H H I I H H H H H H H I I I I I. Use the test based on total runs to test for randomness of the infection.

13. Toss a coin 50 times, recording the sequence of heads and tails, and then test for randomness by means of total runs.

14. Write down a sequence of a's and b's totaling 50 letters that you feel is random. Test the randomness by means of total runs.

15. The following data represent the percentages of defective articles turned out daily by a single workman for a period of 25 consecutive working days. Use the total runs test for runs above and below the median to see if the sequence behaves like a random sequence.

Day	1	2	3	4	5	6	7	8	9	10	11	12	13
%	8.2	9.4	11.1	10.4	8.6	10.3	12.3	12.0	9.3	9.7	8.9	10.0	11.8

14	15	16	17	18	19	20	21	22	23	24	25
9.9	10.9	9.4	8.4	10.1	12.2	11.9	10.3	11.4	8.8	7.4	11.2

Analysis
of Variance

1. INTRODUCTION

Perhaps the problem that arises more frequently than any other in statistical work is that of testing whether two samples differ significantly with respect to some property. In Chapter 7 this problem was solved by testing the equality of two population means or two population proportions. In Chapter 11 it was solved by testing whether two population distributions were identical.

The reason this type of problem occurs so frequently is that experimentalists often design an experiment to compare a new technique or process with a standard one. For example, an educator may believe that he has discovered a better way of teaching foreign languages than that being used at his institution; or a chemist may have discovered a new plastic that he believes will be superior to the one being manufactured at his plant. In either case, an experiment would be designed to test whether the new method or material was in fact superior to the old one.

Situations often occur, however, in which there are several methods or products rather than just two that are competing against each other. For example, a manufacturer of cake mixes may vary the amount of a certain ingredient to obtain five different mixes that he would like to compare for quality. Or, a business firm may have four different calculating machines that it would like to compare with respect to performance.

Now it is usually very inefficient to compare several samples by comparing them two at a time. If one had, say, six samples to compare, there would be fifteen such comparison pairs. Furthermore, the probability associated with testing a single difference is no longer applicable when testing several differences simultaneously. Another disadvantage of the method based upon comparing only pairs of samples is that experimentalists who are accustomed to comparing only two samples at a time may be led into designing poor experiments to accomplish their ultimate objective. The manufacturer of cake mixes, for example, who changed only a single ingredient at a time and then retained only the better of two mixes each time might well miss out on a much better mix obtained by varying several ingredients by different amounts and considering various combinations of mixes simultaneously. In agricultural experiments that are concerned with testing different types and amounts of fertilizers and different seed varieties it has been found very inefficient not to consider different combinations of these quantities simultaneously.

In view of the foregoing discussion, it seems clear that a new method is needed to solve some of the problems related to several samples. One of the methods that has been designed to solve problems of this type for continuous variables is known as the *analysis of variance*. As the name might indicate, the method consists of analyzing the variance of the sample into useful components. Although the method has been developed to treat a wide variety of problems, only two of the easier applications are considered in this chapter.

2. ONE VARIABLE OF CLASSIFICATION

The simplest type of analysis-of-variance model is the one in which observations are classified into groups on the basis of a single property. For example, in studying the marketing weights of rabbits, one might wish to classify rabbits on the basis of the number in a litter; or, in studying the degree of political conservatism in voters, one might wish to classify voters on the basis of income.

For the purpose of explaining the analysis-of-variance technique, consider the data of Table 1. These data represent the scores made by 24 soldiers in an experiment to determine whether shooting accuracy is affected by methods of sighting: (a) with the right eye open, (b) with the left eye open, (c) with both eyes open. Twenty-four soldiers were selected at random from a certain training base and then split into three equal groups corresponding to the three sighting methods. After each group had become familiar with its sighting method, the experiment was conducted by allowing each participant to shoot the same number of rounds at a target.

If there is no advantage in one sighting method over either of the others, these scores could be treated as those of 24 randomly selected soldiers who used any one of the three sighting methods. It is assumed that such scores are normally distributed. However, if the three sighting methods are not equally good, it is necessary to modify the normality assumption to the extent of assuming that each of the three sighting methods has its own normal distribution of scores. In problems like

TABLE 1

Right	Left	Both
44	40	51
39	37	47
33	28	37
56	53	52
43	38	42
56	51	63
47	45	46
58	60	62

this, when differences occur they usually occur in the means rather than in the standard deviations; therefore, it is assumed that the standard deviations of the three normal populations are equal.

If the population means corresponding to the three sighting methods are denoted by μ_1, μ_2, and μ_3, then the problem reduces to one of testing the hypothesis

$$H_0: \mu_1 = \mu_2 = \mu_3.$$

The foregoing assumptions are the same as those made in Chapter 7 for testing the equality of two means by small-sample methods and which permitted the use of Student's t distribution. Unfortunately that distribution cannot be used in solving the present problem and therefore a new approach is needed. Such an approach can be based on comparing two different estimates of the common variance, σ^2, of the three populations.

If the hypothesis H_0 is true the classification of the data into three columns is meaningless and the entire set of measurements can be treated as a sample of size 24 from a normal population. If σ^2 denotes the variance of this population, an estimate of σ^2 can be obtained by means of the familiar sample variance based on those 24 measurements. However, there are several other ways of obtaining valid estimates of σ^2. For example, the sample variance of the first column of measurements is a valid estimate of σ^2 although it is not nearly as good as the estimate based on all the measurements. Similarly, the sample variances of the second and third columns are also valid estimates of σ^2. Furthermore, the mean of the three column estimates is a valid estimate of σ^2 and nearly as good as the familiar estimate based on combining the three sets of measurements. If s_1^2, s_2^2, and s_3^2 denote the sample variances for the three columns, this last estimate, which will be denoted by V_c, is

$$(1) \qquad\qquad V_c = \frac{s_1^2 + s_2^2 + s_3^2}{3}.$$

The subscript c is used here to indicate that the estimate is based on the column variances.

Another quite different type of estimate of σ^2 can be obtained by using the relationship between the variance of a sample mean and the variance of the population, namely $\sigma_{\bar{x}}^2 = \sigma^2/n$. It is convenient here to express this relationship in the form

$$(2) \qquad\qquad \sigma^2 = n\sigma_{\bar{x}}^2.$$

Suppose several samples of size n each have been taken from some population. If the sample means have been calculated, then the sample variance of those sample means will be a valid estimate of $\sigma_{\bar{x}}^2$. In general, the sample variance of a set of measurements is a valid estimate of the population variance of the measurements regardless of whether those measurements happen to be simple measurements, or means of simple measurements, or other functions of simple measurements. From (2) it follows that if an estimate of $\sigma_{\bar{x}}^2$ is available, it may be multiplied by n to yield an estimate of σ^2. In the present problem there are three such sample means that may be used to construct an estimate of $\sigma_{\bar{x}}^2$. They are the three column means, which will be denoted by $\bar{x}_1$, $\bar{x}_2$, and $\bar{x}_3$. If $\tilde{x}$ denotes the mean of those three column means, then an estimate of $\sigma_{\bar{x}}^2$ is given by $\sum_{i=1}^{3}(\bar{x}_i - \tilde{x})^2/2$. Since those means are based on samples of size 8 each, it follows that $n = 8$ and hence from (2) that the desired estimate of σ^2 is given by

$$(3) \qquad V_m = 8 \, \frac{\sum\limits_{i=1}^{3}(\bar{x}_i - \tilde{x})^2}{2} \, .$$

The subscript m is used here to indicate that the estimate is based on the means of the columns.

Since V_c and V_m are both valid estimates of σ^2 when H_0 is true, it follows that they should be approximately equal in value, and therefore that their ratio should have a value close to 1. If, however, H_0 is not true and the column means differ considerably, the two estimates V_c and V_m will be seen to differ considerably in value. Because the estimate V_c is based on calculating the variances of each column separately, it will be unaffected by changing the means of the various columns, for the variance of a set of measurements is independent of the value of their mean. It is clear from (3), however, that the estimate V_m will be directly affected and will increase in value as the sample means move apart. Thus it appears that the ratio of V_m and V_c will differ considerably from 1 when H_0 is not true. This ratio will be used as the desired quantity for testing the hypothesis H_0. It is denoted by the letter F; hence

$$(4) \qquad F = \frac{V_m}{V_c} \, .$$

The discussion thus far has been mostly of the qualitative type, stating that F can be expected to have a value close to 1 when H_0 is true and to have a value considerably larger than 1 when H_0 is not true and the population means differ widely. This information is not sufficient for constructing a test based on probability; it is necessary to know what the distribution of F is before such a test can be performed.

Just as in the case of other sampling distributions, it is possible to approximate the distribution of F by carrying out repeated sampling experiments of the type being considered here and constructing the histogram of the resulting F values; however, the exact sampling distribution of F can be obtained by mathematical methods. It turns out that the distribution of F depends only upon how many data were available for the numerator estimate of σ^2 and how many were available for the denominator estimate. Table XI in the appendix lists the 5 per cent and the 1 per cent right-tail critical values of F corresponding to different values of the parameters ν_1 and ν_2, which are called the number of degrees of freedom in the numerator and denominator of F.

The degrees of freedom here are those that one would naturally associate with the sample variances being used. Since the number of degrees of freedom for the usual estimate of σ^2 is given by $\nu = n - 1$, or one less than the number of measurements, the number of degrees of freedom for the numerator of F in this problem is given by $\nu_1 = 2$ because the estimate is based on the three sample means. The number of degrees of freedom for the denominator of F in this problem is $\nu_2 = 21$ because each column variance contributes 7 degrees of freedom and all three column variances are employed.

Now return to the particular problem that motivated the preceding discussion. Calculations with the data of Table 1 yield the values $\bar{x}_1 = 47$, $\bar{x}_2 = 44$, $\bar{x}_3 = 50$, $s_1{}^2 = 81.1$, $s_2{}^2 = 106.3$, and $s_3{}^2 = 82.3$. As a result, it follows from (1) that $V_c = 89.9$. Additional calculations yield the value $\Sigma(\bar{x}_i - \tilde{x})^2/2 = 9$; hence it follows from (3) that $V_m = 72$. The value of F is therefore given by

$$F = \frac{V_m}{V_c} = \frac{72}{89.9} = .80.$$

From Table XI it will be found that the 5 per cent critical value of F corresponding to $\nu_1 = 2$ and $\nu_2 = 21$ is 3.47. Since $F = .80$ for this problem, the hypothesis is accepted. The data are in agreement with the view that accuracy of shooting is not affected by which of the three sighting methods is used. It would not have been necessary to consult Table XI for this problem because F values in the neighborhood of 1 are to be expected when H_0 is true, and therefore a value of $F < 1$ could not possibly lie in the critical region of large F values.

Although the approach used to arrive at the F variable for testing the hypothesis that a set of column means are equal seems quite different from that used in Chapter 7 for testing the equality of two column means, it can be shown that the F test, when applied to testing the equality of two column means, is equivalent to the t test for the same problem. Thus, the test based on F is a generalization of the earlier two column test based on t.

The foregoing problem is a special case of more general problems of this type, in which one has, say, r rows and c columns of data and in which one wishes to test the hypothesis that the column population means are equal. For the purpose of considering such problems, it is convenient to introduce the following notation.

Let x_{ij} denote the ith measurement in the jth column of a table of measurements, of which Table 1 is a special case. Let r denote the number of rows, and c the number of columns in this table. This notation is displayed in Table 2.

TABLE 2

$$
\begin{array}{ccccc}
x_{11} & x_{12} & \cdots & x_{1j} & \cdots & x_{1c} \\
x_{21} & x_{22} & \cdots & x_{2j} & \cdots & x_{2c} \\
\cdot & \cdot & & \cdot & & \cdot \\
\cdot & \cdot & & \cdot & & \cdot \\
\cdot & \cdot & & \cdot & & \cdot \\
x_{i1} & x_{i2} & \cdots & x_{ij} & \cdots & x_{ic} \\
\cdot & \cdot & & \cdot & & \cdot \\
\cdot & \cdot & & \cdot & & \cdot \\
\cdot & \cdot & & \cdot & & \cdot \\
x_{r1} & x_{r2} & \cdots & x_{rj} & \cdots & x_{rc} \\
\hline
\bar{x}_{.1} & \bar{x}_{.2} & \cdots & \bar{x}_{.j} & \cdots & \bar{x}_{.c}
\end{array}
$$

The mean of the jth column measurements is denoted by the symbol $\bar{x}_{.j}$. The dot is placed in front of the j to indicate that the mean was obtained from summing on the index i (rows). In section 3 it is necessary to sum over columns as well; therefore, some notation such as this is needed to keep straight whether one is summing over rows or columns.

In terms of this new notation, the numerator of F is given by the formula

(5)
$$
V_m = r \frac{\sum_{j=1}^{c} (\bar{x}_{.j} - \bar{x})^2}{c - 1}.
$$

Here $\bar{x}$ denotes the mean of the column means, which is the same as the mean of the entire set of measurements. It replaces $\tilde{x}$, which was used earlier in (3). The quantity $\Sigma(\bar{x}_{.j} - \bar{x})^2/(c - 1)$ is an estimate of $\sigma_{\bar{x}.j}^2$, where $\bar{x}_{.j}$ denotes a typical column mean based on r measurements. The application of formula (2) with $n = r$ to this situation yields formula (5).

In terms of this same notation, the denominator of F is given by the formula

(6)
$$
V_c = \frac{\sum_{j=1}^{c} \sum_{i=1}^{r} (x_{ij} - \bar{x}_{.j})^2}{c(r - 1)}.
$$

The quantity $\Sigma(x_{ij} - \bar{x}._j)^2/(r - 1)$ is the sample variance of the measurements in the jth column. If it is denoted by s_j^2, then (6) can be written in the form

$$\frac{s_1^2 + s_2^2 + \cdots + s_c^2}{c}.$$

Thus (6) corresponds to (1) and gives the mean of the column variances. The ratio of (5) and (6) supplies the desired F variable, with the degrees of freedom given by $v_1 = c - 1$ and $v_2 = c(r - 1)$; hence

(7)
$$F = \frac{rc(r - 1)}{c - 1} \frac{\sum\limits_{j=1}^{c}(\bar{x}._j - \bar{x})^2}{\sum\limits_{j=1}^{c}\sum\limits_{i=1}^{r}(x_{ij} - \bar{x}._j)^2}.$$

3. TWO VARIABLES OF CLASSIFICATION

The foregoing analysis-of-variance problem was relatively simple because there was only one classification variable, namely the method of sighting. In an experiment of this type one could consider many other variables that might influence the accuracy of shooting. For example, one might compare different positions of firing, different brands of guns, or different brands of bullets. Analysis-of-variance methods have been designed to treat any number of classification variables; however, the discussion here is limited to two such variables. The methods for more than two variables are very similar to those for two variables.

The problem that was considered in section 2 can be modified to yield a problem that would normally be solved by the methods of this section. Assume that instead of having drawn a random sample of 24 soldiers from the base a random sample of only 8 soldiers had been drawn. Then it would have been necessary for each of the 8 soldiers to become acquainted with all three methods of sighting. After that, each soldier would have been instructed to fire the same number of rounds with each of the three sighting methods. Thus the three scores in the first row of Table 1 would represent the three scores made by the first soldier. In such an experiment one would randomize the order in which the different sighting methods were employed by the marksmen so that none of the methods would have an advantage with respect to practice.

The second variable of classification here is the individual. Since it is well known that there is large variation in the skill of individuals in shooting, it would seem desirable to control this feature of the variability of scores so that any differences that might be caused by the different sighting methods could be recognized. Large individual differences among the 24 soldiers of the earlier experiment might obliterate any moderate differences arising because of the different sighting methods.

In the two-variable analysis-of-variance setup one assumes that each of the variables x_{ij} in Table 2 is an independent normal variable with a common variance σ^2. This means, for example, that in repeated gunnery experiments of the type being discussed the same 8 soldiers would use each of the three sighting methods each time the experiment was run. This differs from the one-variable of classification setup in which fresh sets of 24 soldiers would be selected each time. For the two-variable situation it is also necessary to make a few more assumptions about the basic variables, but these assumptions are not discussed here.

Just as in the earlier method, one finds two estimates of the common variance σ^2 and then uses the ratio of the two estimates to obtain an F value. The method of finding such estimates is based upon taking the natural variance estimate and analyzing it into useful components. This procedure gave rise to the name "analysis of variance." The natural variance estimate for Table 2 is the quantity

$$\frac{\sum_{i=1}^{r} \sum_{j=1}^{c} (x_{ij} - \bar{x})^2}{rc - 1}.$$

Only the numerator of this estimate is used in the following analysis. Now it can be shown by simple algebraic manipulations that the following formula holds:

$$(8) \quad \sum_{i=1}^{r} \sum_{j=1}^{c} (x_{ij} - \bar{x})^2 = \sum_{i=1}^{r} \sum_{j=1}^{c} (\bar{x}_{i.} - \bar{x})^2 + \sum_{i=1}^{r} \sum_{j=1}^{c} (\bar{x}_{.j} - \bar{x})^2$$

$$+ \sum_{i=1}^{r} \sum_{j=1}^{c} (x_{ij} - \bar{x}_{i.} - \bar{x}_{.j} + \bar{x})^2.$$

It can also be shown that each of the three sums of squares on the right side of (8), if divided by the proper constant, is a valid estimate of σ^2 when it is assumed that there are no real differences in the row means or the column means. These three estimates are

$$V_r = \frac{\sum\limits_{i=1}^{r}\sum\limits_{j=1}^{c}(\bar{x}_{i\cdot} - \bar{x})^2}{r - 1} = c\,\frac{\sum\limits_{i=1}^{r}(\bar{x}_{i\cdot} - \bar{x})^2}{r - 1},$$

$$V_c = \frac{\sum\limits_{i=1}^{r}\sum\limits_{j=1}^{c}(\bar{x}_{\cdot j} - \bar{x})^2}{c - 1} = r\,\frac{\sum\limits_{j=1}^{c}(\bar{x}_{\cdot j} - \bar{x})^2}{c - 1},$$

$$V_e = \frac{\sum\limits_{i=1}^{r}\sum\limits_{j=1}^{c}(x_{ij} - \bar{x}_{i\cdot} - \bar{x}_{\cdot j} + \bar{x})^2}{(r - 1)(c - 1)}.$$

The subscripts here on V refer to rows, columns, and experimental error. The expression for V_c is precisely the same as that for V_m given by (5). The expression for V_r is similar, except that it measures row variation rather than column variation; therefore, if there are large differences in shooting skill among soldiers, this quantity will tend to be considerably larger than if there were no individual differences. The expression for V_e essentially measures the variation in the data after the variation caused by column differences and row differences has been eliminated. It serves as an estimate of σ^2 unaffected by sighting differences and individual differences.

For the purpose of testing the hypothesis that all the theoretical column means are equal, the estimates to use are V_c and V_e. Thus the test reduces to computing the value of F given by

(9)
$$F = \frac{r(r - 1)\sum\limits_{j=1}^{c}(\bar{x}_{\cdot j} - \bar{x})^2}{\sum\limits_{i=1}^{r}\sum\limits_{j=1}^{c}(x_{ij} - \bar{x}_{i\cdot} - \bar{x}_{\cdot j} + \bar{x})^2},$$

$$\nu_1 = c - 1, \qquad \nu_2 = (r - 1)(c - 1).$$

The values of ν_1 and ν_2 in F are always the denominators needed to make the corresponding sums of squares valid estimates of σ^2. The mathematical theory for this problem shows that the F distribution is valid here whether or not there are real differences in the row means.

In the two-variable scheme it is also possible to test the hypothesis that the theoretical row means are equal, which implies that there are no differences among the 8 soldiers with respect to shooting skill. Here one uses the estimates V_r and V_e, and one forms the F ratio given by

(10)
$$F = \frac{c(c-1)\sum\limits_{i=1}^{r}(\bar{x}_{i.} - \bar{x})^2}{\sum\limits_{i=1}^{r}\sum\limits_{j=1}^{c}(x_{ij} - \bar{x}_{i.} - \bar{x}_{.j} + \bar{x})^2},$$
$$\nu_1 = r - 1, \qquad \nu_2 = (r-1)(c-1).$$

In view of the fact that the more sources of variation one can control in an experiment the more likely one is to detect differences of experimental interest, the F test based on eliminating variation due to individual differences in shooting skill and given by formula (9) should be a more delicate test than the one used in section 2 and given by formula (7). For the purpose of comparing these two tests, consider the application of formula (9) to the data of Table 1.

The numerator sum of squares is the same as in the earlier test; therefore, its numerical value need not be computed. It is usually easier to compute the denominator sum of squares by means of formula (8) than it is to compute it directly from its definition. Thus one computes the left side of (8) as well as the first two sums of squares on the right side and then obtains the desired sum of squares by subtraction. Earlier computations gave

$$\sum_{i=1}^{8}\sum_{j=1}^{3}(\bar{x}_{.j} - \bar{x})^2 = 8(18) = 144.$$

The first sum of squares on the right side of (8) was computed in the same manner as the second sum of squares. Computations for the data of Table 1 yielded the values

$$\sum_{i=1}^{8}\sum_{j=1}^{3}(x_{ij} - \bar{x})^2 = 2032,$$

and

$$\sum_{j=1}^{3}\sum_{i=1}^{8}(\bar{x}_{i.} - \bar{x})^2 = 1768.$$

Consequently, formula (8) yields the value

$$\sum_{i=1}^{8}\sum_{j=1}^{3}(x_{ij} - \bar{x}_{i.} - \bar{x}_{.j} + \bar{x})^2 = 2032 - 1768 - 144 = 120.$$

The value of F as given by formula (9) then becomes

$$F = \frac{8 \cdot 7(18)}{120} = 8.4,$$
$$\nu_1 = 2, \qquad \nu_2 = 14.$$

From Table XI it will be found that the 5 per cent critical value of F corresponding to $\nu_1 = 2$ and $\nu_2 = 14$ is 3.74. Since $F = 8.4$ is in the critical region, the hypothesis H_0 is rejected.

The conclusion here is contrary to that made for the same data in section 2. Actually, the data for Table 1 were obtained for a group of 8 soldiers; consequently, only the second method is applicable here. The first method required that the scores should be those for 24 randomly selected soldiers. The purpose of using the same data for both methods was to point out the similarities and the differences of the two methods and to stress the fact that it usually pays to introduce important classification variables in the analysis of variance technique if one wishes to obtain a delicate test for testing a set of theoretical means. If there had been no appreciable individual differences in shooting skill, nothing would have been gained by designing the experiment to measure and eliminate this source of variation in the test, in which case the method in section 2 would have been preferable. The application of formula (10) shows, however, that $F = 29.5$, $\nu_1 = 7$, $\nu_2 = 14$. Since the 5 per cent critical value of F is 2.77, this means that there is large variation in the row means, hence large variation in individual shooting skill.

4. COMPUTING FORMULAS

If a calculating machine is available for obtaining the sums of squares that are needed to apply the F test, it is usually best to use formulas that require one to find only sums and sums of squares of the entries of Table 2. These calculating formulas can be obtained by simple algebraic manipulations. The first two of the following formulas are those needed for (7), whereas all the formulas with the exception of (12) are needed for (9) and (10).

$$(11) \qquad \sum_{j=1}^{c}(\bar{x}_{\cdot j} - \bar{x})^2 = \frac{1}{r^2}\sum_{j=1}^{c}\left(\sum_{i=1}^{r}x_{ij}\right)^2 - \frac{1}{r^2 c}\left(\sum_{j=1}^{c}\sum_{i=1}^{r}x_{ij}\right)^2$$

$$(12) \qquad \sum_{j=1}^{c}\sum_{i=1}^{r}(x_{ij} - \bar{x}_{\cdot j})^2 = \sum_{j=1}^{c}\sum_{i=1}^{r}x_{ij}^2 - \frac{1}{r}\sum_{j=1}^{c}\left(\sum_{i=1}^{r}x_{ij}\right)^2$$

$$(13) \qquad \sum_{i=1}^{r}(\bar{x}_{i\cdot} - \bar{x})^2 = \frac{1}{c^2}\sum_{i=1}^{r}\left(\sum_{j=1}^{c}x_{ij}\right)^2 - \frac{1}{c^2 r}\left(\sum_{i=1}^{r}\sum_{j=1}^{c}x_{ij}\right)^2$$

$$(14) \qquad \sum_{i=1}^{r}\sum_{j=1}^{c}(x_{ij} - \bar{x})^2 = \sum_{i=1}^{r}\sum_{j=1}^{c}x_{ij}^2 - \frac{1}{rc}\left(\sum_{i=1}^{r}\sum_{j=1}^{c}x_{ij}\right)^2.$$

For the purpose of illustrating the use of these computational formulas, a second set of experimental data will be analyzed by means of the analysis of variance technique. The data are displayed in Table 3 and represent the yields of potatoes on four plots of ground, each of which was divided into five subplots. For each plot five different fertilizers were assigned at random to the five subplots. The problem is to test whether the five fertilizers are equally effective with respect to mean yield.

Calculations will yield the following sums:

$$\sum_{i=1}^{4} \sum_{j=1}^{5} x_{ij} = 6320, \qquad \sum_{i=1}^{4} \sum_{j=1}^{5} x_{ij}^{2} = 2{,}018{,}650.$$

Additional calculations will yield the values

$$\sum_{j=1}^{5} \left(\sum_{i=1}^{4} x_{ij} \right)^{2} = 8{,}039{,}328, \qquad \sum_{i=1}^{4} \left(\sum_{j=1}^{5} x_{ij} \right)^{2} = 10{,}017{,}750.$$

As a result, formulas (11), (13), and (14) yield

$$\sum_{j=1}^{5} (\bar{x}_{.j} - \bar{x})^{2} = \frac{8{,}039{,}328}{16} - \frac{(6320)^{2}}{80} = 3178$$

$$\sum_{i=1}^{4} (\bar{x}_{i.} - \bar{x})^{2} = \frac{10{,}017{,}750}{25} - \frac{(6320)^{2}}{100} = 1286$$

$$\sum_{i=1}^{4} \sum_{j=1}^{5} (x_{ij} - \bar{x})^{2} = 2{,}018{,}650 - \frac{(6320)^{2}}{20} = 21{,}530.$$

The denominator sum of squares in (9) can now be obtained by means of formula (8). Thus

$$\sum_{i=1}^{4} \sum_{j=1}^{5} (x_{ij} - \bar{x}_{i.} - \bar{x}_{.j} + \bar{x})^{2} = 21{,}530 - 5(1286) - 4(3178)$$

$$= 2388.$$

The value of F in (9) is therefore given by

$$F = \frac{4 \cdot 3 \cdot 3{,}178}{2388} = 16.0$$

$$\nu_{1} = 4, \qquad \nu_{2} = 12.$$

From Table XI it will be found that the 5 per cent critical value of F corresponding to $v_1 = 4$ and $v_2 = 12$ is 3.26. Since $F = 16.0$ is in the critical region, the hypothesis that the fertilizers are equally effective is rejected. Fertilizers E and C appear to be superior to the other fertilizers.

TABLE 3

Fertilizer

		A	B	C	D	E
	1	310	353	366	299	367
Plot	2	284	293	335	264	314
	3	307	306	339	311	377
	4	267	308	312	266	342

The method presented in section 2 is easily generalized to apply to the situation in which the number of measurements in the various columns is not the same. It is also fairly easy to generalize the methods of section 4 so that they apply to the situation in which one has several measurements in each cell of Table 2. A more complicated generalization occurs when one extends these methods to the situation in which there are several variables of classification; however, the methods are quite similar to those just explained.

EXERCISES

1. The following data give the yield of a chemical product that resulted from trying 4 different catalysts in the chemical process. Use formula (7) to test to see whether yields are influenced by the catalysts.

I	II	III	IV
36	35	35	34
33	37	39	31
35	36	37	35
34	35	38	32
32	37	39	34
34	36	38	33

2. The following data give the yields of wheat on some experimental plots of ground corresponding to 4 different sulfur treatments for the control of rust. The treatments consisted of dusting before rains, dusting after rains, dusting once each week, and no dusting. Test to see if there are significant differences in yields due to the dusting methods.

Dusting Method

	1	2	3	4
1	5.3	4.4	8.4	7.4
2	3.7	5.1	6.0	4.3
3	14.3	5.4	4.9	3.5
4	6.5	12.1	9.5	3.8

(Plot, rows 1–4)

3. The following data represent the number of units of production per day turned out by 5 workmen using 4 different types of machines. (*a*) Test to see whether the mean productivity is the same for the 4 different machine types. (*b*) Test to see whether the 5 men differ with respect to mean productivity. Use formulas (9) and (10) here.

Machine Type

	1	2	3	4
1	44	38	47	36
2	46	40	52	43
3	34	36	44	32
4	43	38	46	33
5	38	42	49	39

(Workman, rows 1–5)

4. Work problem 2 by the two-variable method to see whether eliminating the variation due to plots will affect the test.

5. For the data of Table 3 in the text, test to see whether there are plot differences in yield.

6. For the data of Table 3, use formula (7) to test whether the fertilizers are equally effective; that is, ignore plot differences.

7. If the number of measurements in the jth column of Table 2 in the text is denoted by n_j and if the n_j are not all equal, then formula (6) in the text must be replaced by the formula

$$V_c = \frac{\sum_{j=1}^{c} \sum_{i=1}^{n_j} (x_{ij} - \bar{x}_{.j})^2}{\sum_{j=1}^{c} (n_j - 1)}.$$

(*a*) Explain how this formula reduces to (6) when the n_j are equal. (*b*) Show that this formula is a weighted mean of the column variances.

8. For the situation of problem 7, formula (5) in the text must be replaced by the formula

$$V_m = \frac{\sum_{j=1}^{c} n_j(\bar{x}_{.j} - \bar{x})^2}{c - 1}.$$

(a) Explain the equivalence of this formula to (5) when the n_j are equal. (b) Explain why this formula is the natural generalization of (5) for unequal n_j.

9. For the following data on the scores made by pupils taught arithmetic by three different methods, use the formulas of Problems 7 and 8 to form the appropriate F test and test for equality of column means.

	Methods	
116	132	108
117	137	96
138	131	131
100	108	130
125	111	111
130	130	126
134	140	
124		
114		

10. In problem 2 use Student's t test to determine whether dusting had any effect upon yield. That is, combine the data for the first three columns and treat the measurements as though they were a sample of size 12 from a normal population. The last column measurements may be treated as a sample of size 4 from a second normal population.

C H A P T E R 13

Time Series
and Index Numbers

1. INTRODUCTION

The statistical methods that have been presented in the preceding chapters require the use of random samples for making the appropriate estimate or decision. Unfortunately, many sets of observations that have been taken over a period of time do not behave like random samples from some stable population. This is particularly true of certain sets of economic data, such as the price of stocks, the cost of living, or the consumption of tobacco. As a consequence, standard statistical techniques cannot be applied to such data. It is the purpose of this chapter to consider methods for treating data of this type.

A set of observations taken over a period of time is called a time

TABLE 1

Gross Private Domestic Investment in Billions of Dollars,
Based on 1958 Prices, for the Years 1929–1958

1929—40.6	1939—25.1	1949—45.4
1930—27.8	1940—33.4	1950—64.4
1931—17.3	1941—42.3	1951—66.9
1932—4.9	1942—21.7	1952—58.6
1933—5.1	1943—12.9	1953—59.1
1934—9.1	1944—14.5	1954—56.7
1935—18.3	1945—20.1	1955—72.1
1936—24.6	1946—49.0	1956—73.1
1937—31.0	1947—48.8	1957—67.0
1938—18.0	1948—57.2	1958—53.5

278

TABLE 2

Call-Money Rates from 1860 to 1934 for the Month of January

6.7	7.2	2.1	2.7	2.4	3.3
5.8	5.5	4.2	4.2	3.0	4.3
6.5	2.8	3.7	3.1	2.6	4.3
6.1	5.8	3.3	4.6	2.1	4.2
7.0	5.4	7.7	5.8	1.9	7.1
7.0	9.8	3.9	2.3	2.1	4.6
5.5	3.1	2.4	2.2	4.1	1.6
7.2	5.0	4.0	8.6	4.8	2.6
5.6	4.8	1.0	6.2	8.2	1.0
12.0	5.4	1.4	4.8	6.7	1.0
6.2	4.5	4.9	1.8	4.6	
6.5	1.9	1.8	4.7	4.3	
8.8	1.2	2.5	3.2	4.4	

series. Economists in particular have studied such series extensively because so many of the interesting problems of economics involve them. They have also been studied in the physical sciences in connection with periodic phenomena of various kinds. A few illustrations of time-series data are given in Tables 1, 2, and 3.

The graphs of these three time series, in which neighboring points

TABLE 3

Annual Precipitation in Inches for Los Angeles
from 1878 to 1957

21	19	21	11	15	8
17	22	15	20	14	11
19	8	14	15	18	7
6	13	24	6	18	14
11	12	5	8	27	25
14	14	18	9	12	4
40	5	10	19	20	14
11	9	17	19	31	12
17	11	23	9	7	14
16	12	17	8	23	13
21	13	23	13	17	
33	15	8	19	13	
13	12	17	11	16	
13	19	9	19	4	

have been joined by straight-line segments, are given in Figs. 1, 2, and 3. The first two are typical economic time series, whereas the third should be of interest to anyone concerned about the weather and its predictability. The series given by Tables 2 and 3 will be used to illustrate some of the methods that are applied in time-series analysis. They were chosen because of their length and because they differ considerably in some of their properties.

In studying time series, the first question that needs to be answered is whether the series really depends upon time. A number of statistical tests, such as the one in Chapter 11 based on runs, can be used to answer this question.

If it is quite certain that the series is time dependent, the next step is to estimate the nature of this dependence upon time. Since only the larger movements of the series over time are of major interest, this means fitting a fairly smooth curve to the graph of the series, similar to the fitting of a regression line to a set of points, as explained in Chapter 9. Regression methods are available for obtaining such an estimate; however, another method based on moving averages is commonly employed to carry out this estimation.

After the major portion of the dependence of the series on time has been estimated, the final problem is to determine whether the resulting relationship can be used to predict the future course of the series with any reliability. The ability to predict the future of economic time series is, of course, the dream and desire of every economist. Many statistical techniques have been proposed for making such predictions; some of these are discussed briefly in a later section.

The preceding three phases in the study of time series are considered in their natural order in the following sections.

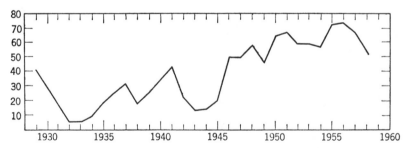

Fig. 1   The graph of private domestic investments for 1929 to 1958.

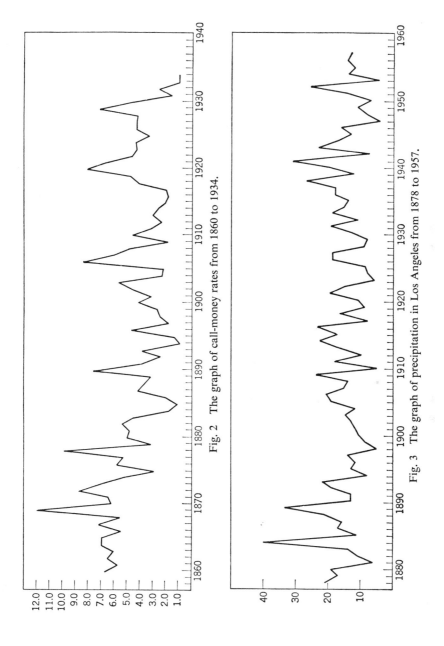

Fig. 2   The graph of call-money rates from 1860 to 1934.

Fig. 3   The graph of precipitation in Los Angeles from 1878 to 1957.

2. TESTS

It is often clear by merely inspecting their graphs that many familiar time series are changing in a fairly regular manner with time. For example, if the series consisted of the weekly height measurements of a growing plant, it is obvious that the measurements would be time-dependent because they would be increasing with time. The graph of the purchasing power of the dollar for the last fifty years would also be expected to show a strong dependence on time because, as any old-timer will tell you, the value of the dollar has been shrinking over that period of time. However, if the series consisted of the yields of common stocks, the production of coal, or the percentage of the laboring force employed, all taken annually during the last fifty years, then it is not so clear that there would be a definite dependence on time.

The difficulty with inspecting the graph of a time series, and thereby trying to determine whether the series behaves like a random sample from some stable population or whether it depends upon time, is that the variation of a random series will often deceive one into believing that the series is dependent on time. Most individuals looking at a time series tend to see regular patterns of movement in the series, whether such regularity is present or not. For example, if one lets his imagination have a free hand, he will undoubtedly see some fairly regular movements in the series shown graphically in Fig. 4. This series was obtained by taking random samples from a normal population with zero mean and unit standard deviation, and therefore there should be no time dependence in it. The data that yielded Fig. 4 are given in Table 4. For series that are not obviously time dependent, it is necessary to apply some statistical test for randomness before one is justified in proceeding further in the analysis

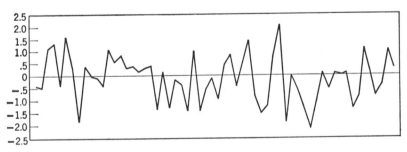

Fig. 4   The graph of random samples from a standard normal population.

TABLE 4

Random Samples Taken from a Standard Normal Population

−.4	−.1	−1.4	−.9	2.1	.0
−.5	−.4	.2	.5	−1.9	.1
1.1	1.1	−1.3	.8	.0	−1.3
1.3	.6	−.2	−.4	−.6	−.8
−.4	.8	−.3	.5	−1.4	1.1
1.7	.3	−1.4	1.5	−2.2	.2
.3	.4	1.0	−.8	−1.0	−.8
−1.9	.2	−1.4	−1.5	.1	−.4
.4	.3	−.5	−1.2	−.5	1.1
.0	.4	−.1	.8	.1	.3

of the series. In selecting a randomization test, it is desirable to consider what alternatives to randomization should be postulated; therefore, such alternatives are considered next.

For many years students of time-series analysis have been concerned principally in determining whether cycles exist in various economic time series. The more ardent advocates of business-cycle analysis attempt to decompose a time series into a long-time trend, cycles, and random effects. The seasonal variation in a time series, which would be found, for example, in monthly department-store sales, is not treated as a business cycle and is often removed from the series before studying the series. To qualify as a business cycle, the cycle should normally exceed a year in length.

In view of the preceding remarks, the natural alternative to randomness in an economic time series is a dependence on time that may involve a long-time trend, together with some reasonably long cycles. This is illustrated in the sketch shown in Fig. 5, which was constructed by taking

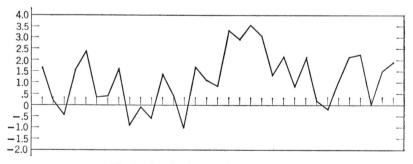

Fig. 5   Graph of an artificial time series.

a two-wave cycle and superimposing it upon a straight-line trend and then adding some random deviations. The data corresponding to this sketch are given in Table 5. In this table one reads down columns to obtain consecutive values. It would be very naïve, of course, to expect an actual economic time series to possess a strict cycle; all that can be hoped for is that there will be some fair degree of approximation to one or more cycles. It would be more realistic to speak of the type of cycle considered in economic time-series analysis as an undulation or oscillation rather than as a cycle, because the latter term implies regular recurrence and such regularity is seldom found in economic data.

TABLE 5

Artificial Time Series Consisting of a Trend, a Cycle,
and Random Deviations

1.7	.4	.4	2.9	2.1	.0
.2	1.6	−1.0	3.6	.2	1.5
−.4	−.9	1.7	3.1	−.2	1.9
1.6	−.1	1.1	1.3	1.1	
2.4	.6	.8	2.2	2.2	
.3	1.3	3.3	.8	2.3	

Now that some more or less intuitive notions as to what constitutes reasonable alternatives to randomness in economic time series are available, it is time to consider appropriate tests for randomness. This is done in the next section.

2.1 Runs

One of the simplest tests to determine whether a time series behaves like a random sequence is that based on the total number of runs, denoted by u, in the series. This test is described in section 5 of Chapter 11. Since most economic time series that are studied contain a large number of terms, the large sample normal approximation for the statistic u, which is described in Table X in the appendix, is ordinarily used to make the test.

If an alternative existed of the type discussed in the preceding section and illustrated in Fig. 5, there would be a tendency for long runs of a's and b's to occur, hence for the total number of runs, u, to be smaller than expected under randomness. This property of the test is discussed further in the last paragraph of this section. In applying the runs test to economic time series one therefore uses a one-sided test with the critical region containing only small values of u. Since the large-sample normal approximation formulas are

$$\mu_u = \frac{2n_1n_2}{n_1 + n_2} + 1$$

and

$$\sigma_u = \sqrt{\frac{2n_1n_2(2n_1n_2 - n_1 - n_2)}{(n_1 + n_2)^2(n_1 + n_2 - 1)}},$$

it follows that the critical region for this test should consist of those values of z satisfying the inequality $z < -1.64$, in which

$$z = \frac{u - \mu_u}{\sigma_u}.$$

As an illustration of how to apply this test, consider the data of Table 3. The median for those data will be found to be 14. If those years in which the precipitation was 14 inches are ignored, the values in Table 3 will give rise to the following sequence of a's and b's, where a denotes a value above the median and b denotes a value below the median and where the sequence has been arranged in rows rather than in columns:

$a, a, a, b, b, a, b, a, a, a, a, b, b, a, a, b, b, b, b, b, b, b, b, a, b, a, a,$
$a, a, b, a, b, a, a, a, a, b, a, b, b, a, a, b, b, b, a, a, b, b, b, a, b, a, a,$
$a, a, a, b, a, a, b, a, a, b, a, b, b, b, b, a, b, b, b.$

The total number of runs in this sequence is 34; hence $u = 34$. Since the number of a's and b's is given by $n_1 = 37$ and $n_2 = 36$, the formulas for the mean and standard deviation of u yield

$$\mu_u = 37.5$$

$$\sigma_u = 4.24.$$

The value of z corresponding to $u = 34$ is therefore

$$z = \frac{34 - 37.5}{4.24} = -.83.$$

Since the critical region for this test consists of those values of z satisfying $z < -1.64$, this result is not significant. On the basis of the runs test, the precipitation for Los Angeles from 1878 to 1957 behaves like a random sequence; hence it constitutes a time series that appears to be independent of time. This test is made slightly more accurate if u is replaced by $u + \frac{1}{2}$. The $\frac{1}{2}$ correction is similar to the same kind of correction employed in applying a normal approximation to the binomial distribution. This correction will yield the value $z = -.71$ in place of $-.83$.

As a second illustration, consider the application of this test to the data of Table 2. The median for those data will be found to be 4.3. If the years for which the rate was 4.3 are ignored, the Table 2 values will give rise to the following sequence of a's and b's:

$a, a, a, a, a, a, a, a, a, a, a, a, a, a, a, b, a, a, a, b, a, a, a, a, b,$
$b, b, b, b, b, a, b, b, b, b, b, a, b, b, b, b, b, a, a, b, b, a, a, a, b,$
$a, b, b, b, b, b, b, b, b, a, a, a, a, a, b, b, a, a, b, b, b, b.$

The total number of runs here is 20; hence $u = 20$. Since $n_1 = 37$ and $n_2 = 35$ here, the mean and standard deviation formulas yield

$$\mu_u = 37.0$$
$$\sigma_u = 4.21.$$

The value of z corresponding to $u = 20$, when using the $\frac{1}{2}$ correction, is therefore

$$z = \frac{20.5 - 37.0}{4.21} = -3.92.$$

Since this value of z is in the critical region of the test, the hypothesis of randomness is rejected in favor of a dependence of the series on time, which produces too few runs. If a horizontal line at the median height of 4.3 is drawn on the graph of Fig. 2, it will be observed that the first one-third of this series lies mostly above this line, whereas the remaining two-thirds of the series contains several fairly long sections lying below this line. Thus the lack of randomness appears to be caused partly by an early downward trend in the series and partly by a persistence of the series to remain low, or high, for several years at a time.

If a series possesses a long upward, or downward, trend, the total number of runs will tend to be small because of a few long runs at the beginning of the series and at the end of the series. If the series possesses a cycle that is fairly long in terms of the time between observations, the total number of runs will again tend to be small because most of the runs will be longer than expected under randomness. This tendency is illustrated in Fig. 5. Thus it appears that either a trend or cyclical movements will give rise to a small number of total runs. If a significant value of u is obtained, an inspection of the graph of the series will often reveal which of these two causes is operating or whether both are present. It is possible to eliminate the necessity of such geometrical judgments by applying a test that responds to a trend but that is relatively unaffected by cyclical movements. Thus one can frequently determine whether a lack of randomness, as indicated by the runs test, is due to cyclical movements only or whether a trend is also present. A number of tests other than that based on runs for testing randomness in a time series can be used, but they are not quite so easy to explain, and therefore they are not included here.

3. ESTIMATION

If the runs test, or any similar test, has verified that the time series being studied does depend on time, then the next phase of the investigation is to estimate this time dependence. Now most economic time series are quite erratic in appearance, so that it is difficult to determine by inspection any underlying regularity that may exist. Since short-term variation is of little interest and, except for seasonal variation, is not likely to possess enough regularity to be meaningful anyway, one attempts to estimate the longer movements only. The problem, therefore, is to eliminate the erratic and short-term fluctuations so that the remaining long-range dependence on time can be recognized.

3.1 Smoothing by Means of Moving Averages

One of the favorite methods for eliminating erratic and short-term movements in a time series is that of moving averages. As its name implies, successive averages are computed in moving along in the series. An operation that eliminates erratic and short-term movements is called a *smoothing* operation because it tends to make the graph of the time series appear smooth. Thus moving averages are basically smoothing devices. The number of terms used in a moving average will determine the degree of smoothness that results. Ordinarily, the more terms one uses in the average, the smoother the outcome.

Let the terms of the time series be denoted by $x_1, x_2, x_3, \ldots, x_n$. Then, for example, the three-term moving-average series is constructed from it by taking successive averages of three consecutive terms and placing the average opposite the middle term of the three terms being averaged. The first few terms in such a moving-average series, together with their location with respect to the original series, would be

$$x_1$$

$$x_2 \qquad \frac{x_1 + x_2 + x_3}{3}$$

$$x_3 \qquad \frac{x_2 + x_3 + x_4}{3}$$

$$x_4 \qquad \frac{x_3 + x_4 + x_5}{3}$$

$$\cdot \qquad \cdot$$
$$\cdot \qquad \cdot$$
$$\cdot \qquad \cdot$$

A twelve-term moving average is often used on economic time series that consist of monthly data because a moving average of this length is especially effective in smoothing out seasonal variation as well as erratic variation. The terms of a moving average of this type should be located halfway between the sixth and seventh terms used in the average; however, for the sake of convenience, the average is usually placed opposite the seventh term. A more precise location method is to take the mean of two consecutive twelve-term moving averages and place it opposite the seventh term of the thirteen terms involved in the two moving averages. Although this device gives the correct location of such terms, it requires additional lengthy computations, and, since it seldom alters the moving-average series appreciably, it is usually omitted. A similar convention of placing the average opposite the first term beyond the middle is often used for other moving averages based on an even number of terms. Shorter moving averages, such as a five-term moving average, are usually long enough to eliminate erratic variation and produce satisfactory smoothness and are to be preferred when working with annual data or with nonseasonal data.

To illustrate the smoothing effects of moving averages, a three-term and also a nine-term moving average were computed for the data of Table 2. The computations needed for moving averages are most easily carried out by first finding the proper sums by addition and subtraction. For example, after the first sum, $x_1 + x_2 + x_3$, is obtained for a three-term moving average, the next sum, which is $x_2 + x_3 + x_4$, is obtained by adding x_4 and subtracting x_1 from the preceding sum. This technique of adding the next term of the time series and subtracting the first element of the moving average sum to obtain the next sum for the moving average is especially helpful when computing, say, a twelve-term moving average.

The computations for the first ten terms of the three-term moving average of Table 2 would proceed as follows:

x	Sum of 3 Terms	Average
6.7		
5.8	19.0	6.3
6.5	18.4	6.1
6.1	19.6	6.5
7.0	20.1	6.7
7.0	19.5	6.5
5.5	19.7	6.6
7.2	18.3	6.1
5.6	24.8	8.3
12.0	23.8	7.9
6.2	24.7	8.2
6.5	.	.
.	.	.
.	.	.
.	.	.

The results of these computations, together with similar computations for the rest of the series of Table 2, are given in Table 6 and are displayed graphically in Fig. 6. The three-term moving average appears to have eliminated much of the erratic variation in the series; however, there is still a considerable amount of short-term variation remaining. Similar calculations for a nine-term moving average yielded the data of Table 7 and the graph displayed in Fig. 7. This smoothing operation has certainly eliminated most of the short-term variation that still remained after the three-term moving average was applied.

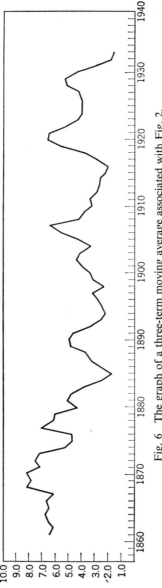

Fig. 6   The graph of a three-term moving average associated with Fig. 2.

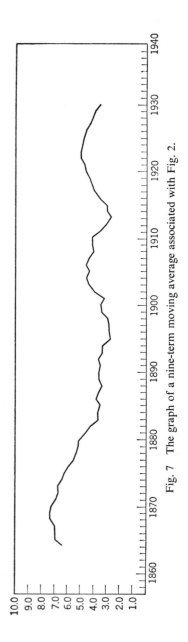

Fig. 7   The graph of a nine-term moving average associated with Fig. 2.

TABLE 6

Three-Term Moving Average Applied to Table 2

6.3	5.2	3.3	3.3	2.7	4.0
6.1	4.7	3.7	4.0	2.6	4.3
6.5	4.7	4.9	4.5	2.2	5.2
6.7	7.0	5.0	4.2	2.0	5.3
6.5	6.1	4.7	3.4	2.7	4.4
6.6	6.0	3.4	4.4	3.7	2.9
6.1	4.3	2.5	5.7	5.7	1.7
8.3	5.1	2.1	6.5	6.6	1.5
7.9	4.9	2.4	4.3	6.5	
8.2	3.9	2.7	3.8	5.2	
7.2	2.5	3.1	3.2	4.4	
7.5	1.7	2.3	3.4	4.0	
7.2	2.5	3.1	2.9	4.0	

TABLE 7

Nine-Term Moving Average Applied to Table 2

6.4	5.9	3.4	3.5	2.9	4.9
7.0	5.5	3.6	3.2	2.6	4.8
7.0	5.3	3.6	4.0	2.9	4.6
7.0	5.2	3.5	4.4	2.9	4.2
7.3	5.1	3.6	4.6	3.5	4.0
7.3	4.6	3.4	4.4	3.9	3.7
7.2	4.2	3.3	4.6	4.1	3.4
6.9	3.6	2.7	4.4	4.3	
6.7	3.6	2.8	4.0	4.6	
6.7	3.5	2.8	4.1	4.7	
6.4	3.8	2.9	4.1	5.0	
6.1	3.6	3.4	3.4	5.0	

3.2 Weaknesses of Moving Averages

Although Figs. 6 and 7 would seem to indicate that moving averages are very effective in smoothing a time series and thus enable one to estimate the underlying long-range time dependence of a time series, there are several properties of moving averages that must be understood before one can hope to use them intelligently.

Moving averages tend to deflate, or depress, the magnitude of oscillations in a series. The larger the number of terms employed in the average, the greater the deflation. A comparison of Figs. 2, 6, and 7 will show how the high oscillations of the original series are damped somewhat by the three-term moving average and are thoroughly deflated by the nine-term moving average. Thus, the greater the degree of smoothing, the less realistic the resulting movements.

Not only do moving averages deflate the magnitudes of movements, but they also anticipate rapid changes before the changes occur. For example, the large rise in call-money rates for the year 1869, corresponding to the tenth point of Fig. 2, showed its effect on the three-term moving average for the year 1868, which corresponds to the eighth point of Fig. 6. Thus one would receive the impression from the moving average that the money rate suddenly rose one year in advance of its actual rise. This effect is due to the fact that the three-term moving average for 1868 uses the data for 1867 and 1869 and thus is heavily influenced by the large 1869 value. Of course, if moving averages have a tendency to anticipate rapid changes, they must also have a tendency to prolong such changes.

Although the two preceding properties of moving averages are not at all desirable, they can be taken into account when interpreting such averages. A third property that can cause considerable difficulty is the tendency of moving averages to produce cyclical movements in data, even though such movements do not exist in the original data. For example, if one starts with a set of random data and applies a moving average to it, one may generate a new series that appears to have fairly regular cyclical movements in it. The practical implication of this property of moving averages is that the business analyst who uses moving averages to smooth his data, while in the process of trying to discover business cycles, is likely to come up with some nonexistent cycles.

As an illustration of this tendency of moving averages to produce what appear to be cyclical movements in data, a five-term moving average was applied to the data of Table 4. Since these data are random samples from a standard normal population, there is no time dependence in the data, and therefore there are no underlying cyclical movements present. An inspection of Fig. 4 certainly does not reveal any systematic movements in these data, although some cycle enthusiasts with clairvoyant powers might discern some regularity. The results of applying a five-term moving average to the data of Table 4 are shown in Fig. 8. This graph seems to show some rather pronounced oscillations. A comparison of this graph with that of Fig. 6 would seem to indicate that there is not a great deal of difference between the degree of regularity of movement in

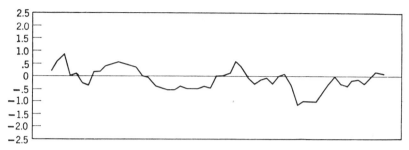

Fig. 8   The graph of a five-term moving average associated with Fig. 4.

the two series; yet the series giving rise to Fig. 8 is a random series, whereas that giving rise to Fig. 6 is an actual economic time series.

Some of the minor faults of moving averages can be remedied to a considerable extent by introducing weighted moving averages. Instead of calculating the mean of, say, five consecutive terms for a five-term moving average, one might attach weights such as 1, 2, 4, 2, 1 to the respective terms on the grounds that the middle term should have the greatest influence on the average that is to replace it. These weights are quite arbitrary, and other sets of weights could have been chosen. Weighted moving averages, such as this one, do not deflate a time series nearly so much as a simple moving average does. Furthermore, they do not stretch out the influence of a sudden change so much as a simple moving average of the same number of terms. They are, however, subject to the same weakness as simple moving averages in that they tend to introduce spurious cyclical movements.

In view of the earlier discussion about the cycle-producing effects of moving averages, it follows that one needs to show extreme caution in claiming cyclical movements in a time series merely because they appear to exist in the moving-average series. It is necessary to check the original series very carefully for any movement that was suggested by a moving average applied to the series. There are methods available for checking on postulated cyclical movements, one of which is discussed very briefly in section 4. Thus it is possible to circumvent the cycle-producing effects of moving averages.

The estimation of the larger movements of a time series by means of moving averages is quite subjective because the estimate depends considerably on the number of terms used in the moving average. For example, the estimate given by Fig. 6 differs considerably from that given by Fig. 7, yet the same series is being estimated in each case. An estimate such as that given by Fig. 7 should be looked upon as an estimate of an underlying structure that is not defined explicitly and whose economic interpretation is often obscure. Such an estimate differs from the customary estimates of statistics that have been studied in the preceding chapters because one cannot state explicitly what is being estimated and how accurate the estimate is. Nevertheless, moving averages are very useful in helping one to eliminate the uninteresting features of a time series and thus assist in the study of more basic features of the series.

If a mathematical model has been postulated for the underlying structure of a time series, then it is possible to determine the accuracy of the estimate given by a moving average. Methods have been developed in the physical sciences for treating this problem; however, the mathematical models that are postulated there are seldom very realistic for economic time series. As a consequence, moving-average methods in economic studies are usually treated as a combined qualitative-quantitative tool rather than as a strictly quantitative one.

The student may wonder why regression methods, similar to those employed in Chapter 9, are not used to estimate the underlying structure of a time series. It is easy to generalize the least-squares method used for fitting a straight line to a set of points to fit a more general type of curve to the graph of a time series. The difficulty is that no simple class of curves will suffice to fit most time-series graphs because of the extremely variable nature of such graphs. The computations become exceedingly lengthy for any curve that is likely to do a satisfactory job of fitting the points, although this objection is becoming less serious now that elaborate high-speed computing facilities are available. A more serious criticism is that there is seldom any good economic justification for picking a particular type of curve to fit the data.

3.3 Adjustment for Seasonal Variation

In the preceding discussions of time series only annual data were considered. If the series consists of monthly data and if one wishes to estimate only the more important movements in the series, it is desirable to eliminate first any seasonal variation that may be present. A second reason for eliminating seasonal variation is that one can study short-term trends more easily when pronounced seasonal fluctuations are missing. For example, suppose one wished to know whether department-store sales were increasing during

TABLE 8

	J	F	M	A	M	J	J	A	S	O	N	D
1951	96	90	98	99	103	99	84	93	112	112	134	184
1952	83	83	92	103	108	105	84	98	112	120	134	196
1953	85	88	103	115	108	108	89	98	112	115	136	192
1954	83	86	89	110	106	106	88	98	112	118	137	200

1954, as compared to earlier years, and that only the data of Table 8 were available. It is difficult to inspect Table 8 and determine whether sales during 1954 are rising or falling because of the heavy seasonal pattern in sales; it would be much easier to do so if the seasonal variation were not present.

One of the simplest methods for eliminating seasonal variation is to apply a twelve-term moving average to the series. However, if one does not wish to smooth the data this much, this method is not completely satisfactory. There are methods that are not subject to the smoothing criticism and that, at the same time, yield more reliable results. One of the most popular of these methods is discussed next.

Consider the problem of adjusting the data of department-store sales (index values) shown in Table 8 for seasonal variation. This means replacing each monthly sales index by a value that will represent what the sales are that month if allowance is made for seasonal variation. The mechanics of the proposed method is explained first, after which the reasoning behind the method is given.

One first applies a twelve-term moving average to the data, centering each value opposite the seventh term in the average. As explained in section 3.1, a more precise location method is available, but it hardly justifies the extra computational labor involved. More data than those shown in Table 8 are needed to find moving averages for the first half year of 1951 and the last half year of 1954. Such additional data obtained from other sources were used to compute the moving averages for Table 8. The results of those computations are given in Table 9. These values represent approximate average yearly sales for the middle of the year located at the indicated month.

TABLE 9

	J	F	M	A	M	J	J	A	S	O	N	D
1951	109	108	108	107	108	109	109	108	107	106	107	107
1952	108	108	108	108	109	109	110	110	110	111	112	112
1953	113	113	113	113	113	113	112	112	112	111	110	110
1954	110	110	110	110	110	110	111	111	111	111	111	111

TABLE 10

	J	F	M	A	M	J	J	A	S	O	N	D
1951	88	83	91	93	95	91	77	86	105	106	125	172
1952	77	77	85	95	99	96	76	89	102	108	120	175
1953	75	78	91	102	96	96	79	88	100	104	124	175
1954	75	78	81	100	96	96	79	88	101	106	123	180
Means	79	79	87	98	96	95	78	88	102	106	123	175

Each entry in Table 8 is now divided by its corresponding entry in Table 9 and multiplied by 100 to yield the set of crude seasonal-index numbers shown in Table 10.

The next step in the adjustment consists in calculating a mean seasonal index for each month. This is accomplished by calculating the mean of each column in Table 10. These means are shown in the last row of Table 10. If the means do not total 1200 it is necessary to adjust them until they do. In this illustration the means sum to 1206; hence one should multiply each mean by 1200/1206. Since 1206 differs from 1200 by only $\frac{1}{2}$ per cent, this refinement has been ignored here because the other computations have been carried only to the nearest 1 per cent. The resulting means are called *seasonal index numbers* because they represent average monthly rate of sales. If the index numbers were divided by 12, they would yield an average percentage of annual sales corresponding to each month.

The final step in the seasonal adjustment is to divide each entry in Table 8 by the correct monthly seasonal index number from Table 10, treating the latter as decimal fractions. For example, all the entries in the January column of Table 8 would be divided by .79 because 79 is the seasonal index number for January in Table 10. The resulting values, which are shown in Table 11, represent sales for the corresponding dates when allowance is made for seasonal variation.

TABLE 11

Seasonally Adjusted Department-Store Sales

	J	F	M	A	M	J	J	A	S	O	N	D
1951	122	114	113	101	107	104	108	106	110	106	109	105
1952	105	105	106	105	112	111	108	111	110	113	109	112
1953	108	111	118	117	112	114	114	111	110	108	111	110
1954	105	109	102	112	110	112	113	111	110	111	111	114

Data that have been adjusted for seasonal variation enable one to determine whether a series is increasing or decreasing during the period of a year without being deceived by apparent increases or decreases caused by natural seasonal variation. Thus one is not able to compare the sales for November and December of 1953 and determine whether department-store sales are really picking up, or dropping, because the annual Christmas buying splurge masks any underlying increase or decrease. The adjusted values of Table 11, however, show that there might have been a very slight decrease then, when account is taken of the natural seasonal variation in the data.

The reasoning behind the foregoing adjustment methods runs somewhat as follows. Suppose the value of any entry in Table 8 is assumed to be expressible as the product of three quantities: (1) a number that represents the underlying basic series value, (2) a number that represents the seasonal-index value, and (3) a number that represents the erratic, or random, part of the series, all for the date in question. If these components are denoted by B, S, and E, respectively, then the value of the entry is assumed to be given by $B \cdot S \cdot E$.

The application of a twelve-term moving average to a series of this kind will usually eliminate most of the seasonal component (S) and also most of the erratic component (E), and leave the underlying basic component (B) only slightly changed. Thus the entries in Table 9 represent estimates of B values. Since the first step in the preceding adjustment is to divide the original series values by their twelve-term moving-average values, the resulting series should consist essentially of $S \cdot E$ values because one is essentially performing the division $B \cdot S \cdot E/B$. Thus the entries in Table 10 are estimates of $S \cdot E$ values. Since the seasonal (S) values for a given column of this table are constant, by taking the mean of the column, most of the erratic component (E) will be eliminated, thereby leaving only the desired S value. This follows from the assumption that the erratic element E should possess a mean of 1 because it is a factor of series terms and that therefore the mean of a sample of such quantities should be close to 1. Thus the entries in the last row of Table 10 represent estimates of S values. Finally, if the original series values ($B \cdot S \cdot E$) are divided by their S values, the resulting series should represent $B \cdot E$ values, that is, original series values with the seasonal component eliminated.

The assumption that a time series can be decomposed into the product of three such factors is sometimes replaced by the assumption that the series can be expressed as the sum of three such components. In the preceding adjustment method one would then subtract quantities rather than divide them.

4. PREDICTION

There are two major reasons for attempting to estimate the principal movements of an economic time series. First, it is hoped that the estimate will reveal trends and oscillations that can be accounted for on the basis of reasonable economic factors. Economists would like to be able to explain the larger oscillations of economic time series on the basis of economic theory. It would be rather frustrating to them to find that such series were not reacting to the impact of supposedly important economic factors. Thus the analysis of economic time series is a kind of laboratory work for economists who are interested in explaining the dynamics of economic systems.

The second major interest in the estimation of economic time-series movements is the hope that the estimate can be used for predicting the future course of the series. Predicting the stock market with some degree of reliability would, of course, satisfy most individuals, but few time-series analysts are optimistic enough to believe that they can do much with such a sensitive and variable series.

An estimate that has been obtained by means of a moving average is useful for studying the effects of economic factors in the past, but it is not capable of predicting the future unless some method for extending the smoothed series is given. Various methods have been suggested for analyzing the smoothed series further so that it can be extended into the future. For many years the commonest method of performing such an analysis was that of decomposing the series into various parts such that the sum, or the product, of the parts would yield the original series. This is similar to what was done in section 3.3 in explaining the logic behind the seasonal adjustment procedure. These parts, or components, have usually consisted of a trend, cycles, and erratic elements. For monthly data, seasonal variation is usually eliminated first in a manner such as that described in section 3.3.

If a series can be decomposed into the sum (or product) of such components, then it is easy to extend the series into the future by merely extending the trend and the cycles and adding (or multiplying) the extended components.

The possibility of decomposing a series in this manner is discussed first for artificial series and then for economic series. Methods for treating economic time series have evolved from those that were created for handling periodic data in the physical sciences, which in turn were patterned after techniques for analyzing artificial series.

4.1 Artificial Time Series

If a time series has been built up from strictly mathematical components, as in the artificial series shown in Fig. 5, then methods exist for decomposing the series into its basic parts. The major difficulty is, of course, to discover the lengths of the underlying cycles. One simple method for attempting to do this is based on serial correlation. By *serial correlation* is meant the correlation between pairs of values of a time series that are a fixed distance apart. The fixed distance between pairs of values is called the *lag*. In speaking of serial correlation, it is always necessary to specify the lag. One might state, for example, that the value of the serial-correlation coefficient with lag 6 is .7. As before, let $x_1, x_2, x_3, \ldots, x_n$ denote the n terms of a time series and consider what is meant by the serial-correlation coefficient with lag k, where k is any positive integer.

First, one lists the x values in a column and then opposite each x value the value in the time series that is k time intervals further along in the series. For a general time series, this listing would assume the following form:

$$
\begin{array}{cc}
x & y \\
x_1 & x_{1+k} \\
x_2 & x_{2+k} \\
x_3 & x_{3+k} \\
\cdot & \cdot \\
\cdot & \cdot \\
\cdot & \cdot
\end{array}
$$

The second-column values are treated as the y values in calculating the ordinary correlation coefficient between the two columns of values. Since there will be no y terms available to associate with the last k values of x, the last k pairs are ignored in the calculations.

Suppose a time series consisted of a strict cycle such as that displayed in Fig. 9. Then if one chooses a lag of 8, which is the number of time units between the high points on two consecutive waves and also the distance between pairs of points that occupy the same relative position on two

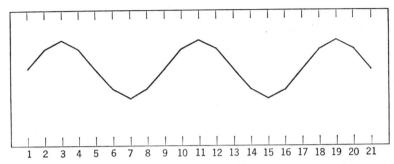

Fig. 9   A cylical series of period 8.

neighboring waves, the x and y values in the preceding listing would be identical. For example, the value of x_7 is the distance up to the trough on the first wave, whereas x_{15} is the distance up to the trough on the second wave; therefore, these two values are identical. But when corresponding x and y values are equal, the value of the correlation coefficient is 1. If a lag of 16 had been chosen, the same conclusion would have been obtained; however, there would have been considerably fewer pairs of values available for calculating the correlation coefficient with this lag. Thus it appears that a value of the serial correlation coefficient with lag k which is near to 1 may indicate the existence of a cycle with a distance of approximately k time units or some simple fraction of k, such as $k/2$ or $k/3$, between crests of neighboring waves. Other possibilities could also give rise to a value near 1, but they have been ignored here.

In order to be able to use serial correlation to discover cyclical components in a series, it is necessary to calculate the value of the serial-correlation coefficient for all lags from $k = 1$ up to the largest value of k that is considered reasonable and possible. The graph of these serial-correlation-coefficient values as a function of the lag is called the *correlogram*. From it one can observe the lags that seem to correspond to cycles in the series. If there are several different cycles hidden in the time series, the correlogram might be expected to show a value close to 1 for those lags that correspond to the cycles, and it should have small, or negative, values for lags that are not close to cycle lags. Serial-correlation methods have proved very useful in the physical sciences for discovering cycles and for analyzing the nature of certain types of time series.

After the lengths of the cycles have been discovered in an artificial time series, which consists of, say, a trend and the sum of several cyclical components plus some random deviations, it is not difficult to decompose the series. One such method, for example, is based on applying the proper moving averages to the series and isolating one cyclical component at a time.

4.2 Economic Time Series

The preceding discussion was concerned with a technique that has been used in the decomposition of a mathematical time series. The interesting question, of course, is whether methods such as this one, which have been designed for ideal series, are also capable of decomposing economic time series. The answer, unfortunately, is that these methods are successful only if the series is quite regular in behavior. The serial-correlation technique, for example, will discover a cyclical movement only if it is fairly regular. Similarly, moving averages will be effective in the decomposition of a series only if the components are quite stable.

In most economic time series the distance between crests of waves is usually highly variable, so that even the larger movements would not respond very well to the serial-correlation and moving-average techniques of decomposition. Furthermore, the erratic component is often very large compared to much of the oscillation, with the result that even fairly regular movements are often masked out by such irregularities. In view of the lack of stability in most economic time series, it is not surprising to learn that the decomposition methods designed for physical phenomena have not proved very effective when applied to economic data. Economic time series are much more difficult to treat than those encountered in the physical sciences.

Because of the failure of the physical sciences' decomposition methods to yield reliable forecasts for economic time series, economists have devised their own decomposition techniques. The most popular of these assumes that a time series can be expressed as a product of four components, which will be devoted by the letters T, C, S, and E, and which are called trend, cyclical, seasonal, and erratic components. Another popular model assumes that these four components are added rather than multiplied to produce the series. Since a sum can be expressed as a product by means of logarithms, it will suffice to discuss the product model only. Thus, assume that the value of any term in a time series can be obtained from the corresponding term in the product $T \cdot C \cdot S \cdot E$. This model differs from the one introduced in section 3.3 only in that the quantity B there has been expressed as the product of a trend component T and a cyclical component C. The latter component is conceived of as being made up of various business cycles.

The first step in the decomposition of this product is to determine the trend factor T. If the word trend is understood to mean the overall upward or downward tendency of the series, then T is treated as a linear function of the time t and it can be found by fitting a straight line to the points of the graph of the time series. The formulas for doing this are available in the chapter on regression. The second step in the decomposition is to divide the time series values by their corresponding fitted straight line values. This will yield the values of $C \cdot S \cdot E$. One can now proceed to determine the seasonal component S and the cyclical component C by means of the techniques used in section 3.3, because C merely plays the role of B there. Since the erratic component E can be determined by division, all four components are now determined.

After the decomposition has been performed, the problem is how to use it to predict future values of the series. The predicted value of T is obtained by substituting the desired value of t in the equation of the fitted straight line. The corresponding value of S is also readily obtained from the table of S values that results from determining the seasonal component. Since the erratic component is assumed to be unpredictable, it is ignored. The remaining cyclical component C is also unpredictable unless further assumptions are made concerning its nature. If it is assumed to be made up of several fairly regular cycles, then one can try to determine the nature of those cycles and project them forward to the desired point in time to obtain a predicted C value. The product of the three predicted component values would then yield the desired forecast of the series.

Although the preceding analysis sounds promising, the difficulty lies in forecasting the value of C because, for most economic time series, this component cannot be expressed in terms of regular cycles. This is precisely why the decomposition methods of the physical sciences failed on economic time series. Unless C can be expressed satisfactorily in terms of a few fairly well defined business cycles, there is not much that one can do to predict a time series by these methods other than to predict on the basis of its trend and seasonal component. Unfortunately, the problem of how to discover business cycles, if indeed they exist, is a very difficult one and one on which there is very little agreement among economists. It follows, therefore, that the decomposition procedure should not be treated as a well established technique for predicting a time series. Any statistical device that sheds light on the structure of a time series should prove useful to someone who understands all the economic factors operating to generate the series, and therefore should enable him to forecast with more assurance than before. The decomposition technique is such a device but it certainly is not a tool for the amateur forecaster.

Another disturbing feature of the decomposition procedure for prediction, besides that of not yielding results, is the difficulty of interpreting the components that have been isolated. In a dynamic economic system it is difficult to pick out economic factors that contribute only to the gradual growth, or decline, of the series, other factors that contribute only to cyclical movements, and still other factors that have only a purely random effect on the series. Thus many inventions and new processes in industry have been introduced at random times, but they certainly have contributed to the steady growth, or decline, of certain industries. It is very difficult to decompose dynamic factors in an economic time series in this artificial mathematical manner.

In recent years economists have become interested in new methods for studying time series that are based on investigating the relationship between successive terms of the series. In this new approach the terms of a series are treated as a set of random variables that possess certain probability properties. For mathematical convenience a time series is assumed to extend to infinity in both past and future time; therefore it is conveniently expressed in the form

$$\ldots, x_{-2}, x_{-1}, x_0, x_1, x_2, \ldots$$

The subscript on any x denotes the number of time units in the future, if it is positive, and in the past, if it is negative. A set of random variables such as this is called a *stochastic process*.

In terms of the preceding notation, various assumptions concerning these random variables can be introduced which will correspond to how the terms of an economic time series might be expected to be related to each other. One of the simplest models of this type assumes that the relationship between consecutive terms is given by the formula

$$(1) \qquad\qquad x_t = \beta x_{t-1} + e_t.$$

The quantity β is a constant and the quantities $\ldots e_{-2}, e_{-1}, e_0, e_1, e_2, \ldots$ are a set of random variables which are usually assumed to be independent and to possess the same distribution. In words, this model states that the value of any term in the series depends only upon the value of the term immediately preceding it in time and upon an erratic, that is, random, additive component. One would hardly expect that very many time series can be explained by such a simple model because this model assumes that the entire past history of the series, except for the term one time unit back, is of no value in predicting the future course of the series. This weakness can easily be overcome, however, by assuming a more sophisticated model such as

(2) $$x_t = \beta_1 x_{t-1} + \beta_2 x_{t-2} + \cdots + \beta_k x_{t-k} + e_t.$$

Here the value of any term depends upon the values of the k terms immediately preceding it, where k may be chosen sufficiently large to include enough past history to satisfy one's desires.

The preceding stochastic-process model has been applied with much success to some of the problems of engineering communication theory. Although economic time series do not possess properties as attractive as those of the series of communication theory, there is enough similarity to give some hope that these newer methods may yield better forecasts than those obtained by the decomposition.

One obvious weakness of the stochastic-process approach, which also applies to the decomposition method, is that the prediction of a future value of a time series is based exclusively upon the values of that same series in the past. One would expect that a knowledge of the behavior of other related series should contribute to a better forecast. This certainly would be true, for example, if one variable had a tendency to follow the movements of another variable one time unit later, because then the latest value of the leading variable could be used to forecast the value of the lagging variable. Variables such as wholesale and retail prices are an illustration of such possibilities. Considerations such as the foregoing would lead one to generalize model (2) to include additional sets of pertinent variables on the right side of the equation. This would give rise to a grand stochastic linear-regression model, which presumably should do better at forecasting than the earlier simpler models. The calculations needed to determine a regression function of this magnitude would be rather formidable. However, now that high-speed computing facilities are available, the opportunities for trying out such other approaches to the forecasting problem have increased remarkably. A prominent economic statistician was overheard waxing enthusiastic about his success with an elaborate linear-regression model for prediction. His enthusiasm, however, may possibly have been based on his personal success in the stock market rather than upon a scientific appraisal of his methods. The best that one can hope for in a method of predicting economic time series is to outdo those who do not possess such methods because the economic factors upon which any predictive scheme is based are not likely to remain static very long. The problem of prediction is a difficult but fascinating one, and new approaches to a solution will always find a sympathetic audience among those who have not succeeded with the aid of current methods. Problems are plentiful and await the attack of imaginative minds.

5. INDEX NUMBERS

The discussion in section 3.3 on how to adjust a time series for seasonal variation introduced the concept of an index number. The purpose there was to obtain a number for each month that represented department-store sales for that month relative to the monthly average for the year. This kind of index number is but a special case of more general index numbers that arise in various economic problems. Since index numbers are usually constructed for certain economic time series, they constitute one phase of the problem of how to treat time series. A brief discussion of some of the factors involved in their construction is therefore desirable here.

The basic objective of index numbers is to compare some economic quantity, such as the cost of living, at different periods of time. The problem is quite simple, for example, if one limits oneself to a single commodity and restricts oneself to two years. Thus it would be easy to compare the cost of eggs for two consecutive years by dividing the average cost for the second year by the average cost for the first year. Such averages can be obtained from government publications. A ratio of this kind when multiplied by 100 is an example of a simple index number. The problem of comparison becomes more difficult when more than one commodity and more than one year are considered. If one commodity only is being considered over a period of years, a simple solution consists in dividing the yearly prices by the price for the first year of the set and then multiplying these ratios by 100. The first year is called the base year; consequently, the second year is really the first comparison year. An illustration of this procedure is given in Table 12 for the average prices received by farmers for eggs during the years 1950–1956.

These index values merely tell one how the price of eggs for any year compares with the price in 1950. No attempt is made to consider changing economic factors, such as feed and labor costs, to determine how much the farmer really benefited by some of the indicated increased prices.

If more than one commodity is being considered, the problem becomes more difficult. For example, if one considered only eggs and bread, it is not obvious how the prices of those two commodities should be combined for two consecutive years to give a ratio that tells one whether the combined price of those two commodities has increased or decreased over the period of time. For problems of this more complicated sort it is necessary to introduce weighted index numbers.

Perhaps the best known weighted index, and certainly the one that has caused more controversy than any other, is the Consumer Price Index, which is published regularly by the government. This index is designed to measure price changes over a period of time of goods purchased by the typical consumer. Since the construction of a price index displays all the difficulties inherent in index-number construction, the following discussion is limited to price indexes.

Suppose it is agreed to consider a fixed set of goods on which to base a price index. For example, one might select a set of 100 common goods and services, such as milk, bread, meat, rent, and insurance. Suppose further that the average prices and quantities purchased of these goods are known for two consecutive years. In this connection, it is convenient to introduce the notation p_0 and q_0 for the price and quantity purchased, respectively, of a typical commodity during the first, or base, year.

TABLE 12

Year	Prices of Eggs in Cents per Dozen	Index Prices Relative to 1950
1950	31.2	100
1951	42.6	137
1952	40.5	130
1953	45.8	147
1954	46.3	148
1955	32.2	103
1956	46.6	149

Similarly, p_1 and q_1 denote the price and quantity purchased of this commodity during the second, or first comparison, year.

Now the total amount of money spent by consumers during the base year for a commodity is merely the product of its price p_0 by the amount purchased q_0; consequently, the total amount of money that was spent by consumers for the set of goods being considered is given by the expression

$$\sum p_0 q_0.$$

This sum is assumed to extend over all the commodities in the set. If the consumers had bought exactly the same amounts of these goods during the second year as they had during the first year, the total cost to them during the second year would have been

$$\sum p_1 q_0$$

because the price of the typical commodity changed from p_0 to p_1. The ratio of this second quantity to the first, namely,

(1) $$\frac{\sum p_1 q_0}{\sum p_0 q_0},$$

is a measure of the change in price of the set of goods from the first to the second year. The numerical value of this ratio determines how much prices have risen or fallen during the period being studied. For example, if the value were 1.03, prices would have increased 3 per cent, whereas if it were .98, prices would have decreased 2 per cent.

The index given by (1) is a reasonably good measure of the change in prices of consumer goods for a time interval of a year; however, if one wished to compare prices over a longer period of time, such as five or ten years, then this index possesses serious weaknesses. When the prices of certain commodities increase considerably, the consumer is likely to cut down on the amounts of those commodities that he will purchase. As a consequence, the numbers q_0, which denote the amounts purchased the first year, no longer represent satisfactory estimates of the amounts purchased in later years. It is not realistic to calculate what it would cost a family today to buy the same goods that it bought ten years ago and use those costs to estimate its present cost of living. Since the consumer is likely to buy less of the goods that increased in value and more of those that decreased in value, there will be a tendency for this index number to overestimate the present cost of living.

One method of making the index number up to date with respect to changes in the quantities of goods purchased is to replace the weights q_0 by the weights q_1. Thus one could introduce the index

(2)
$$\frac{\sum p_1 q_1}{\sum p_0 q_1}.$$

This index is the ratio of the total amount spent on this year's purchases to the total amount that would have been spent last year if this year's quantities of goods had been purchased then. Of course, this index is subject to the same kind of criticism as that raised against (1) when the time interval is several years rather than one year. It is just as unrealistic to compare present purchases with hypothetical past purchases as it was to compare past purchases with hypothetical future purchases. The longer the time interval between the two comparison dates, the more serious the criticism.

TABLE 13

Year	Cattle		Hogs		Sheep	
	Price	Consumption	Price	Consumption	Price	Consumption
1950	20	95	15	104	10	60
1954	16	120	25	90	7	69

For the purpose of observing the differential effects of these two weighting methods, consider the problem of calculating a price index for the cost of meat for the year 1954 when using 1950 as the base year. Data on the average annual consumption in pounds of various types of meat and the prices paid to farmers in cents per pound for those two years are given in Table 13. Since these data give the prices paid to the farmer rather than the prices paid by the consumer, the resulting indexes will not be consumer price indexes; however, they will illustrate the differences between formulas (1) and (2) very nicely.

Since the 1950 price and consumption figures are the p_0 and q_0 values and the 1954 figures are the p_1 and q_1 values, it follows that

$$\sum p_0 q_0 = 20 \cdot 95 + 15 \cdot 104 + 10 \cdot 60 = 4{,}060$$

and

$$\sum p_1 q_0 = 16 \cdot 95 + 25 \cdot 104 + 7 \cdot 60 = 4{,}540.$$

Consequently, the value of (1) is given by

$$\frac{\sum p_1 q_0}{\sum q_0 p_0} = 1.12.$$

Similar calculations will yield

$$\sum p_0 q_1 = 20 \cdot 120 + 15 \cdot 90 + 10 \cdot 69 = 4,440$$
$$\sum p_1 q_1 = 16 \cdot 120 + 25 \cdot 90 + 7 \cdot 69 = 4,653.$$

As a result, the value of (2) for this problem is

$$\frac{\sum p_1 q_1}{\sum p_0 q_1} = 1.05.$$

Formula (1) would indicate that prices had risen about 12 per cent from 1950 to 1954; however, formula (2) would suggest only a 5 per cent increase.

A good compromise between the two indexes (1) and (2) would seem to be some sort of average of the two. As a matter of fact, serious students of index-number theory have constructed a number of such averages that possess certain desirable theoretical properties. The ordinary mean of (1) and (2), for example, is considered to be a very good index for comparing prices at two different times.

Formulas (1) and (2) are usually called the formulas of Laspeyres and Paasche, respectively, because these two economists were the first to recommend the use of the formulas for measuring price changes. Since they were active during the last century, it is clear that index numbers have been of interest to economists for a long time.

The problem of index-number construction becomes more complicated when yearly prices are to be compared over a period of several years. Formula (1) is considerably easier to use than formula (2) in this situation because formula (2) would require one to use fresh weights for each new year that is added and also require one to recalculate the index values for each of the preceding years. If p_j and q_j denote the price and amount purchased, respectively, of a typical commodity during the jth comparison year, then the index value for the jth comparison year corresponding to formula (1) would be

(3) $$\frac{\sum p_j q_0}{\sum p_0 q_0}.$$

The subscript 0 is always used to indicate the first year in the set of years being compared. In view of the practical advantages of formula (1) over formula (2) for a set of consecutive years, a formula comparable to (3) that corresponds to (2) is seldom used. Because of these same practical considerations, a formula based on the mean, or other combinations, of formulas (1) and (2) is also seldom used for such consecutive data.

The use of formula (3) for estimating the prices of consumer goods for a number of consecutive years is subject to the same criticism as that discussed earlier with respect to formula (1) when the time interval between comparison dates is long. Ideally, fresh base years should be chosen every few years, or whenever there are noticeable changes in the purchasing habits of consumers, so that the base weights q_0 will be realistic weights for present-day purchases. Unfortunately, the cost of determining consumers' purchasing habits is a very expensive undertaking, and therefore the Consumer Price Index published regularly by the government is not revised very often; hence it is subject to the criticism that it is not up to date. A number of years ago some lively debates occurred between representatives of labor and the government over the accuracy of the Consumer Price Index in measuring increased living costs. Labor representatives maintained that the cost of living had risen considerably more than that indicated by the government's Consumer Price Index, in spite of the fact that this index tends to exaggerate the increase. Their arguments against it, however, were based on other undesirable features of the index. Some students of index-number theory feel that it is a mistake to use fixed weights corresponding to any chosen base period and that a different approach to index-number construction should be used.

Many of the other problems that arise in an attempt to construct a satisfactory consumer price index have been glossed over in this brief discussion. There are serious problems in connection with the choice of terms that are to be used in the index, how to take account of the decreased quality of goods, and how to take samples of prices and quantities of goods over the country and combine them into a single index. Synthetic fibers, for example, have replaced many of the cotton and woolen fabrics used exclusively in clothing a few years ago; consequently, it is difficult to compare the cost of clothing now with what it was then. Continued high prices of a commodity may cause consumers to shift to a substitute, such as shifting from butter to margarine, and gradually cease buying the original commodity. Does this mean that they are eating just as well, or would they really prefer butter? Questions such as these are more closely related to economics than to statistics, and therefore they would be out of

place in this book. The purpose of this section was to give a brief introduction to index numbers without exposing their nonelementary features;
therefore, let this suffice for the present until you are prepared to assess
their virtues and their shortcomings through more specialized study.

EXERCISES

1. Apply the runs test for randomness to the time series given in Table 4 in
the text. Comment on your result.

2. The following data give the prices of American railroad stocks from 1880
to 1936. Read down columns. Test for randomness by means of the runs test.
Comment on your result.

45	47	52	103	61	124
56	42	64	94	60	91
53	49	78	93	58	32
52	48	84	93	68	25
47	37	68	83	65	42
38	36	86	73	81	32
47	37	100	83	91	41
50	36	98	81	98	
47	42	74	62	115	
45	51	96	66	131	

3. The following data give the monthly call-money rates for five consecutive
years. Each column corresponds to a year. Test for randomness by means of
the runs test.

4.6	5.8	2.3	2.2	8.6
2.4	2.9	1.8	2.2	4.6
3.9	6.0	1.8	3.2	4.9
5.1	4.2	1.4	3.2	9.5
5.6	2.4	1.6	2.4	4.2
2.8	3.1	1.1	2.5	3.2
3.5	2.5	1.0	2.3	3.0
3.8	2.0	.9	2.1	4.4
10.8	2.3	1.5	3.6	9.4
7.6	2.7	2.0	5.3	5.2
4.9	5.2	2.8	7.7	7.5
6.8	5.5	3.1	16.0	14.0

4. Apply the runs test to the time series of problem 13.

5. Give an illustration by means of numbers or a graph of an artificial time
series that has a regular cycle but for which the runs test would probably claim
randomness.

6. Apply a 3-term moving average to the data of problem 2 and graph both series. Do any cyclical movements appear to be present?

7. Apply a 3-term moving average to the data of Table 5 in the text and graph the result.

8. Draw 50 1-digit random numbers from Table II in the appendix and apply a 5-term moving average to them. Graph the result and observe whether any cyclical movements have been generated.

9. Apply a 5-term moving average to the data of Table 5 and graph the result. Compare this result with that of problem 7.

10. Fit a straight line by the method of Chapter 9 to the data of Table 5 in the text to obtain an estimate of the underlying trend.

11. What moving average would you apply to the data of Table 5 if you wished to eliminate the 2-cycle wave as well as the random component and thus estimate the underlying trend?

12. Use the method explained in the text to obtain seasonal index numbers for the data of problem 3. In performing the computations, obtain entries for the three middle years only.

13. The following data represent the monthly amounts of magazine advertising in ten-thousands of lines for four consecutive years. Use the method explained in the text to adjust these data for seasonal variation. In performing the computations, obtain entries for the two middle years only. Each column corresponds to one year.

254	245	268	250
301	285	316	302
326	321	360	342
350	368	408	388
358	343	387	364
301	306	355	335
242	258	286	245
223	216	243	206
276	281	316	260
341	350	376	302
357	349	383	304
318	317	362	282

14. Calculate the serial correlation coefficient with lag 12 for the data of Table 8 in the text and comment about its value.

15. Calculate the serial correlation coefficient with lag 12 for the data of problem 13. Comment on your result.

16. The following data give the mortgage loans paid off during the year as a percentage of the gross mortgage portfolio from 1929 to 1958. (a) Graph the data. (b) Apply the runs test for randomness. (c) Does a linear trend appear to

be present? How would you test for a linear trend? Read the data a row at a time.

    16.8, 16.6, 19.2, 19.8, 21.1, 27.9, 28.3, 23.0, 21.3, 18.3,
    20.4, 21.4, 21.0, 22.1, 25.0, 25.9, 26.2, 28.6, 26.0, 22.4,
    21.1, 25.5, 22.9, 22.4, 20.9, 20.1, 21.5, 18.4, 16.1, 15.8.

17. For the series of problem 16, does a fairly regular cycle appear to be present? If you believe it does, apply a moving average with the number of terms equal to the distance between waves and observe whether it kills off the assumed cycle.

18. In problem 17 calculate the serial correlation for a lag equal to the assumed cycle length and comment on your result.

19. The following data give the number of workers in transportation and public utilities in ten-thousands of employees from 1929 to 1958. Use various techniques to study the series for randomness, trend, and cycles. Read the data a row at a time.

    391, 368, 324, 280, 266, 274, 277, 296, 311, 284,
    291, 301, 325, 343, 362, 380, 387, 402, 412, 414,
    395, 398, 417, 418, 422, 401, 406, 416, 415, 390.

20. The following data give the prices in dollars per box and the production in millions of boxes of citrus fruit from 1935 to 1938. Calculate price indexes, using 1935 as the base year. Comment about these index values.

	1935	1936	1937	1938
Oranges	1.37 33	1.04 30	1.55 46	.55 41
Lemons	3.15 8	1.35 8	4.95 9	1.10 11

21. Given the following fictitious prices and quantities of three commodities purchased by a family for the years 1957 and 1959, use them to calculate the increase, or decrease, in prices from 1957 to 1959 (a) if the amounts purchased are ignored, (b) if index formula (1) is employed, (c) if index formula (2) is employed, (d) if the mean of formulas (1) and (2) is employed.

	1957		1959	
	Price	Quantity	Price	Quantity
Meat	60¢	400 lb	70¢	350 lb
Eggs	70¢	100 doz	50¢	120 doz
Bread	25¢	200 loaves	30¢	180 loaves

22. Explain why formula (2) is likely to underestimate the increase in prices for the average consumer.

23. Suppose the price index on rent for the year 1959, with 1950 as the base year, is 130 for San Francisco and 120 for Philadelphia. What information do these indexes supply concerning relative rental costs in the two cities?

24. Construct a set of fictitious prices and quantities of two commodities for two years such that formula (1) will show an increase in prices but formula (2) will show a decrease in prices.

25. Do as in problem 24, but now have (1) show a decrease and (2) show an increase. Is a situation like this likely to arise in real life?

26. Discuss some of the practical difficulties in determining the average price of meat for use in a consumer price index.

Appendix

The following tables are modifications or condensations of tables found in other books or journals. I wish to take this opportunity to express my appreciation to the authors and publishers from whom these tables were obtained.

Tables I, IV and XI are modifications of similar tables found in the author's book, *Introduction to Mathematical Statistics*, 3rd edition, John Wiley & Sons, 1962. Table XI originally came from *Statistical Methods* by G. Snedecor, Collegiate Press, Iowa State College.

Tables V and VII are from the book *Statistics, An Introduction* by D. A. S. Fraser and published by John Wiley & Sons, 1958. These tables originally came from the journal articles "Tables of percentage points of the incomplete beta function" and "Tables of the percentage points of the χ^2 distribution" by C. M. Thompson in *Biometrika*, Vol. 32 (1941), E. S. Pearson editor.

The McGraw-Hill Book Company granted the author permission to extract parts of Table A-20 from *Introduction to Statistical Analysis*, 2nd edition, by W. J. Dixon and F. J. Massey. This extraction is found in Table VIII.

Table IX was obtained from the material in the article "Distribution of the sums of squares of rank differences for small numbers of individuals," *Annals of Mathematical Statistics*, Vol. 9 (1938), by E. G. Olds, and with his consent.

Table X was extracted from C. Eisenhart and F. Swed, "Tables for testing randomness of grouping in a sequence of alternatives," *Annals of Mathematical Statistics*, Vol. 14 (1943), with permission from the authors.

P. G. H.

USE OF SQUARE ROOT TABLE

To obtain the square root of a number, mark off the digits in blocks of 2, starting at the decimal point. If the number is larger than 1 and the block farthest to the left contains only one digit, use the column $\sqrt{N}$; if it contains two digits use $\sqrt{10N}$. If the number is smaller than 1 and the first nonzero digit to the right of the decimal point is preceded by a zero in its block, use the column $\sqrt{N}$, otherwise use $\sqrt{10N}$. Each block of digits in the number corresponds to a single digit in the answer. Examples:

$\sqrt{241.67} = \sqrt{2|41.|67}$; hence use $\sqrt{N}$ column for $\sqrt{242.} \doteq 15.6$.

$\sqrt{.0024167} = \sqrt{.00|24|16|7}$; hence use $\sqrt{10N}$ column for $\sqrt{.00242} \doteq .0492$.

TABLE I. Squares and Square Roots

N	N²	√N	√10N	N	N²	√N	√10N
1.00	1.0000	1.00000	3.16228	**1.50**	2.2500	1.22474	3.87298
1.01	1.0201	1.00499	3.17805	1.51	2.2801	1.22882	3.88587
1.02	1.0404	1.00995	3.19374	1.52	2.3104	1.23288	3.89872
1.03	1.0609	1.01489	3.20936	1.53	2.3409	1.23693	3.91152
1.04	1.0816	1.01980	3.22490	1.54	2.3716	1.24097	3.92428
1.05	1.1025	1.02470	3.24037	1.55	2.4025	1.24499	3.93700
1.06	1.1236	1.02956	3.25576	1.56	2.4336	1.24900	3.94968
1.07	1.1449	1.03441	3.27109	1.57	2.4649	1.25300	3.96232
1.08	1.1664	1.03923	3.28634	1.58	2.4964	1.25698	3.97492
1.09	1.1881	1.04403	3.30151	1.59	2.5281	1.26095	3.98748
1.10	1.2100	1.04881	3.31662	**1.60**	2.5600	1.26491	4.00000
1.11	1.2321	1.05357	3.33167	1.61	2.5921	1.26886	4.01248
1.12	1.2544	1.05830	3.34664	1.62	2.6244	1.27279	4.02492
1.13	1.2769	1.06301	3.36155	1.63	2.6569	1.27671	4.03733
1.14	1.2996	1.06771	3.37639	1.64	2.6896	1.28062	4.04969
1.15	1.3225	1.07238	3.39116	1.65	2.7225	1.28452	4.06202
1.16	1.3456	1.07703	3.40588	1.66	2.7556	1.28841	4.07431
1.17	1.3689	1.08167	3.42053	1.67	2.7889	1.29228	4.08656
1.18	1.3924	1.08628	3.43511	1.68	2.8224	1.29615	4.09878
1.19	1.4161	1.09087	3.44964	1.69	2.8561	1.30000	4.11096
1.20	1.4400	1.09545	3.46410	**1.70**	2.8900	1.30384	4.12311
1.21	1.4641	1.10000	3.47851	1.71	2.9241	1.30767	4.13521
1.22	1.4884	1.10454	3.49285	1.72	2.9584	1.31149	4.14729
1.23	1.5129	1.10905	3.50714	1.73	2.9929	1.31529	4.15933
1.24	1.5376	1.11355	3.52136	1.74	3.0276	1.31909	4.17133
1.25	1.5625	1.11803	3.53553	1.75	3.0625	1.32288	4.18330
1.26	1.5876	1.12250	3.54965	1.76	3.0976	1.32665	4.19524
1.27	1.6129	1.12694	3.56371	1.77	3.1329	1.33041	4.20714
1.28	1.6384	1.13137	3.57771	1.78	3.1684	1.33417	4.21900
1.29	1.6641	1.13578	3.59166	1.79	3.2041	1.33791	4.23084
1.30	1.6900	1.14018	3.60555	**1.80**	3.2400	1.34164	4.24264
1.31	1.7161	1.14455	3.61939	1.81	3.2761	1.34536	4.25441
1.32	1.7424	1.14891	3.63318	1.82	3.3124	1.34907	4.26615
1.33	1.7689	1.15326	3.64692	1.83	3.3489	1.35277	4.27785
1.34	1.7956	1.15758	3.66060	1.84	3.3856	1.35647	4.28952
1.35	1.8225	1.16190	3.67423	1.85	3.4225	1.36015	4.30116
1.36	1.8496	1.16619	3.68782	1.86	3.4596	1.36382	4.31277
1.37	1.8769	1.17047	3.70135	1.87	3.4969	1.36748	4.32435
1.38	1.9044	1.17473	3.71484	1.88	3.5344	1.37113	4.33590
1.39	1.9321	1.17898	3.72827	1.89	3.5721	1.37477	4.34741
1.40	1.9600	1.18322	3.74166	**1.90**	3.6100	1.37840	4.35890
1.41	1.9881	1.18743	3.75500	1.91	3.6481	1.38203	4.37035
1.42	2.0164	1.19164	3.76829	1.92	3.6864	1.38564	4.38178
1.43	2.0449	1.19583	3.78153	1.93	3.7249	1.38924	4.39318
1.44	2.0736	1.20000	3.79473	1.94	3.7636	1.39284	4.40454
1.45	2.1025	1.20416	3.80789	1.95	3.8025	1.39642	4.41588
1.46	2.1316	1.20830	3.82099	1.96	3.8416	1.40000	4.42719
1.47	2.1609	1.21244	3.83406	1.97	3.8809	1.40357	4.43847
1.48	2.1904	1.21655	3.84708	1.98	3.9204	1.40712	4.44972
1.49	2.2201	1.22066	3.86005	1.99	3.9601	1.41067	4.46094
1.50	2.2500	1.22474	3.87298	**2.00**	4.0000	1.41421	4.47214
N	N²	√N	√10N	N	N²	√N	√10N

N	N²	√N	√10N	N	N²	√N	√10N
2.00	4.0000	1.41421	4.47214	**2.50**	6.2500	1.58114	5.00000
2.01	4.0401	1.41774	4.48330	2.51	6.3001	1.58430	5.00999
2.02	4.0804	1.42127	4.49444	2.52	6.3504	1.58745	5.01996
2.03	4.1209	1.42478	4.50555	2.53	6.4009	1.59060	5.02991
2.04	4.1616	1.42829	4.51664	2.54	6.4516	1.59374	5.03984
2.05	4.2025	1.43178	4.52769	2.55	6.5025	1.59687	5.04975
2.06	4.2436	1.43527	4.53872	2.56	6.5536	1.60000	5.05964
2.07	4.2849	1.43875	4.54973	2.57	6.6049	1.60312	5.06952
2.08	4.3264	1.44222	4.56070	2.58	6.6564	1.60624	5.07937
2.09	4.3681	1.44568	4.57165	2.59	6.7081	1.60935	5.08920
2.10	4.4100	1.44914	4.58258	**2.60**	6.7600	1.61245	5.09902
2.11	4.4521	1.45258	4.59347	2.61	6.8121	1.61555	5.10882
2.12	4.4944	1.45602	4.60435	2.62	6.8644	1.61864	5.11859
2.13	4.5369	1.45945	4.61519	2.63	6.9169	1.62173	5.12835
2.14	4.5796	1.46287	4.62601	2.64	6.9696	1.62481	5.13809
2.15	4.6225	1.46629	4.63681	2.65	7.0225	1.62788	5.14782
2.16	4.6656	1.46969	4.64758	2.66	7.0756	1.63095	5.15752
2.17	4.7089	1.47309	4.65833	2.67	7.1289	1.63401	5.16720
2.18	4.7524	1.47648	4.66905	2.68	7.1824	1.63707	5.17687
2.19	4.7961	1.47986	4.67974	2.69	7.2361	1.64012	5.18652
2.20	4.8400	1.48324	4.69042	**2.70**	7.2900	1.64317	5.19615
2.21	4.8841	1.48661	4.70106	2.71	7.3441	1.64621	5.20577
2.22	4.9284	1.48997	4.71169	2.72	7.3984	1.64924	5.21536
2.23	4.9729	1.49332	4.72229	2.73	7.4529	1.65227	5.22494
2.24	5.0176	1.49666	4.73286	2.74	7.5076	1.65529	5.23450
2.25	5.0625	1.50000	4.74342	2.75	7.5625	1.65831	5.24404
2.26	5.1076	1.50333	4.75395	2.76	7.6176	1.66132	5.25357
2.27	5.1529	1.50665	4.76445	2.77	7.6729	1.66433	5.26308
2.28	5.1984	1.50997	4.77493	2.78	7.7284	1.66733	5.27257
2.29	5.2441	1.51327	4.78539	2.79	7.7841	1.67033	5.28205
2.30	5.2900	1.51658	4.79583	**2.80**	7.8400	1.67332	5.29150
2.31	5.3361	1.51987	4.80625	2.81	7.8961	1.67631	5.30094
2.32	5.3824	1.52315	4.81664	2.82	7.9524	1.67929	5.31037
2.33	5.4289	1.52643	4.82701	2.83	8.0089	1.68226	5.31977
2.34	5.4756	1.52971	4.83735	2.84	8.0656	1.68523	5.32917
2.35	5.5225	1.53297	4.84768	2.85	8.1225	1.68819	5.33854
2.36	5.5696	1.53623	4.85798	2.86	8.1796	1.69115	5.34790
2.37	5.6169	1.53948	4.86826	2.87	8.2369	1.69411	5.35724
2.38	5.6644	1.54272	4.87852	2.88	8.2944	1.69706	5.36656
2.39	5.7121	1.54596	4.88876	2.89	8.3521	1.70000	5.37587
2.40	5.7600	1.54919	4.89898	**2.90**	8.4100	1.70294	5.38516
2.41	5.8081	1.55242	4.90918	2.91	8.4681	1.70587	5.39444
2.42	5.8564	1.55563	4.91935	2.92	8.5264	1.70880	5.40370
2.43	5.9049	1.55885	4.92950	2.93	8.5849	1.71172	5.41295
2.44	5.9536	1.56205	4.93964	2.94	8.6436	1.71464	5.42218
2.45	6.0025	1.56525	4.94975	2.95	8.7025	1.71756	5.43139
2.46	6.0516	1.56844	4.95984	2.96	8.7616	1.72047	5.44059
2.47	6.1009	1.57162	4.96991	2.97	8.8209	1.72337	5.44977
2.48	6.1504	1.57480	4.97996	2.98	8.8804	1.72627	5.45894
2.49	6.2001	1.57797	4.98999	2.99	8.9401	1.72916	5.46809
2.50	6.2500	1.58114	5.00000	**3.00**	9.0000	1.73205	5.47723
N	N²	√N	√10N	N	N²	√N	√10N

N	N²	√N	√10N	N	N²	√N	√10N
3.00	9.0000	1.73205	5.47723	**3.50**	12.2500	1.87083	5.91608
3.01	9.0601	1.73494	5.48635	3.51	12.3201	1.87350	5.92453
3.02	9.1204	1.73781	5.49545	3.52	12.3904	1.87617	5.93296
3.03	9.1809	1.74069	5.50454	3.53	12.4609	1.87883	5.94138
3.04	9.2416	1.74356	5.51362	3.54	12.5316	1.88149	5.94979
3.05	9.3025	1.74642	5.52268	3.55	12.6025	1.88414	5.95819
3.06	9.3636	1.74929	5.53173	3.56	12.6736	1.88680	5.96657
3.07	9.4249	1.75214	5.54076	3.57	12.7449	1.88944	5.97495
3.08	9.4864	1.75499	5.54977	3.58	12.8164	1.89209	5.98331
3.09	9.5481	1.75784	5.55878	3.59	12.8881	1.89473	5.99166
3.10	9.6100	1.76068	5.56776	**3.60**	12.9600	1.89737	6.00000
3.11	9.6721	1.76352	5.57674	3.61	13.0321	1.90000	6.00833
3.12	9.7344	1.76635	5.58570	3.62	13.1044	1.90263	6.01664
3.13	9.7969	1.76918	5.59464	3.63	13.1769	1.90526	6.02495
3.14	9.8596	1.77200	5.60357	3.64	13.2496	1.90788	6.03324
3.15	9.9225	1.77482	5.61249	3.65	13.3225	1.91050	6.04152
3.16	9.9856	1.77764	5.62139	3.66	13.3956	1.91311	6.04979
3.17	10.0489	1.78045	5.63028	3.67	13.4689	1.91572	6.05805
3.18	10.1124	1.78326	5.63915	3.68	13.5424	1.91833	6.06630
3.19	10.1761	1.78606	5.64801	3.69	13.6161	1.92094	6.07454
3.20	10.2400	1.78885	5.65685	**3.70**	13.6900	1.92354	6.08276
3.21	10.3041	1.79165	5.66569	3.71	13.7641	1.92614	6.09098
3.22	10.3684	1.79444	5.67450	3.72	13.8384	1.92873	6.09918
3.23	10.4329	1.79722	5.68331	3.73	13.9129	1.93132	6.10737
3.24	10.4976	1.80000	5.69210	3.74	13.9876	1.93391	6.11555
3.25	10.5625	1.80278	5.70088	3.75	14.0625	1.93649	6.12372
3.26	10.6276	1.80555	5.70964	3.76	14.1376	1.93907	6.13188
3.27	10.6929	1.80831	5.71839	3.77	14.2129	1.94165	6.14003
3.28	10.7584	1.81108	5.72713	3.78	14.2884	1.94422	6.14817
3.29	10.8241	1.81384	5.73585	3.79	14.3641	1.94679	6.15630
3.30	10.8900	1.81659	5.74456	**3.80**	14.4400	1.94936	6.16441
3.31	10.9561	1.81934	5.75326	3.81	14.5161	1.95192	6.17252
3.32	11.0224	1.82209	5.76194	3.82	14.5924	1.95448	6.18061
3.33	11.0889	1.82483	5.77062	3.83	14.6689	1.95704	6.18870
3.34	11.1556	1.82757	5.77927	3.84	14.7456	1.95959	6.19677
3.35	11.2225	1.83030	5.78792	3.85	14.8225	1.96214	6.20484
3.36	11.2896	1.83303	5.79655	3.86	14.8996	1.96469	6.21289
3.37	11.3569	1.83576	5.80517	3.87	14.9769	1.96723	6.22093
3.38	11.4244	1.83848	5.81378	3.88	15.0544	1.96977	6.22896
3.39	11.4921	1.84120	5.82237	3.89	15.1321	1.97231	6.23699
3.40	11.5600	1.84391	5.83095	**3.90**	15.2100	1.97484	6.24500
3.41	11.6281	1.84662	5.83952	3.91	15.2881	1.97737	6.25300
3.42	11.6964	1.84932	5.84808	3.92	15.3664	1.97990	6.26099
3.43	11.7649	1.85203	5.85662	3.93	15.4449	1.98242	6.26897
3.44	11.8336	1.85472	5.86515	3.94	15.5236	1.98494	6.27694
3.45	11.9025	1.85742	5.87367	3.95	15.6025	1.98746	6.28490
3.46	11.9716	1.86011	5.88218	3.96	15.6816	1.98997	6.29285
3.47	12.0409	1.86279	5.89067	3.97	15.7609	1.99249	6.30079
3.48	12.1104	1.86548	5.89915	3.98	15.8404	1.99499	6.30872
3.49	12.1801	1.86815	5.90762	3.99	15.9201	1.99750	6.31664
3.50	12.2500	1.87083	5.91608	**4.00**	16.0000	2.00000	6.32456
N	N²	√N,	√10N	N	N²	√N	√10N

Squares and Square Roots (*Continued*)

N	N²	√N̄	√10N	N	N²	√N̄	√10N
4.00	16.0000	2.00000	6.32456	**4.50**	20.2500	2.12132	6.70820
4.01	16.0801	2.00250	6.33246	4.51	20.3401	2.12368	6.71565
4.02	16.1604	2.00499	6.34035	4.52	20.4304	2.12603	6.72309
4.03	16.2409	2.00749	6.34823	4.53	20.5209	2.12838	6.73053
4.04	16.3216	2.00998	6.35610	4.54	20.6116	2.13073	6.73795
4.05	16.4025	2.01246	6.36396	4.55	20.7025	2.13307	6.74537
4.06	16.4836	2.01494	6.37181	4.56	20.7936	2.13542	6.75278
4.07	16.5649	2.01742	6.37966	4.57	20.8849	2.13776	6.76018
4.08	16.6464	2.01990	6.38749	4.58	20.9764	2.14009	6.76757
4.09	16.7281	2.02237	6.39531	4.59	21.0681	2.14243	6.77495
4.10	16.8100	2.02485	6.40312	**4.60**	21.1600	2.14476	6.78233
4.11	16.8921	2.02731	6.41093	4.61	21.2521	2.14709	6.78970
4.12	16.9744	2.02978	6.41872	4.62	21.3444	2.14942	6.79706
4.13	17.0569	2.03224	6.42651	4.63	21.4369	2.15174	6.80441
4.14	17.1396	2.03470	6.43428	4.64	21.5296	2.15407	6.81175
4.15	17.2225	2.03715	6.44205	4.65	21.6225	2.15639	6.81909
4.16	17.3056	2.03961	6.44981	4.66	21.7156	2.15870	6.82642
4.17	17.3889	2.04206	6.45755	4.67	21.8089	2.16102	6.83374
4.18	17.4724	2.04450	6.46529	4.68	21.9024	2.16333	6.84105
4.19	17.5561	2.04695	6.47302	4.69	21.9961	2.16564	6.84836
4.20	17.6400	2.04939	6.48074	**4.70**	22.0900	2.16795	6.85565
4.21	17.7241	2.05183	6.48845	4.71	22.1841	2.17025	6.86294
4.22	17.8084	2.05426	6.49615	4.72	22.2784	2.17256	6.87023
4.23	17.8929	2.05670	6.50384	4.73	22.3729	2.17486	6.87750
4.24	17.9776	2.05913	6.51153	4.74	22.4676	2.17715	6.88477
4.25	18.0625	2.06155	6.51920	4.75	22.5625	2.17945	6.89202
4.26	18.1476	2.06398	6.52687	4.76	22.6576	2.18174	6.89928
4.27	18.2329	2.06640	6.53452	4.77	22.7529	2.18403	6.90652
4.28	18.3184	2.06882	6.54217	4.78	22.8484	2.18632	6.91375
4.29	18.4041	2.07123	6.54981	4.79	22.9441	2.18861	6.92098
4.30	18.4900	2.07364	6.55744	**4.80**	23.0400	2.19089	6.92820
4.31	18.5761	2.07605	6.56506	4.81	23.1361	2.19317	6.93542
4.32	18.6624	2.07846	6.57267	4.82	23.2324	2.19545	6.94262
4.33	18.7489	2.08087	6.58027	4.83	23.3289	2.19773	6.94982
4.34	18.8356	2.08327	6.58787	4.84	23.4256	2.20000	6.95701
4.35	18.9225	2.08567	6.59545	4.85	23.5225	2.20227	6.96419
4.36	19.0096	2.08806	6.60303	4.86	23.6196	2.20454	6.97137
4.37	19.0969	2.09045	6.61060	4.87	23.7169	2.20681	6.97854
4.38	19.1844	2.09284	6.61816	4.88	23.8144	2.20907	6.98570
4.39	19.2721	2.09523	6.62571	4.89	23.9121	2.21133	6.99285
4.40	19.3600	2.09762	6.63325	**4.90**	24.0100	2.21359	7.00000
4.41	19.4481	2.10000	6.64078	4.91	24.1081	2.21585	7.00714
4.42	19.5364	2.10238	6.64831	4.92	24.2064	2.21811	7.01427
4.43	19.6249	2.10476	6.65582	4.93	24.3049	2.22036	7.02140
4.44	19.7136	2.10713	6.66333	4.94	24.4036	2.22261	7.02851
4.45	19.8025	2.10950	6.67083	4.95	24.5025	2.22486	7.03562
4.46	19.8916	2.11187	6.67832	4.96	24.6016	2.22711	7.04273
4.47	19.9809	2.11424	6.68581	4.97	24.7009	2.22935	7.04982
4.48	20.0704	2.11660	6.69328	4.98	24.8004	2.23159	7.05691
4.49	20.1601	2.11896	6.70075	4.99	24.9001	2.23383	7.06399
4.50	20.2500	2.12132	6.70820	**5.00**	25.0000	2.23607	7.07107
N	N²	√N̄	√10N	N	N²	√N̄	√10N

Squares and Square Roots (*Continued*)

N	N²	√N	√10N	N	N²	√N	√10N
5.00	25.0000	2.23607	7.07107	**5.50**	30.2500	2.34521	7.41620
5.01	25.1001	2.23830	7.07814	5.51	30.3601	2.34734	7.42294
5.02	25.2004	2.24054	7.08520	5.52	30.4704	2.34947	7.42967
5.03	25.3009	2.24277	7.09225	5.53	30.5809	2.35160	7.43640
5.04	25.4016	2.24499	7.09930	5.54	30.6916	2.35372	7.44312
5.05	25.5025	2.24722	7.10634	5.55	30.8025	2.35584	7.44983
5.06	25.6036	2.24944	7.11337	5.56	30.9136	2.35797	7.45654
5.07	25.7049	2.25167	7.12039	5.57	31.0249	2.36008	7.46324
5.08	25.8064	2.25389	7.12741	5.58	31.1364	2.36220	7.46994
5.09	25.9081	2.25610	7.13442	5.59	31.2481	2.36432	7.47663
5.10	26.0100	2.25832	7.14143	**5.60**	31.3600	2.36643	7.48331
5.11	26.1121	2.26053	7.14843	5.61	31.4721	2.36854	7.48999
5.12	26.2144	2.26274	7.15542	5.62	31.5844	2.37065	7.49667
5.13	26.3169	2.26495	7.16240	5.63	31.6969	2.37276	7.50333
5.14	26.4196	2.26716	7.16938	5.64	31.8096	2.37487	7.50999
5.15	26.5225	2.26936	7.17635	5.65	31.9225	2.37697	7.51665
5.16	26.6256	2.27156	7.18331	5.66	32.0356	2.37908	7.52330
5.17	26.7289	2.27376	7.19027	5.67	32.1489	2.38118	7.52994
5.18	26.8324	2.27596	7.19722	5.68	32.2624	2.38328	7.53658
5.19	26.9361	2.27816	7.20417	5.69	32.3761	2.38537	7.54321
5.20	27.0400	2.28035	7.21110	**5.70**	32.4900	2.38747	7.54983
5.21	27.1441	2.28254	7.21803	5.71	32.6041	2.38956	7.55645
5.22	27.2484	2.28473	7.22496	5.72	32.7184	2.39165	7.56307
5.23	27.3529	2.28692	7.23187	5.73	32.8329	2.39374	7.56968
5.24	27.4576	2.28910	7.23878	5.74	32.9476	2.39583	7.57628
5.25	27.5625	2.29129	7.24569	5.75	33.0625	2.39792	7.58288
5.26	27.6676	2.29347	7.25259	5.76	33.1776	2.40000	7.58947
5.27	27.7729	2.29565	7.25948	5.77	33.2929	2.40208	7.59605
5.28	27.8784	2.29783	7.26636	5.78	33.4084	2.40416	7.60263
5.29	27.9841	2.30000	7.27324	5.79	33.5241	2.40624	7.60920
5.30	28.0900	2.30217	7.28011	**5.80**	33.6400	2.40832	7.61577
5.31	28.1961	2.30434	7.28697	5.81	33.7561	2.41039	7.62234
5.32	28.3024	2.30651	7.29383	5.82	33.8724	2.41247	7.62889
5.33	28.4089	2.30868	7.30068	5.83	33.9889	2.41454	7.63544
5.34	28.5156	2.31084	7.30753	5.84	34.1056	2.41661	7.64199
5.35	28.6225	2.31301	7.31437	5.85	34.2225	2.41868	7.64853
5.36	28.7296	2.31517	7.32120	5.86	34.3396	2.42074	7.65506
5.37	28.8369	2.31733	7.32803	5.87	34.4569	2.42281	7.66159
5.38	28.9444	2.31948	7.33485	5.88	34.5744	2.42487	7.66812
5.39	29.0521	2.32164	7.34166	5.89	34.6921	2.42693	7.67463
5.40	29.1600	2.32379	7.34847	**5.90**	34.8100	2.42899	7.68115
5.41	29.2681	2.32594	7.35527	5.91	34.9281	2.43105	7.68765
5.42	29.3764	2.32809	7.36206	5.92	35.0464	2.43311	7.69415
5.43	29.4849	2.33024	7.36885	5.93	35.1649	2.43516	7.70065
5.44	29.5936	2.33238	7.37564	5.94	35.2836	2.43721	7.70714
5.45	29.7025	2.33452	7.38241	5.95	35.4025	2.43926	7.71362
5.46	29.8116	2.33666	7.38918	5.96	35.5216	2.44131	7.72010
5.47	29.9209	2.33880	7.39594	5.97	35.6409	2.44336	7.72658
5.48	30.0304	2.34094	7.40270	5.98	35.7604	2.44540	7.73305
5.49	30.1401	2.34307	7.40945	5.99	35.8801	2.44745	7.73951
5.50	30.2500	2.34521	7.41620	**6.00**	36.0000	2.44949	7.74597
N	N²	√N	√10N	N	N²	√N	√10N

N	N²	√N	√10N	N	N²	√N	√10N
6.00	36.0000	2.44949	7.74597	**6.50**	42.2500	2.54951	8.06226
6.01	36.1201	2.45153	7.75242	6.51	42.3801	2.55147	8.06846
6.02	36.2404	2.45357	7.75887	6.52	42.5104	2.55343	8.07465
6.03	36.3609	2.45561	7.76531	6.53	42.6409	2.55539	8.08084
6.04	36.4816	2.45764	7.77174	6.54	42.7716	2.55734	8.08703
6.05	36.6025	2.45967	7.77817	6.55	42.9025	2.55930	8.09321
6.06	36.7236	2.46171	7.78460	6.56	43.0336	2.56125	8.09938
6.07	36.8449	2.46374	7.79102	6.57	43.1649	2.56320	8.10555
6.08	36.9664	2.46577	7.79744	6.58	43.2964	2.56515	8.11172
6.09	37.0881	2.46779	7.80385	6.59	43.4281	2.56710	8.11788
6.10	37.2100	2.46982	7.81025	**6.60**	43.5600	2.56905	8.12404
6.11	37.3321	2.47184	7.81665	6.61	43.6921	2.57099	8.13019
6.12	37.4544	2.47386	7.82304	6.62	43.8244	2.57294	8.13634
6.13	37.5769	2.47588	7.82943	6.63	43.9569	2.57488	8.14248
6.14	37.6996	2.47790	7.83582	6.64	44.0896	2.57682	8.14862
6.15	37.8225	2.47992	7.84219	6.65	44.2225	2.57876	8.15475
6.16	37.9456	2.48193	7.84857	6.66	44.3556	2.58070	8.16088
6.17	38.0689	2.48395	7.85493	6.67	44.4889	2.58263	8.16701
6.18	38.1924	2.48596	7.86130	6.68	44.6224	2.58457	8.17313
6.19	38.3161	2.48797	7.86766	6.69	44.7561	2.58650	8.17924
6.20	38.4400	2.48998	7.87401	**6.70**	44.8900	2.58844	8.18535
6.21	38.5641	2.49199	7.88036	6.71	45.0241	2.59037	8.19146
6.22	38.6884	2.49399	7.88670	6.72	45.1584	2.59230	8.19756
6.23	38.8129	2.49600	7.89303	6.73	45.2929	2.59422	8.20366
6.24	38.9376	2.49800	7.89937	6.74	45.4276	2.59615	8.20975
6.25	39.0625	2.50000	7.90569	6.75	45.5625	2.59808	8.21584
6.26	39.1876	2.50200	7.91202	6.76	45.6976	2.60000	8.22192
6.27	39.3129	2.50400	7.91833	6.77	45.8329	2.60192	8.22800
6.28	39.4384	2.50599	7.92465	6.78	45.9684	2.60384	8.23408
6.29	39.5641	2.50799	7.93095	6.79	46.1041	2.60576	8.24015
6.30	39.6900	2.50998	7.93725	**6.80**	46.2400	2.60768	8.24621
6.31	39.8161	2.51197	7.94355	6.81	46.3761	2.60960	8.25227
6.32	39.9424	2.51396	7.94984	6.82	46.5124	2.61151	8.25833
6.33	40.0689	2.51595	7.95613	6.83	46.6489	2.61343	8.26438
6.34	40.1956	2.51794	7.96241	6.84	46.7856	2.61534	8.27043
6.35	40.3225	2.51992	7.96869	6.85	46.9225	2.61725	8.27647
6.36	40.4496	2.52190	7.97496	6.86	47.0596	2.61916	8.28251
6.37	40.5769	2.52389	7.98123	6.87	47.1969	2.62107	8.28855
6.38	40.7044	2.52587	7.98749	6.88	47.3344	2.62298	8.29458
6.39	40.8321	2.52784	7.99375	6.89	47.4721	2.62488	8.30060
6.40	40.9600	2.52982	8.00000	**6.90**	47.6100	2.62679	8.30662
6.41	41.0881	2.53180	8.00625	6.91	47.7481	2.62869	8.31264
6.42	41.2164	2.53377	8.01249	6.92	47.8864	2.63059	8.31865
6.43	41.3449	2.53574	8.01873	6.93	48.0249	2.63249	8.32466
6.44	41.4736	2.53772	8.02496	6.94	48.1636	2.63439	8.33067
6.45	41.6025	2.53969	8.03119	6.95	48.3025	2.63629	8.33667
6.46	41.7316	2.54165	8.03741	6.96	48.4416	2.63818	8.34266
6.47	41.8609	2.54362	8.04363	6.97	48.5809	2.64008	8.34865
6.48	41.9904	2.54558	8.04984	6.98	48.7204	2.64197	8.35464
6.49	42.1201	2.54755	8.05605	6.99	48.8601	2.64386	8.36062
6.50	42.2500	2.54951	8.06226	**7.00**	49.0000	2.64575	8.36660
N	N²	√N	√10N	N	N²	√N	√10N

Squares and Square Roots (*Continued*)

N	N²	√N	√10N	N	N²	√N	√10N
7.00	49.0000	2.64575	8.36660	**7.50**	56.2500	2.73861	8.66025
7.01	49.1401	2.64764	8.37257	7.51	56.4001	2.74044	8.66603
7.02	49.2804	2.64953	8.37854	7.52	56.5504	2.74226	8.67179
7.03	49.4209	2.65141	8.38451	7.53	56.7009	2.74408	8.67756
7.04	49.5616	2.65330	8.39047	7.54	56.8516	2.74591	8.68332
7.05	49.7025	2.65518	8.39643	7.55	57.0025	2.74773	8.68907
7.06	49.8436	2.65707	8.40238	7.56	57.1536	2.74955	8.69483
7.07	49.9849	2.65895	8.40833	7.57	57.3049	2.75136	8.70057
7.08	50.1264	2.66083	8.41427	7.58	57.4564	2.75318	8.70632
7.09	50.2681	2.66271	8.42021	7.59	57.6081	2.75500	8.71206
7.10	50.4100	2.66458	8.42615	**7.60**	57.7600	2.75681	8.71780
7.11	50.5521	2.66646	8.43208	7.61	57.9121	2.75862	8.72353
7.12	50.6944	2.66833	8.43801	7.62	58.0644	2.76043	8.72926
7.13	50.8369	2.67021	8.44393	7.63	58.2169	2.76225	8.73499
7.14	50.9796	2.67208	8.44985	7.64	58.3696	2.76405	8.74071
7.15	51.1225	2.67395	8.45577	7.65	58.5225	2.76586	8.74643
7.16	51.2656	2.67582	8.46168	7.66	58.6756	2.76767	8.75214
7.17	51.4089	2.67769	8.46759	7.67	58.8289	2.76948	8.75785
7.18	51.5524	2.67955	8.47349	7.68	58.9824	2.77128	8.76356
7.19	51.6961	2.68142	8.47939	7.69	59.1361	2.77308	8.76926
7.20	51.8400	2.68328	8.48528	**7.70**	59.2900	2.77489	8.77496
7.21	51.9841	2.68514	8.49117	7.71	59.4441	2.77669	8.78066
7.22	52.1284	2.68701	8.49706	7.72	59.5984	2.77849	8.78635
7.23	52.2729	2.68887	8.50294	7.73	59.7529	2.78029	8.79204
7.24	52.4176	2.69072	8.50882	7.74	59.9076	2.78209	8.79773
7.25	52.5625	2.69258	8.51469	7.75	60.0625	2.78388	8.80341
7.26	52.7076	2.69444	8.52056	7.76	60.2176	2.78568	8.80909
7.27	52.8529	2.69629	8.52643	7.77	60.3729	2.78747	8.81476
7.28	52.9984	2.69815	8.53229	7.78	60.5284	2.78927	8.82043
7.29	53.1441	2.70000	8.53815	7.79	60.6841	2.79106	8.82610
7.30	53.2900	2.70185	8.54400	**7.80**	60.8400	2.79285	8.83176
7.31	53.4361	2.70370	8.54985	7.81	60.9961	2.79464	8.83742
7.32	53.5824	2.70555	8.55570	7.82	61.1524	2.79643	8.84308
7.33	53.7289	2.70740	8.56154	7.83	61.3089	2.79821	8.84873
7.34	53.8756	2.70924	8.56738	7.84	61.4656	2.80000	8.85438
7.35	54.0225	2.71109	8.57321	7.85	61.6225	2.80179	8.86002
7.36	54.1696	2.71293	8.57904	7.86	61.7796	2.80357	8.86566
7.37	54.3169	2.71477	8.58487	7.87	61.9369	2.80535	8.87130
7.38	54.4644	2.71662	8.59069	7.88	62.0944	2.80713	8.87694
7.39	54.6121	2.71846	8.59651	7.89	62.2521	2.80891	3.88257
7.40	54.7600	2.72029	8.60233	**7.90**	62.4100	2.81069	8.88819
7.41	54.9081	2.72213	8.60814	7.91	62.5681	2.81247	8.89382
7.42	55.0564	2.72397	8.61394	7.92	62.7264	2.81425	8.89944
7.43	55.2049	2.72580	8.61974	7.93	62.8849	2.81603	8.90505
7.44	55.3536	2.72764	8.62554	7.94	63.0436	2.81780	8.91067
7.45	55.5025	2.72947	8.63134	7.95	63.2025	2.81957	8.91628
7.46	55.6516	2.73130	8.63713	7.96	63.3616	2.82135	8.92188
7.47	55.8009	2.73313	8.64292	7.97	63.5209	2.82312	8.92749
7.48	55.9504	2.73496	8.64870	7.98	63.6804	2.82489	8.93308
7.49	56.1001	2.73679	8.65448	7.99	63.8401	2.82666	8.93868
7.50	56.2500	2.73861	8.66025	**8.00**	64.0000	2.82843	8.94427
N	N²	√N	√10N	N	N²	√N	√10N

N	N²	√N	√10N	N	N²	√N	√10N
8.00	64.0000	2.82843	8.94427	**8.50**	72.2500	2.91548	9.21954
8.01	64.1601	2.83019	8.94986	8.51	72.4201	2.91719	9.22497
8.02	64.3204	2.83196	8.95545	8.52	72.5904	2.91890	9.23038
8.03	64.4809	2.83373	8.96103	8.53	72.7609	2.92062	9.23580
8.04	64.6416	2.83549	8.96660	8.54	72.9316	2.92233	9.24121
8.05	64.8025	2.83725	8.97218	8.55	73.1025	2.92404	9.24662
8.06	64.9636	2.83901	8.97775	8.56	73.2736	2.92575	9.25203
8.07	65 1249	2.84077	8.98332	8.57	73.4449	2.92746	9.25743
8.08	65.2864	2.84253	8.98888	8.58	73.6164	2.92916	9.26283
8.09	65.4481	2.84429	8.99444	8.59	73.7881	2.93087	9.26823
8.10	65.6100	2.84605	9.00000	**8.60**	73.9600	2.93258	9.27362
8.11	65.7721	2.84781	9.00555	8.61	74.1321	2.93428	9.27901
8.12	65.9344	2.84956	9.01110	8.62	74.3044	2.93598	9.28440
8.13	66.0969	2.85132	9.01665	8.63	74.4769	2.93769	9.28978
8.14	66.2596	2.85307	9.02219	8.64	74.6496	2.93939	9.29516
8.15	66.4225	2.85482	9.02774	8.65	74.8225	2.94109	9.30054
8.16	66.5856	2.85657	9.03327	8.66	74.9956	2.94279	9.30591
8.17	66.7489	2.85832	9.03881	8.67	75.1689	2.94449	9.31128
8.18	66.9124	2.86007	9.04434	8.68	75.3424	2.94618	9.31665
8.19	67.0761	2.86182	9.04986	8.69	75.5161	2.94788	9.32202
8.20	67.2400	2.86356	9.05539	**8.70**	75.6900	2.94958	9.32738
8.21	67.4041	2.86531	9.06091	8.71	75.8641	2.95127	9.33274
8.22	67.5684	2.86705	9.06642	8.72	76.0384	2.95296	9.33809
8.23	67.7329	2.86880	9.07193	8.73	76.2129	2.95466	9.34345
8.24	67.8976	2.87054	9.07744	8.74	76.3876	2.95635	9.34880
8.25	68.0625	2.87228	9.08295	8.75	76.5625	2.95804	9.35414
8.26	68.2276	2.87402	9.08845	8.76	76.7376	2.95973	9.35949
8.27	68.3929	2.87576	9.09395	8.77	76.9129	2.96142	9.36483
8.28	68.5584	2.87750	9.09945	8.78	77.0884	2.96311	9.37017
8.29	68.7241	2.87924	9.10494	8.79	77.2641	2.96479	9.37550
8.30	68.8900	2.88097	9.11043	**8.80**	77.4400	2.96648	9.38083
8.31	69.0561	2.88271	9.11592	8.81	77.6161	2.96816	9.38616
8.32	69.2224	2.88444	9.12140	8.82	77.7924	2.96985	9.39149
8.33	69.3889	2.88617	9.12688	8.83	77.9689	2.97153	9.39681
8.34	69.5556	2.88791	9.13236	8.84	78.1456	2.97321	9.40213
8.35	69.7225	2.88964	9.13783	8.85	78.3225	2.97489	9.40744
8.36	69.8896	2.89137	9.14330	8.86	78.4996	2.97658	9.41276
8.37	70.0569	2.89310	9.14877	8.87	78.6769	2.97825	9.41807
8.38	70.2244	2.89482	9.15423	8.88	78.8544	2.97993	9.42338
8.39	70.3921	2.89655	9.15969	8.89	79.0321	2.98161	9.42868
8.40	70.5600	2.89828	9.16515	**8.90**	79.2100	2.98329	9.43398
8.41	70.7281	2.90000	9.17061	8.91	79.3881	2.98496	9.43928
8.42	70.8964	2.90172	9.17606	8.92	79.5664	2.98664	9.44458
8.43	71.0649	2.90345	9.18150	8.93	79.7449	2.98831	9.44987
8.44	71.2336	2.90517	9.18695	8.94	79.9236	2.98998	9.45516
8.45	71.4025	2.90689	9.19239	8.95	80.1025	2.99166	9.46044
8.46	71.5716	2.90861	9.19783	8.96	80.2816	2.99333	9.46573
8.47	71.7409	2.91033	9.20326	8.97	80.4609	2.99500	9.47101
8.48	71.9104	2.91204	9.20869	8.98	80.6404	2.99666	9.47629
8.49	72.0801	2.91376	9.21412	8.99	80.8201	2.99833	9.48156
8.50	72.2500	2.91548	9.21954	**9.00**	81.0000	3.00000	9.48683
N	N²	√N	√10N	N	N²	√N	√10N

Squares and Square Roots (*Continued*)

N	N²	√N	√10N	N	N²	√N	√10N
9.00	81.0000	3.00000	9.48683	**9.50**	90.2500	3.08221	9.74679
9.01	81.1801	3.00167	9.49210	9.51	90.4401	3.08383	9.75192
9.02	81.3604	3.00333	9.49737	9.52	90.6304	3.08545	9.75705
9.03	81.5409	3.00500	9.50263	9.53	90.8209	3.08707	9.76217
9.04	81.7216	3.00666	9.50789	9.54	91.0116	3.08869	9.76729
9.05	81.9025	3.00832	9.51315	9.55	91.2025	3.09031	9.77241
9.06	82.0836	3.00998	9.51840	9.56	91.3936	3.09192	9.77753
9.07	82.2649	3.01164	9.52365	9.57	91.5849	3.09354	9.78264
9.08	82.4464	3.01330	9.52890	9.58	91.7764	3.09516	9.78775
9.09	82.6281	3.01496	9.53415	9.59	91.9681	3.09677	9.79285
9.10	82.8100	3.01662	9.53939	**9.60**	92.1600	3.09839	9.79796
9.11	82.9921	3.01828	9.54463	9.61	92.3521	3.10000	9.80306
9.12	83.1744	3.01993	9.54987	9.62	92.5444	3.10161	9.80816
9.13	83.3569	3.02159	9.55510	9.63	92.7369	3.10322	9.81326
9.14	83.5396	3.02324	9.56033	9.64	92.9296	3.10483	9.81835
9.15	83.7225	3.02490	9.56556	9.65	93.1225	3.10644	9.82344
9.16	83.9056	3.02655	9.57079	9.66	93.3156	3.10805	9.82853
9.17	84.0889	3.02820	9.57601	9.67	93.5089	3.10966	9.83362
9.18	84.2724	3.02985	9.58123	9.68	93.7024	3.11127	9.83870
9.19	84.4561	3.03150	9.58645	9.69	93.8961	3.11288	9.84378
9.20	84.6400	3.03315	9.59166	**9.70**	94.0900	3.11448	9.84886
9.21	84.8241	3.03480	9.59687	9.71	94.2841	3.11609	9.85393
9.22	85.0084	3.03645	9.60208	9.72	94.4784	3.11769	9.85901
9.23	85.1929	3.03809	9.60729	9.73	94.6729	3.11929	9.86408
9.24	85.3776	3.03974	9.61249	9.74	94.8676	3.12090	9.86914
9.25	85.5625	3.04138	9.61769	9.75	95.0625	3.12250	9.87421
9.26	85.7476	3.04302	9.62289	9.76	95.2576	3.12410	9.87927
9.27	85.9329	3.04467	9.62808	9.77	95.4529	3.12570	9.88433
9.28	86.1184	3.04631	9.63328	9.78	95.6484	3.12730	9.88939
9.29	86.3041	3.04795	9.63846	9.79	95.8441	3.12890	9.89444
9.30	86.4900	3.04959	9.64365	**9.80**	96.0400	3.13050	9.89949
9.31	86.6761	3.05123	9.64883	9.81	96.2361	3.13209	9.90454
9.32	86.8624	3.05287	9.65401	9.82	96.4324	3.13369	9.90959
9.33	87.0489	3.05450	9.65919	9.83	96.6289	3.13528	9.91464
9.34	87.2356	3.05614	9.66437	9.84	96.8256	3.13688	9.91968
9.35	87.4225	3.05778	9.66954	9.85	97.0225	3.13847	9.92472
9.36	87.6096	3.05941	9.67471	9.86	97.2196	3.14006	9.92975
9.37	87.7969	3.06105	9.67988	9.87	97.4169	3.14166	9.93479
9.38	87.9844	3.06268	9.68504	9.88	97.6144	3.14325	9.93982
9.39	88.1721	3.06431	9.69020	9.89	97.8121	3.14484	9.94485
9.40	88.3600	3.06594	9.69536	**9.90**	98.0100	3.14643	9.94987
9.41	88.5481	3.06757	9.70052	9.91	98.2081	3.14802	9.95490
9.42	88.7364	3.06920	9.70567	9.92	98.4064	3.14960	9.95992
9.43	88.9249	3.07083	9.71082	9.93	98.6049	3.15119	9.96494
9.44	89.1136	3.07246	9.71597	9.94	98.8036	3.15278	9.96995
9.45	89.3025	3.07409	9.72111	9.95	99.0025	3.15436	9.97497
9.46	89.4916	3.07571	9.72625	9.96	99.2016	3.15595	9.97998
9.47	89.6809	3.07734	9.73139	9.97	99.4009	3.15753	9.98499
9.48	89.8704	3.07896	9.73653	9.98	99.6004	3.15911	9.98999
9.49	90.0601	3.08058	9.74166	9.99	99.8001	3.16070	9.99500
9.50	90.2500	3.08221	9.74679	**10.00**	100.000	3.16228	10.0000
N	N²	√N	√10N	N	N²	√N	√10N

TABLE II. Random Digits

03991	10461	93716	16894	98953	73231	39528	72484	82474	25593
38555	95554	32886	59780	09958	18065	81616	18711	53342	44276
17546	73704	92052	46215	15917	06253	07586	16120	82641	22820
32643	52861	95819	06831	19640	99413	90767	04235	13574	17200
69572	68777	39510	35905	85244	35159	40188	28193	29593	88627
24122	66591	27699	06494	03152	19121	34414	82157	86887	55087
61196	30231	92962	61773	22109	78508	63439	75363	44989	16822
30532	21704	10274	12202	94205	20380	67049	09070	93399	45547
03788	97599	75867	20717	82037	10268	79495	04146	52162	90286
48228	63379	85783	47619	87481	37220	91704	30552	04737	21031
88618	19161	41290	67312	71857	15957	48545	35247	18619	13674
71299	23853	05870	01119	92784	26340	75122	11724	74627	73707
27954	58909	82444	99005	04921	73701	92904	13141	32392	19763
80863	00514	20247	81759	45197	25332	69902	63742	78464	22501
33564	60780	48460	85558	15191	18782	94972	11598	62095	36787
90899	75754	60833	25983	01291	41349	19152	00023	12302	80783
78038	70267	43529	06318	38384	74761	36024	00867	76378	41605
55986	66485	88722	56736	66164	49431	94458	74284	05041	49807
87539	08823	94813	31900	54155	83436	54158	34243	46978	35482
16818	60311	74457	90561	72848	11834	75051	93029	47665	64382
34677	58300	74910	64345	19325	81549	60365	94653	35075	33949
45305	07521	61318	31855	14413	70951	83799	42402	56623	34442
59747	67277	76503	34513	39663	77544	32960	07405	36409	83232
16520	69676	11654	99893	02181	68161	19322	53845	57620	52606
68652	27376	92852	55866	88448	03584	11220	94747	07399	37408
79375	95220	01159	63267	10622	48391	31751	57260	68980	05339
33521	26665	55823	47641	86225	31704	88492	99382	14454	04504
59589	49067	66821	41575	49767	04037	30934	47744	07481	83828
20554	91409	96277	48257	50816	97616	22888	48893	27499	98748
59404	72059	43947	51680	43852	59693	78212	16993	35902	91386
42614	29297	01918	28316	25163	01889	70014	15021	68971	11403
34994	41374	70071	14736	65251	07629	37239	33295	18477	65622
99385	41600	11133	07586	36815	43625	18637	37509	14707	93997
66497	68646	78138	66559	64397	11692	05327	82162	83745	22567
48509	23929	27482	45476	04515	25624	95096	67946	16930	33361
15470	48355	88651	22596	83761	60873	43253	84145	20368	07126
20094	98977	74843	93413	14387	06345	80854	09279	41196	37480
73788	06533	28597	20405	51321	92246	80088	77074	66919	31678
60530	45128	74022	84617	72472	00008	80890	18002	35352	54131
44372	15486	65741	14014	05466	55306	93128	18464	79982	68416
18611	19241	66083	24653	84609	58232	41849	84547	46850	52326
58319	15997	08355	60860	29735	47762	46352	33049	69248	93460
61199	67940	55121	29281	59076	07936	11087	96294	14013	31792
18627	90872	00911	98936	76355	93779	52701	08337	56303	87315
00441	58997	14060	40619	29549	69616	57275	36898	81304	48585
32624	68691	14845	46672	61958	77100	20857	73156	70284	24326
65961	73488	41839	55382	17267	70943	15633	84924	90415	93614
20288	34060	39685	23309	10061	68829	92694	48297	39904	02115
59362	95938	74416	53166	35208	33374	77613	19019	88152	00080
99782	93478	53152	67433	35663	52972	38688	32486	45134	63545

TABLE II (*Continued*)

27767	43584	85301	88977	29490	69714	94015	64874	32444	48277
13025	14338	54066	15243	47724	66733	74108	88222	88570	74015
80217	36292	98525	24335	24432	24896	62880	87873	95160	59221
10875	62004	90391	61105	57411	06368	11748	12102	80580	41867
54127	57326	26629	19087	24472	88779	17944	05600	60478	03343
60311	42824	37301	42678	45990	43242	66067	42792	95043	52680
49739	71484	92003	98086	76668	73209	54244	91030	45547	70818
78626	51594	16453	94614	39014	97066	30945	57589	31732	57260
66692	13986	99837	00582	81232	44987	69170	37403	86995	90307
44071	28091	07362	97703	76447	42537	08345	88975	35841	85771
59820	96163	78851	16499	87064	13075	73035	41207	74699	09310
25704	91035	26313	77463	55387	72681	47431	43905	31048	56699
22304	90314	78438	66276	18396	73538	43277	58874	11466	16082
17710	59621	15292	76139	59526	52113	53856	30743	08670	84741
25852	58905	55018	56374	35824	71708	30540	27886	61732	75454
46780	56487	75211	10271	36633	68424	17374	52003	70707	70214
59849	96169	87195	46092	26787	60939	59202	11973	02902	33250
47670	07654	30342	40277	11049	72049	83012	09832	25571	77628
94304	71803	73465	09819	58869	35220	09504	96412	90193	79568
08105	59987	21437	36786	49226	77837	98524	97831	65704	09514
64281	61826	18555	64937	64654	25843	41145	42820	14924	39650
66847	70495	32350	02985	01755	14750	48968	38603	70312	05682
72461	33230	21529	53424	72877	17334	39283	04149	90850	64618
21032	91050	13058	16218	06554	07850	73950	79552	24781	89683
95362	67011	06651	16136	57216	39618	49856	99326	40902	05069
49712	97380	10404	55452	09971	59481	37006	22186	72682	07385
58275	61764	97586	54716	61459	21647	87417	17198	21443	41808
89514	11788	68224	23417	46376	25366	94746	49580	01176	28838
15472	50669	48139	36732	26825	05511	12459	91314	80582	71944
12120	86124	51247	44302	87112	21476	14713	71181	13177	55292
95294	00556	70481	06905	21785	41101	49386	54480	23604	23554
66986	34099	74474	20740	47458	64809	06312	88940	15995	69321
80620	51790	11436	38072	40405	68032	60942	00307	11897	92674
55411	85667	77535	99892	71209	92061	92329	98932	78284	46347
95083	06783	28102	57816	85561	29671	77936	63574	31384	51924
90726	57166	98884	08583	95889	57067	38101	77756	11657	13897
68984	83620	89747	98882	92613	89719	39641	69457	91339	22502
36421	16489	18059	51061	67667	60631	84054	40455	99396	63680
92638	40333	67054	16067	24700	71594	47468	03577	57649	63266
21036	82808	77501	97427	76479	68562	43321	31370	28977	23896
13173	33365	41468	85149	49554	17994	91178	10174	29420	90438
86716	38746	94559	37559	49678	53119	98189	81851	29651	84215
92581	02262	41615	70360	64114	58660	96717	54244	10701	41393
12470	56500	50273	93113	41794	86861	39448	93136	25722	08564
01016	00857	41396	80504	90670	08289	58137	17820	22751	36518
34030	60726	25807	24260	71529	78920	47648	13885	70669	93406
50259	46345	06170	97965	88302	98041	11947	56203	19324	20504
73959	76145	60808	54444	74412	81105	69181	96845	38525	11600
46874	37088	80940	44893	10408	3622.`	14004	23153	69249	05747
60883	52109	19516	90120	46759	71643	62342	07589	08899	05985

TABLE III.　Binomial Coefficients $\dfrac{n!}{x!(n-x)!}$

n \ x	2	3	4	5	6	7	8	9	10
2	1								
3	3	1							
4	6	4	1						
5	10	10	5	1					
6	15	20	15	6	1				
7	21	35	35	21	7	1			
8	28	56	70	56	28	8	1		
9	36	84	126	126	84	36	9	1	
10	45	120	210	252	210	120	45	10	1
11	55	165	330	462	462	330	165	55	11
12	66	220	495	792	924	792	495	220	66
13	78	286	715	1,287	1,716	1,716	1,287	715	286
14	91	364	1,001	2,002	3,003	3,432	3,003	2,002	1,001
15	105	455	1,365	3,003	5,005	6,435	6,435	5,005	3,003
16	120	560	1,820	4,368	8,008	11,440	12,870	11,440	8,008
17	136	680	2,380	6,188	12,376	19,448	24,310	24,310	19,448
18	153	816	3,060	8,568	18,564	31,824	43,758	48,620	43,758
19	171	969	3,876	11,628	27,132	50,388	75,582	92,378	92,378
20	190	1,140	4,845	15,504	38,760	77,520	125,970	167,960	184,756

TABLE IV. Areas of a Standard Normal Distribution

An entry in the table is the proportion under the
entire curve which is between $z = 0$ and a positive
value of z. Areas for negative values of z are
obtained by symmetry.

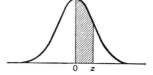

z	.00	.01	.02	.03	.04	.05	.06	.07	.08	.09
0.0	.0000	.0040	.0080	.0120	.0160	.0199	.0239	.0279	.0319	.0359
0.1	.0398	.0438	.0478	.0517	.0557	.0596	.0636	.0675	.0714	.0753
0.2	.0793	.0832	.0871	.0910	.0948	.0987	.1026	.1064	.1103	.1141
0.3	.1179	.1217	.1255	.1293	.1331	.1368	.1406	.1443	.1480	.1517
0.4	.1554	.1591	.1628	.1664	.1700	.1736	.1772	.1808	.1844	.1879
0.5	.1915	.1950	.1985	.2019	.2054	.2088	.2123	.2157	.2190	.2224
0.6	.2257	.2291	.2324	.2357	.2389	.2422	.2454	.2486	.2517	.2549
0.7	.2580	.2611	.2642	.2673	.2703	.2734	.2764	.2794	.2823	.2852
0.8	.2881	.2910	.2939	.2967	.2995	.3023	.3051	.3078	.3106	.3133
0.9	.3159	.3186	.3212	.3238	.3264	.3289	.3315	.3340	.3365	.3389
1.0	.3413	.3438	.3461	.3485	.3508	.3531	.3554	.3577	.3599	.3621
1.1	.3643	.3665	.3686	.3708	.3729	.3749	.3770	.3790	.3810	.3830
1.2	.3849	.3869	.3888	.3907	.3925	.3944	.3962	.3980	.3997	.4015
1.3	.4032	.4049	.4066	.4082	.4099	.4115	.4131	.4147	.4162	.4177
1.4	.4192	.4207	.4222	.4236	.4251	.4265	.4279	.4292	.4306	.4319
1.5	.4332	.4345	.4357	.4370	.4382	.4394	.4406	.4418	.4429	.4441
1.6	.4452	.4463	.4474	.4484	.4495	.4505	.4515	.4525	.4535	.4545
1.7	.4554	.4564	.4573	.4582	.4591	.4599	.4608	.4616	.4625	.4633
1.8	.4641	.4649	.4656	.4664	.4671	.4678	.4686	.4693	.4699	.4706
1.9	.4713	.4719	.4726	.4732	.4738	.4744	.4750	.4756	.4761	.4767
2.0	.4772	.4778	.4783	.4788	.4793	.4798	.4803	.4808	.4812	.4817
2.1	.4821	.4826	.4830	.4834	.4838	.4842	.4846	.4850	.4854	.4857
2.2	.4861	.4864	.4868	.4871	.4875	.4878	.4881	.4884	.4887	.4890
2.3	.4893	.4896	.4898	.4901	.4904	.4906	.4909	.4911	.4913	.4916
2.4	.4918	.4920	.4922	.4925	.4927	.4929	.4931	.4932	.4934	.4936
2.5	.4938	.4940	.4941	.4943	.4945	.4946	.4948	.4949	.4951	.4952
2.6	.4953	.4955	.4956	.4957	.4959	.4960	.4961	.4962	.4963	.4964
2.7	.4965	.4966	.4967	.4968	.4969	.4970	.4971	.4972	.4973	.4974
2.8	.4974	.4975	.4976	.4977	.4977	.4978	.4979	.4979	.4980	.4981
2.9	.4981	.4982	.4982	.4983	.4984	.4984	.4985	.4985	.4986	.4986
3.0	.4987	.4987	.4987	.4988	.4988	.4989	.4989	.4989	.4990	.4990

TABLE V. Student's t Distribution

The first column lists the number of degrees of freedom (ν). The headings of the other columns give probabilities (P) for t to exceed numerically the entry value.

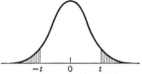

P / ν	0.50	0.25	0.10	0.05	0.025	0.01	0.005
1	1.00000	2.4142	6.3138	12.706	25.452	63.657	127.32
2	0.81650	1.6036	2.9200	4.3027	6.2053	9.9248	14.089
3	0.76489	1.4226	2.3534	3.1825	4.1765	5.8409	7.4533
4	0.74070	1.3444	2.1318	2.7764	3.4954	4.6041	5.5976
5	0.72669	1.3009	2.0150	2.5706	3.1634	4.0321	4.7733
6	0.71756	1.2733	1.9432	2.4469	2.9687	3.7074	4.3168
7	0.71114	1.2543	1.8946	2.3646	2.8412	3.4995	4.0293
8	0.70639	1.2403	1.8595	2.3060	2.7515	3.3554	3.8325
9	0.70272	1.2297	1.8331	2.2622	2.6850	3.2498	3.6897
10	0.69981	1.2213	1.8125	2.2281	2.6338	3.1693	3.5814
11	0.69745	1.2145	1.7959	2.2010	2.5931	3.1058	3.4966
12	0.69548	1.2089	1.7823	2.1788	2.5600	3.0545	3.4284
13	0.69384	1.2041	1.7709	2.1604	2.5326	3.0123	3.3725
14	0.69242	1.2001	1.7613	2.1448	2.5096	2.9768	3.3257
15	0.69120	1.1967	1.7530	2.1315	2.4899	2.9467	3.2860
16	0.69013	1.1937	1.7459	2.1199	2.4729	2.9208	3.2520
17	0.68919	1.1910	1.7396	2.1098	2.4581	2.8982	3.2225
18	0.68837	1.1887	1.7341	2.1009	2.4450	2.8784	3.1966
19	0.68763	1.1866	1.7291	2.0930	2.4334	2.8609	3.1737
20	0.68696	1.1848	1.7247	2.0860	2.4231	2.8453	3.1534
21	0.68635	1.1831	1.7207	2.0796	2.4138	2.8314	3.1352
22	0.68580	1.1816	1.7171	2.0739	2.4055	2.8188	3.1188
23	0.68531	1.1802	1.7139	2.0687	2.3979	2.8073	3.1040
24	0.68485	1.1789	1.7109	2.0639	2.3910	2.7969	3.0905
25	0.68443	1.1777	1.7081	2.0595	2.3846	2.7874	3.0782
26	0.68405	1.1766	1.7056	2.0555	2.3788	2.7787	3.0669
27	0.68370	1.1757	1.7033	2.0518	2.3734	2.7707	3.0565
28	0.68335	1.1748	1.7011	2.0484	2.3685	2.7633	3.0469
29	0.68304	1.1739	1.6991	2.0452	2.3638	2.7564	3.0380
30	0.68276	1.1731	1.6973	2.0423	2.3596	2.7500	3.0298
40	0.68066	1.1673	1.6839	2.0211	2.3289	2.7045	2.9712
60	0.67862	1.1616	1.6707	2.0003	2.2991	2.6603	2.9146
120	0.67656	1.1559	1.6577	1.9799	2.2699	2.6174	2.8599
∞	0.67449	1.1503	1.6449	1.9600	2.2414	2.5758	2.8070

TABLE VI. Values of $w = \dfrac{1}{2}\log_e \dfrac{1+r}{1-r}$

r	w	r	w	r	w	r	w
.00	.000	.25	.255	.50	.549	.75	.973
.01	.010	.26	.266	.51	.563	.76	.996
.02	.020	.27	.277	.52	.576	.77	1.020
.03	.030	.28	.288	.53	.590	.78	1.045
.04	.040	.29	.299	.54	.604	.79	1.071
.05	.050	.30	.310	.55	.618	.80	1.099
.06	.060	.31	.321	.56	.633	.81	1.127
.07	.070	.32	.332	.57	.648	.82	1.157
.08	.080	.33	.343	.58	.662	.83	1.188
.09	.090	.34	.354	.59	.678	.84	1.221
.10	.100	.35	.365	.60	.693	.85	1.256
.11	.110	.36	.377	.61	.709	.86	1.293
.12	.121	.37	.388	.62	.725	.87	1.333
.13	.131	.38	.400	.63	.741	.88	1.376
.14	.141	.39	.412	.64	.758	.89	1.422
.15	.151	.40	.424	.65	.775	.90	1.472
.16	.161	.41	.436	.66	.793	.91	1.528
.17	.172	.42	.448	.67	.811	.92	1.589
.18	.182	.43	.460	.68	.829	.93	1.658
.19	.192	.44	.472	.69	.848	.94	1.738
.20	.203	.45	.485	.70	.867	.95	1.832
.21	.213	.46	.497	.71	.887	.96	1.946
.22	.224	.47	.510	.72	.908	.97	2.092
.23	.234	.48	.523	.73	.929	.98	2.298
.24	.245	.49	.536	.74	.950	.99	2.647

TABLE VII. The χ^2 Distribution

The first column lists the number of degrees of
freedom (v). The headings of the other columns
give probabilities (P) for χ^2 to exceed the entry
value. For $v > 100$, treat $\sqrt{2\chi^2} - \sqrt{2v - 1}$ as a
standard normal variable.

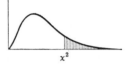

v \ P	0.995	0.975	0.050	0.025	0.010	0.005
1	0.0⁴3927	0.0³9821	3.84146	5.02389	6.63490	7.87944
2	0.010025	0.050636	5.99147	7.37776	9.21034	10.5966
3	0.071721	0.215795	7.81473	9.34840	11.3449	12.8381
4	0.206990	0.484419	9.48773	11.1433	13.2767	14.8602
5	0.411740	0.831211	11.0705	12.8325	15.0863	16.7496
6	0.675727	1.237347	12.5916	14.4494	16.8119	18.5476
7	0.989265	1.68987	14.0671	16.0128	18.4753	20.2777
8	1.344419	2.17973	15.5073	17.5346	20.0902	21.9550
9	1.734926	2.70039	16.9190	19.0228	21.6660	23.5893
10	2.15585	3.24697	18.3070	20.4831	23.2093	25.1882
11	2.60321	3.81575	19.6751	21.9200	24.7250	26.7569
12	3.07382	4.40379	21.0261	23.3367	26.2170	28.2995
13	3.56503	5.00874	22.3621	24.7356	27.6883	29.8194
14	4.07468	5.62872	23.6848	26.1190	29.1413	31.3193
15	4.60094	6.26214	24.9958	27.4884	30.5779	32.8013
16	5.14224	6.90766	26.2962	28.8454	31.9999	34.2672
17	5.69724	7.56418	27.5871	30.1910	33.4087	35.7185
18	6.26481	8.23075	28.8693	31.5264	34.8053	37.1564
19	6.84398	8.90655	30.1435	32.8523	36.1908	38.5822
20	7.43386	9.59083	31.4104	34.1696	37.5662	39.9968
21	8.03366	10.28293	32.6705	35.4789	38.9321	41.4010
22	8.64272	10.9823	33.9244	36.7807	40.2894	42.7956
23	9.26042	11.6885	35.1725	38.0757	41.6384	44.1813
24	9.88623	12.4001	36.4151	39.3641	42.9798	45.5585
25	10.5197	13.1197	37.6525	40.6465	44.3141	46.9278
26	11.1603	13.8439	38.8852	41.9232	45.6417	48.2899
27	11.8076	14.5733	40.1133	43.1944	46.9630	49.6449
28	12.4613	15.3079	41.3372	44.4607	48.2782	50.9933
29	13.1211	16.0471	42.5569	45.7222	49.5879	52.3356
30	13.7867	16.7908	43.7729	46.9792	50.8922	53.6720
40	20.7065	24.4331	55.7585	59.3417	63.6907	66.7659
50	27.9907	32.3574	67.5048	71.4202	76.1539	79.4900
60	35.5346	40.4817	79.0819	83.2976	88.3794	91.9517
70	43.2752	48.7576	90.5312	95.0231	100.425	104.215
80	51.1720	57.1532	101.879	106.629	112.329	116.321
90	59.1963	65.6466	113.145	118.136	124.116	128.299
100	67.3276	74.2219	124.342	129.561	135.807	140.169

TABLE VIII.   Rank-Sum Critical Values

The sample sizes are shown in parentheses (n_1, n_2). The probability associated with a pair of critical values is the probability that $R \leq$ smaller value, or equally, it is the probability that $R \geq$ larger value. These probabilities are the closest ones to .025 and .05 that exist for integer values of R. The approximate .025 values should be used for a two-sided test with $\alpha = .05$, and the approximate .05 values for a one-sided test.

(2, 4)			(4, 4)			(6, 7)		
3	11	.067	11	25	.029	28	56	.026
(2, 5)			12	24	.057	30	54	.051
3	13	.047	(4, 5)			(6, 8)		
(2, 6)			12	28	.032	29	61	.021
3	15	.036	13	27	.056	32	58	.054
4	14	.071	(4, 6)			(6, 9)		
(2, 7)			12	32	.019	31	65	.025
3	17	.028	14	30	.057	33	63	.044
4	16	.056	(4, 7)			(6, 10)		
(2, 8)			13	35	.021	33	69	.028
3	19	.022	15	33	.055	35	67	.047
4	18	.044	(4, 8)			(7, 7)		
(2, 9)			14	38	.024	37	68	.027
3	21	.018	16	36	.055	39	66	.049
4	20	.036	(4, 9)			(7, 8)		
(2, 10)			15	41	.025	39	73	.027
4	22	.030	17	39	.053	41	71	.047
5	21	.061	(4, 10)			(7, 9)		
(3, 3)			16	44	.026	41	78	.027
6	15	.050	18	42	.053	43	76	.045
(3, 4)			(5, 5)			(7, 10)		
6	18	.028	18	37	.028	43	83	.028
7	17	.057	19	36	.048	46	80	.054
(3, 5)			(5, 6)			(8, 8)		
6	21	.018	19	41	.026	49	87	.025
7	20	.036	20	40	.041	52	84	.052
(3, 6)			(5, 7)			(8, 9)		
7	23	.024	20	45	.024	51	93	.023
8	22	.048	22	43	.053	54	90	.046
(3, 7)			(5, 8)			(8, 10)		
8	25	.033	21	49	.023	54	98	.027
9	24	.058	23	47	.047	57	95	.051
(3, 8)			(5, 9)			(9, 9)		
8	28	.024	22	53	.021	63	108	.025
9	27	.042	25	50	.056	66	105	.047
(3, 9)			(5, 10)			(9, 10)		
9	30	.032	24	56	.028	66	114	.027
10	29	.050	26	54	.050	69	111	.047
(3, 10)			(6, 6)			(10, 10)		
9	33	.024	26	52	.021	79	131	.026
11	31	.056	28	50	.047	83	127	.053

TABLE IX. Rank Correlation Coefficient

n	Significance level (one-sided test)	
	.05	.01
4	1.000	
5	.900	1.000
6	.829	.943
7	.714	.893
8	.643	.833
9	.600	.783
10	.564	.746
12	.504	.701
14	.456	.645
16	.425	.601
18	.399	.564
20	.377	.534
22	.359	.508
24	.343	.485
26	.329	.465
28	.317	.448
30	.306	.432

TABLE X. Critical Values for Total Runs (u)

For $n_1 > 20$ or $n_2 > 20$, one may treat u as a normal variable with mean and standard deviation given by

$$\mu_u = \frac{2n_1 n_2}{n_1 + n_2} + 1, \qquad \sigma_u = \sqrt{\frac{2n_1 n_2 (2n_1 n_2 - n_1 - n_2)}{(n_1 + n_2)^2 (n_1 + n_2 - 1)}}$$

The larger of n_1 and n_2

Each cell gives the lower/upper critical value.

smaller of n_1 and n_2	5	6	7	8	9	10	11	12	13	14	15	16	17	18	19	20
2								2/6	2/6	2/6	2/6	2/6	2/6	2/6	2/6	2/6
3		2/8	2/8	2/8	2/8	2/8	2/8	2/8	2/8	2/8	3/8	3/8	3/8	3/8	3/8	3/8
4	2/9	2/9	2/10	3/10	3/10	3/10	3/10	3/10	3/10	3/10	3/10	4/10	4/10	4/10	4/10	4/10
5	2/10	3/10	3/11	3/11	3/12	3/12	4/12	4/12	4/12	4/12	4/12	4/12	4/12	5/12	5/12	5/12
6		3/11	3/12	3/12	4/13	4/13	4/13	4/13	5/14	5/14	5/14	5/14	5/14	5/14	6/14	6/14
7			3/13	4/13	4/14	5/14	5/14	5/14	5/15	5/15	5/15	6/16	6/16	6/16	6/16	6/16
8				4/14	5/14	5/15	5/15	6/16	6/16	6/16	6/16	6/17	7/17	7/17	7/17	7/17
9					5/15	5/16	6/16	6/16	6/17	7/17	7/18	7/18	7/18	8/18	8/18	8/18
10						6/16	6/17	7/17	7/18	7/18	7/18	8/19	8/19	8/19	8/20	9/20
11							7/17	7/18	7/19	8/19	8/19	8/20	9/20	9/20	9/21	9/21
12								7/19	8/19	8/20	8/20	9/21	9/21	9/21	10/22	10/22
13									8/20	9/20	9/21	9/21	10/22	10/22	10/23	10/23
14										9/21	9/22	10/22	10/23	10/23	11/23	11/24
15											10/22	10/23	11/23	11/24	11/24	12/25
16												11/23	11/24	11/25	12/25	12/25
17													11/25	12/25	12/26	13/26
18														12/26	13/26	13/27
19															13/27	13/27
20																14/28

TABLE XI. F Distribution

5% (Roman Type) and 1% (Boldface Type) Points for the Distribution of F

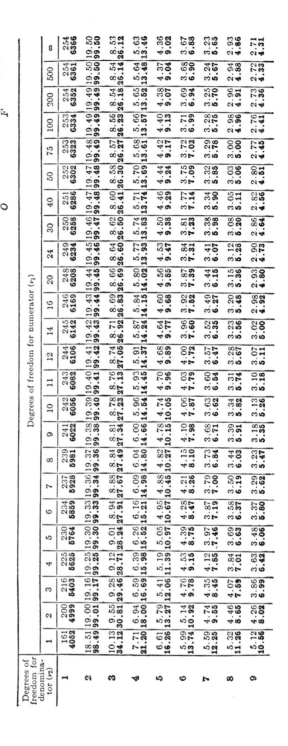

Degrees of freedom for numerator (ν_1)

Degrees of freedom for denominator (ν_2)	1	2	3	4	5	6	7	8	9	10	11	12	14	16	20	24	30	40	50	75	100	200	500	∞
1	161 **4052**	200 **4999**	216 **5403**	225 **5625**	230 **5764**	234 **5859**	237 **5928**	239 **5981**	241 **6022**	242 **6056**	243 **6082**	244 **6106**	245 **6142**	246 **6169**	248 **6208**	249 **6234**	250 **6258**	251 **6286**	252 **6302**	253 **6323**	253 **6334**	254 **6352**	254 **6361**	254 **6366**
2	18.51 **98.49**	19.00 **99.01**	19.16 **99.17**	19.25 **99.25**	19.30 **99.30**	19.33 **99.33**	19.36 **99.34**	19.37 **99.36**	19.38 **99.38**	19.39 **99.40**	19.40 **99.41**	19.41 **99.42**	19.42 **99.43**	19.43 **99.44**	19.44 **99.45**	19.45 **99.46**	19.46 **99.47**	19.47 **99.48**	19.47 **99.48**	19.48 **99.49**	19.49 **99.49**	19.49 **99.49**	19.50 **99.50**	19.50 **99.50**
3	10.13 **34.12**	9.55 **30.81**	9.28 **29.46**	9.12 **28.71**	9.01 **28.24**	8.94 **27.91**	8.88 **27.67**	8.84 **27.49**	8.81 **27.34**	8.78 **27.23**	8.76 **27.13**	8.74 **27.05**	8.71 **26.92**	8.69 **26.83**	8.66 **26.69**	8.64 **26.60**	8.62 **26.50**	8.60 **26.41**	8.58 **26.30**	8.57 **26.27**	8.56 **26.23**	8.54 **26.18**	8.54 **26.14**	8.53 **26.12**
4	7.71 **21.20**	6.94 **18.00**	6.59 **16.69**	6.39 **15.98**	6.26 **15.52**	6.16 **15.21**	6.09 **14.98**	6.04 **14.80**	6.00 **14.66**	5.96 **14.54**	5.93 **14.45**	5.91 **14.37**	5.87 **14.24**	5.84 **14.15**	5.80 **14.02**	5.77 **13.93**	5.74 **13.83**	5.71 **13.74**	5.70 **13.69**	5.68 **13.61**	5.66 **13.57**	5.65 **13.52**	5.64 **13.48**	5.63 **13.46**
5	6.61 **16.26**	5.79 **13.27**	5.41 **12.06**	5.19 **11.39**	5.05 **10.97**	4.95 **10.67**	4.88 **10.45**	4.82 **10.27**	4.78 **10.15**	4.74 **10.05**	4.70 **9.96**	4.68 **9.89**	4.64 **9.77**	4.60 **9.68**	4.56 **9.55**	4.53 **9.47**	4.50 **9.38**	4.46 **9.29**	4.44 **9.24**	4.42 **9.17**	4.40 **9.13**	4.38 **9.07**	4.37 **9.04**	4.36 **9.02**
6	5.99 **13.74**	5.14 **10.92**	4.76 **9.78**	4.53 **9.15**	4.39 **8.75**	4.28 **8.47**	4.21 **8.26**	4.15 **8.10**	4.10 **7.98**	4.06 **7.87**	4.03 **7.79**	4.00 **7.72**	3.96 **7.60**	3.92 **7.52**	3.87 **7.39**	3.84 **7.31**	3.81 **7.23**	3.77 **7.14**	3.75 **7.09**	3.72 **7.02**	3.71 **6.99**	3.69 **6.94**	3.68 **6.90**	3.67 **6.88**
7	5.59 **12.25**	4.74 **9.55**	4.35 **8.45**	4.12 **7.85**	3.97 **7.46**	3.87 **7.19**	3.79 **7.00**	3.73 **6.84**	3.68 **6.71**	3.63 **6.62**	3.60 **6.54**	3.57 **6.47**	3.52 **6.35**	3.49 **6.27**	3.44 **6.15**	3.41 **6.07**	3.38 **5.98**	3.34 **5.90**	3.32 **5.85**	3.29 **5.78**	3.28 **5.75**	3.25 **5.70**	3.24 **5.67**	3.23 **5.65**
8	5.32 **11.26**	4.46 **8.65**	4.07 **7.59**	3.84 **7.01**	3.69 **6.63**	3.58 **6.37**	3.50 **6.19**	3.44 **6.03**	3.39 **5.91**	3.34 **5.82**	3.31 **5.74**	3.28 **5.67**	3.23 **5.56**	3.20 **5.48**	3.15 **5.36**	3.12 **5.28**	3.08 **5.20**	3.05 **5.11**	3.03 **5.06**	3.00 **5.00**	2.98 **4.96**	2.96 **4.91**	2.94 **4.88**	2.93 **4.86**
9	5.12 **10.56**	4.26 **8.02**	3.86 **6.99**	3.63 **6.42**	3.48 **6.06**	3.37 **5.80**	3.29 **5.62**	3.23 **5.47**	3.18 **5.35**	3.13 **5.26**	3.10 **5.18**	3.07 **5.11**	3.02 **5.00**	2.98 **4.92**	2.93 **4.80**	2.90 **4.73**	2.86 **4.64**	2.82 **4.56**	2.80 **4.51**	2.77 **4.45**	2.76 **4.41**	2.73 **4.36**	2.72 **4.33**	2.71 **4.31**

	1	2	3	4	5	6	7	8	9	10	11	12	13	14	15	16	17	18	19	20	21	22	23	24
10	2.54 / 3.91	2.55 / 3.93	2.56 / 3.96	2.59 / 4.01	2.61 / 4.05	2.64 / 4.12	2.67 / 4.17	2.70 / 4.25	2.74 / 4.33	2.77 / 4.41	2.82 / 4.52	2.86 / 4.60	2.91 / 4.71	2.94 / 4.78	2.97 / 4.85	3.02 / 4.95	3.07 / 5.06	3.14 / 5.21	3.22 / 5.39	3.33 / 5.64	3.48 / 5.99	3.71 / 6.55	4.10 / 7.56	4.96 / 10.04
11	2.40 / 3.60	2.41 / 3.62	2.42 / 3.66	2.45 / 3.70	2.47 / 3.74	2.50 / 3.80	2.53 / 3.86	2.57 / 3.94	2.61 / 4.02	2.65 / 4.10	2.70 / 4.21	2.74 / 4.29	2.79 / 4.40	2.82 / 4.46	2.86 / 4.54	2.90 / 4.63	2.95 / 4.74	3.01 / 4.88	3.09 / 5.07	3.20 / 5.32	3.36 / 5.67	3.59 / 6.22	3.98 / 7.20	4.84 / 9.65
12	2.30 / 3.36	2.31 / 3.38	2.32 / 3.41	2.35 / 3.46	2.36 / 3.49	2.40 / 3.56	2.42 / 3.61	2.46 / 3.70	2.50 / 3.78	2.54 / 3.86	2.60 / 3.98	2.64 / 4.05	2.69 / 4.16	2.72 / 4.22	2.76 / 4.30	2.80 / 4.39	2.85 / 4.50	2.92 / 4.65	3.00 / 4.82	3.11 / 5.06	3.26 / 5.41	3.49 / 5.95	3.88 / 6.93	4.75 / 9.33
13	2.21 / 3.16	2.22 / 3.18	2.24 / 3.21	2.26 / 3.27	2.28 / 3.30	2.32 / 3.37	2.34 / 3.42	2.38 / 3.51	2.42 / 3.59	2.46 / 3.67	2.51 / 3.78	2.55 / 3.85	2.60 / 3.96	2.63 / 4.02	2.67 / 4.10	2.72 / 4.19	2.77 / 4.30	2.84 / 4.44	2.92 / 4.62	3.02 / 4.86	3.18 / 5.20	3.41 / 5.74	3.80 / 6.70	4.67 / 9.07
14	2.13 / 3.00	2.14 / 3.02	2.16 / 3.06	2.19 / 3.11	2.21 / 3.14	2.24 / 3.21	2.27 / 3.26	2.31 / 3.34	2.35 / 3.43	2.39 / 3.51	2.44 / 3.62	2.48 / 3.70	2.53 / 3.80	2.56 / 3.86	2.60 / 3.94	2.65 / 4.03	2.70 / 4.14	2.77 / 4.28	2.85 / 4.46	2.96 / 4.69	3.11 / 5.03	3.34 / 5.56	3.74 / 6.51	4.60 / 8.86
15	2.07 / 2.87	2.08 / 2.89	2.10 / 2.92	2.12 / 2.97	2.15 / 3.00	2.18 / 3.07	2.21 / 3.12	2.25 / 3.20	2.29 / 3.29	2.33 / 3.36	2.39 / 3.48	2.43 / 3.56	2.48 / 3.67	2.51 / 3.73	2.55 / 3.80	2.59 / 3.89	2.64 / 4.00	2.70 / 4.14	2.79 / 4.32	2.90 / 4.56	3.06 / 4.89	3.29 / 5.42	3.68 / 6.36	4.54 / 8.68
16	2.01 / 2.75	2.02 / 2.77	2.04 / 2.80	2.07 / 2.86	2.09 / 2.89	2.13 / 2.96	2.16 / 3.01	2.20 / 3.10	2.24 / 3.18	2.28 / 3.25	2.33 / 3.37	2.37 / 3.45	2.42 / 3.55	2.45 / 3.61	2.49 / 3.69	2.54 / 3.78	2.59 / 3.89	2.66 / 4.03	2.74 / 4.20	2.85 / 4.44	3.01 / 4.77	3.24 / 5.29	3.63 / 6.23	4.49 / 8.53
17	1.96 / 2.65	1.97 / 2.67	1.99 / 2.70	2.02 / 2.76	2.04 / 2.79	2.08 / 2.86	2.11 / 2.92	2.15 / 3.00	2.19 / 3.08	2.23 / 3.16	2.29 / 3.27	2.33 / 3.35	2.38 / 3.45	2.41 / 3.52	2.45 / 3.59	2.50 / 3.68	2.55 / 3.79	2.62 / 3.93	2.70 / 4.10	2.81 / 4.34	2.96 / 4.67	3.20 / 5.18	3.59 / 6.11	4.45 / 8.40
18	1.92 / 2.57	1.93 / 2.59	1.95 / 2.62	1.98 / 2.68	2.00 / 2.71	2.04 / 2.78	2.07 / 2.83	2.11 / 2.91	2.15 / 3.00	2.19 / 3.07	2.25 / 3.19	2.29 / 3.27	2.34 / 3.37	2.37 / 3.44	2.41 / 3.51	2.46 / 3.60	2.51 / 3.71	2.58 / 3.85	2.66 / 4.01	2.77 / 4.25	2.93 / 4.58	3.16 / 5.09	3.55 / 6.01	4.41 / 8.28
19	1.88 / 2.49	1.90 / 2.51	1.91 / 2.54	1.94 / 2.60	1.96 / 2.63	2.00 / 2.70	2.02 / 2.76	2.07 / 2.84	2.11 / 2.92	2.15 / 3.00	2.21 / 3.12	2.26 / 3.19	2.31 / 3.30	2.34 / 3.36	2.38 / 3.43	2.43 / 3.52	2.48 / 3.63	2.55 / 3.77	2.63 / 3.94	2.74 / 4.17	2.90 / 4.50	3.13 / 5.01	3.52 / 5.93	4.38 / 8.18
20	1.84 / 2.42	1.85 / 2.44	1.87 / 2.47	1.90 / 2.53	1.92 / 2.56	1.96 / 2.63	1.99 / 2.69	2.04 / 2.77	2.08 / 2.86	2.12 / 2.94	2.18 / 3.05	2.23 / 3.13	2.28 / 3.23	2.31 / 3.30	2.35 / 3.37	2.40 / 3.45	2.45 / 3.56	2.52 / 3.71	2.60 / 3.87	2.71 / 4.10	2.87 / 4.43	3.10 / 4.94	3.49 / 5.85	4.35 / 8.10
21	1.81 / 2.36	1.82 / 2.38	1.84 / 2.42	1.87 / 2.47	1.89 / 2.51	1.93 / 2.58	1.96 / 2.63	2.00 / 2.72	2.05 / 2.80	2.09 / 2.88	2.15 / 3.00	2.20 / 3.07	2.25 / 3.17	2.28 / 3.24	2.32 / 3.31	2.37 / 3.40	2.42 / 3.51	2.49 / 3.65	2.57 / 3.81	2.68 / 4.04	2.84 / 4.37	3.07 / 4.87	3.47 / 5.78	4.32 / 8.02
22	1.78 / 2.31	1.80 / 2.33	1.81 / 2.37	1.84 / 2.42	1.87 / 2.46	1.91 / 2.53	1.93 / 2.58	1.98 / 2.67	2.03 / 2.75	2.07 / 2.83	2.13 / 2.94	2.18 / 3.02	2.23 / 3.12	2.26 / 3.18	2.30 / 3.26	2.35 / 3.35	2.40 / 3.45	2.47 / 3.59	2.55 / 3.76	2.66 / 3.99	2.82 / 4.31	3.05 / 4.82	3.44 / 5.72	4.30 / 7.94
23	1.76 / 2.26	1.77 / 2.28	1.79 / 2.32	1.82 / 2.37	1.84 / 2.41	1.88 / 2.48	1.91 / 2.53	1.96 / 2.62	2.00 / 2.70	2.04 / 2.78	2.10 / 2.89	2.14 / 2.97	2.20 / 3.07	2.24 / 3.14	2.28 / 3.21	2.32 / 3.30	2.38 / 3.41	2.45 / 3.54	2.53 / 3.71	2.64 / 3.94	2.80 / 4.26	3.03 / 4.76	3.42 / 5.66	4.28 / 7.88
24	1.73 / 2.21	1.74 / 2.23	1.76 / 2.27	1.80 / 2.33	1.82 / 2.36	1.86 / 2.44	1.89 / 2.49	1.94 / 2.58	1.98 / 2.66	2.02 / 2.74	2.09 / 2.85	2.13 / 2.93	2.18 / 3.03	2.22 / 3.09	2.26 / 3.17	2.30 / 3.25	2.36 / 3.36	2.43 / 3.50	2.51 / 3.67	2.62 / 3.90	2.78 / 4.22	3.01 / 4.72	3.40 / 5.61	4.26 / 7.82
25	1.71 / 2.17	1.72 / 2.19	1.74 / 2.23	1.77 / 2.29	1.80 / 2.32	1.84 / 2.40	1.87 / 2.45	1.92 / 2.54	1.96 / 2.62	2.00 / 2.70	2.06 / 2.81	2.11 / 2.89	2.16 / 2.99	2.20 / 3.05	2.24 / 3.13	2.28 / 3.21	2.34 / 3.32	2.41 / 3.46	2.49 / 3.63	2.60 / 3.86	2.76 / 4.18	2.99 / 4.68	3.38 / 5.57	4.24 / 7.77

TABLE XI. F Distribution (Continued)

5% (Roman Type) and 1% (Boldface Type) Points for the Distribution of F

Degrees of freedom for numerator (ν_1)

Degrees of freedom for denominator (ν_2)	1	2	3	4	5	6	7	8	9	10	11	12	14	16	20	24	30	40	50	75	100	200	500	∞
26	4.22 / **7.72**	3.37 / **5.53**	2.89 / **4.64**	2.74 / **4.14**	2.59 / **3.82**	2.47 / **3.59**	2.39 / **3.42**	2.32 / **3.29**	2.27 / **3.17**	2.22 / **3.09**	2.18 / **3.02**	2.15 / **2.96**	2.10 / **2.86**	2.05 / **2.77**	1.99 / **2.66**	1.95 / **2.58**	1.90 / **2.50**	1.85 / **2.41**	1.82 / **2.36**	1.78 / **2.28**	1.76 / **2.25**	1.72 / **2.19**	1.70 / **2.15**	1.69 / **2.13**
27	4.21 / **7.68**	3.35 / **5.49**	2.96 / **4.60**	2.73 / **4.11**	2.57 / **3.79**	2.46 / **3.56**	2.37 / **3.39**	2.30 / **3.26**	2.25 / **3.14**	2.20 / **3.06**	2.16 / **2.98**	2.13 / **2.93**	2.08 / **2.83**	2.03 / **2.74**	1.97 / **2.63**	1.93 / **2.55**	1.88 / **2.47**	1.84 / **2.38**	1.80 / **2.33**	1.76 / **2.25**	1.74 / **2.21**	1.71 / **2.16**	1.68 / **2.12**	1.67 / **2.10**
28	4.20 / **7.64**	3.34 / **5.45**	2.95 / **4.57**	2.71 / **4.07**	2.56 / **3.76**	2.44 / **3.53**	2.36 / **3.36**	2.29 / **3.23**	2.24 / **3.11**	2.19 / **3.03**	2.15 / **2.95**	2.12 / **2.90**	2.06 / **2.80**	2.02 / **2.71**	1.96 / **2.60**	1.91 / **2.52**	1.87 / **2.44**	1.81 / **2.35**	1.78 / **2.30**	1.75 / **2.22**	1.72 / **2.18**	1.69 / **2.13**	1.67 / **2.09**	1.65 / **2.06**
29	4.18 / **7.60**	3.33 / **5.42**	2.93 / **4.54**	2.70 / **4.04**	2.54 / **3.73**	2.43 / **3.50**	2.35 / **3.33**	2.28 / **3.20**	2.22 / **3.08**	2.18 / **3.00**	2.14 / **2.92**	2.10 / **2.87**	2.05 / **2.77**	2.00 / **2.68**	1.94 / **2.57**	1.90 / **2.49**	1.85 / **2.41**	1.80 / **2.32**	1.77 / **2.27**	1.73 / **2.19**	1.71 / **2.15**	1.68 / **2.10**	1.65 / **2.06**	1.64 / **2.03**
30	4.17 / **7.56**	3.32 / **5.39**	2.92 / **4.51**	2.69 / **4.02**	2.53 / **3.70**	2.42 / **3.47**	2.34 / **3.30**	2.27 / **3.17**	2.21 / **3.06**	2.16 / **2.98**	2.12 / **2.90**	2.09 / **2.84**	2.04 / **2.74**	1.99 / **2.66**	1.93 / **2.55**	1.89 / **2.47**	1.84 / **2.38**	1.79 / **2.29**	1.76 / **2.24**	1.72 / **2.16**	1.69 / **2.13**	1.66 / **2.07**	1.64 / **2.03**	1.62 / **2.01**
32	4.15 / **7.50**	3.30 / **5.34**	2.90 / **4.46**	2.67 / **3.97**	2.51 / **3.66**	2.40 / **3.42**	2.32 / **3.25**	2.25 / **3.12**	2.19 / **3.01**	2.14 / **2.94**	2.10 / **2.86**	2.07 / **2.80**	2.02 / **2.70**	1.97 / **2.62**	1.91 / **2.51**	1.86 / **2.42**	1.82 / **2.34**	1.76 / **2.25**	1.74 / **2.20**	1.69 / **2.12**	1.67 / **2.08**	1.64 / **2.02**	1.61 / **1.98**	1.59 / **1.96**
34	4.13 / **7.44**	3.28 / **5.29**	2.88 / **4.42**	2.65 / **3.93**	2.49 / **3.61**	2.38 / **3.38**	2.30 / **3.21**	2.23 / **3.08**	2.17 / **2.97**	2.12 / **2.89**	2.08 / **2.82**	2.05 / **2.76**	2.00 / **2.66**	1.95 / **2.58**	1.89 / **2.47**	1.84 / **2.38**	1.80 / **2.30**	1.74 / **2.21**	1.71 / **2.15**	1.67 / **2.08**	1.64 / **2.04**	1.61 / **1.98**	1.59 / **1.94**	1.57 / **1.91**
36	4.11 / **7.39**	3.26 / **5.25**	2.86 / **4.38**	2.63 / **3.89**	2.48 / **3.58**	2.36 / **3.35**	2.28 / **3.18**	2.21 / **3.04**	2.15 / **2.94**	2.10 / **2.86**	2.06 / **2.78**	2.03 / **2.72**	1.98 / **2.62**	1.93 / **2.54**	1.87 / **2.43**	1.82 / **2.35**	1.78 / **2.26**	1.72 / **2.17**	1.69 / **2.12**	1.65 / **2.04**	1.62 / **2.00**	1.59 / **1.94**	1.56 / **1.90**	1.55 / **1.87**
38	4.10 / **7.35**	3.25 / **5.21**	2.85 / **4.34**	2.62 / **3.86**	2.46 / **3.54**	2.35 / **3.32**	2.26 / **3.15**	2.19 / **3.02**	2.14 / **2.91**	2.09 / **2.82**	2.05 / **2.75**	2.02 / **2.69**	1.96 / **2.59**	1.92 / **2.51**	1.85 / **2.40**	1.80 / **2.32**	1.76 / **2.22**	1.71 / **2.14**	1.67 / **2.08**	1.63 / **2.00**	1.60 / **1.97**	1.57 / **1.90**	1.54 / **1.86**	1.53 / **1.84**
40	4.08 / **7.31**	3.23 / **5.18**	2.84 / **4.31**	2.61 / **3.83**	2.45 / **3.51**	2.34 / **3.29**	2.25 / **3.12**	2.18 / **2.99**	2.12 / **2.88**	2.07 / **2.80**	2.04 / **2.73**	2.00 / **2.66**	1.95 / **2.56**	1.90 / **2.49**	1.84 / **2.37**	1.79 / **2.29**	1.74 / **2.20**	1.69 / **2.11**	1.66 / **2.05**	1.61 / **1.97**	1.59 / **1.94**	1.55 / **1.88**	1.53 / **1.84**	1.51 / **1.81**
42	4.07 / **7.27**	3.22 / **5.15**	2.83 / **4.29**	2.59 / **3.80**	2.44 / **3.49**	2.32 / **3.26**	2.24 / **3.10**	2.17 / **2.96**	2.11 / **2.86**	2.06 / **2.77**	2.02 / **2.70**	1.99 / **2.64**	1.94 / **2.54**	1.89 / **2.46**	1.82 / **2.35**	1.78 / **2.26**	1.73 / **2.17**	1.68 / **2.08**	1.64 / **2.02**	1.60 / **1.94**	1.57 / **1.91**	1.54 / **1.85**	1.51 / **1.80**	1.49 / **1.78**
44	4.06 / **7.24**	3.21 / **5.12**	2.82 / **4.26**	2.58 / **3.78**	2.43 / **3.46**	2.31 / **3.24**	2.23 / **3.07**	2.16 / **2.94**	2.10 / **2.84**	2.05 / **2.75**	2.01 / **2.68**	1.98 / **2.62**	1.92 / **2.52**	1.88 / **2.44**	1.81 / **2.32**	1.76 / **2.24**	1.72 / **2.15**	1.66 / **2.06**	1.63 / **2.00**	1.58 / **1.92**	1.56 / **1.88**	1.52 / **1.82**	1.50 / **1.78**	1.48 / **1.75**
46	4.05 / **7.21**	3.20 / **5.10**	2.81 / **4.24**	2.57 / **3.76**	2.42 / **3.44**	2.30 / **3.22**	2.22 / **3.05**	2.14 / **2.92**	2.09 / **2.82**	2.04 / **2.73**	2.00 / **2.66**	1.97 / **2.60**	1.91 / **2.50**	1.87 / **2.42**	1.80 / **2.30**	1.75 / **2.22**	1.71 / **2.13**	1.65 / **2.04**	1.62 / **1.98**	1.57 / **1.90**	1.54 / **1.86**	1.51 / **1.80**	1.48 / **1.76**	1.46 / **1.72**
48	4.04 / **7.19**	3.19 / **5.08**	2.80 / **4.22**	2.56 / **3.74**	2.41 / **3.42**	2.30 / **3.20**	2.21 / **3.04**	2.14 / **2.90**	2.08 / **2.80**	2.03 / **2.71**	1.99 / **2.64**	1.96 / **2.58**	1.90 / **2.48**	1.86 / **2.40**	1.79 / **2.28**	1.74 / **2.20**	1.70 / **2.11**	1.64 / **2.02**	1.61 / **1.96**	1.56 / **1.88**	1.53 / **1.84**	1.50 / **1.78**	1.47 / **1.73**	1.45 / **1.70**

n_2																								
50	1.44 1.68	1.46 1.71	1.48 1.76	1.52 1.82	1.55 1.86	1.60 1.94	1.63 2.00	1.69 2.10	1.74 2.18	1.78 2.26	1.85 2.39	1.90 2.46	1.95 2.56	1.98 2.62	2.02 2.70	2.07 2.78	2.13 2.88	2.20 3.02	2.29 3.18	2.40 3.41	2.56 3.72	2.79 4.20	3.18 5.06	4.03 7.17
55	1.41 1.64	1.43 1.66	1.46 1.71	1.50 1.78	1.52 1.82	1.58 1.90	1.61 1.96	1.67 2.06	1.72 2.15	1.76 2.23	1.83 2.35	1.88 2.43	1.93 2.53	1.97 2.59	2.00 2.66	2.05 2.75	2.11 2.85	2.18 2.98	2.27 3.15	2.38 3.37	2.54 3.68	2.78 4.16	3.17 5.01	4.02 7.12
60	1.39 1.60	1.41 1.63	1.44 1.68	1.48 1.74	1.50 1.79	1.56 1.87	1.59 1.93	1.65 2.03	1.70 2.12	1.75 2.20	1.81 2.32	1.86 2.40	1.92 2.50	1.95 2.56	1.99 2.63	2.04 2.72	2.10 2.82	2.17 2.95	2.25 3.12	2.37 3.34	2.52 3.65	2.76 4.13	3.15 4.98	4.00 7.08
65	1.37 1.56	1.39 1.60	1.42 1.64	1.46 1.71	1.49 1.76	1.54 1.84	1.57 1.90	1.63 2.00	1.68 2.09	1.73 2.18	1.80 2.30	1.85 2.37	1.90 2.47	1.94 2.54	1.98 2.61	2.02 2.70	2.08 2.79	2.15 2.93	2.24 3.09	2.36 3.31	2.51 3.62	2.75 4.10	3.14 4.95	3.99 7.04
70	1.35 1.53	1.37 1.56	1.40 1.62	1.45 1.69	1.47 1.74	1.53 1.82	1.56 1.88	1.62 1.98	1.67 2.07	1.72 2.15	1.79 2.28	1.84 2.35	1.89 2.45	1.93 2.51	1.97 2.59	2.01 2.67	2.07 2.77	2.14 2.91	2.23 3.07	2.35 3.29	2.50 3.60	2.74 4.08	3.13 4.92	3.98 7.01
80	1.32 1.49	1.35 1.52	1.38 1.57	1.42 1.65	1.45 1.70	1.51 1.78	1.54 1.84	1.60 1.94	1.65 2.03	1.70 2.11	1.77 2.24	1.82 2.32	1.88 2.41	1.91 2.48	1.95 2.55	1.99 2.64	2.05 2.74	2.12 2.87	2.21 3.04	2.33 3.25	2.48 3.56	2.72 4.04	3.11 4.88	3.96 6.95
100	1.28 1.43	1.30 1.46	1.34 1.51	1.39 1.59	1.42 1.64	1.48 1.73	1.51 1.79	1.57 1.89	1.63 1.98	1.68 2.06	1.75 2.19	1.79 2.26	1.85 2.36	1.88 2.43	1.92 2.51	1.97 2.59	2.03 2.69	2.10 2.82	2.19 2.99	2.30 3.20	2.46 3.51	2.70 3.98	3.09 4.82	3.94 6.90
125	1.25 1.37	1.27 1.40	1.31 1.46	1.36 1.54	1.39 1.59	1.45 1.68	1.49 1.75	1.55 1.85	1.60 1.94	1.65 2.03	1.72 2.15	1.77 2.23	1.83 2.33	1.86 2.40	1.90 2.47	1.95 2.56	2.01 2.65	2.08 2.79	2.17 2.95	2.29 3.17	2.44 3.47	2.68 3.94	3.07 4.78	3.92 6.84
150	1.22 1.33	1.25 1.37	1.29 1.43	1.34 1.51	1.37 1.56	1.44 1.66	1.47 1.72	1.54 1.83	1.59 1.91	1.64 2.00	1.71 2.12	1.76 2.20	1.82 2.30	1.85 2.37	1.89 2.44	1.94 2.53	2.00 2.62	2.07 2.76	2.16 2.92	2.27 3.13	2.43 3.44	2.67 3.91	3.06 4.75	3.91 6.81
200	1.19 1.28	1.22 1.33	1.26 1.39	1.32 1.48	1.35 1.53	1.42 1.62	1.45 1.69	1.52 1.79	1.57 1.88	1.62 1.97	1.69 2.09	1.74 2.17	1.80 2.28	1.83 2.34	1.87 2.41	1.92 2.50	1.98 2.60	2.05 2.73	2.14 2.90	2.26 3.11	2.41 3.41	2.65 3.88	3.04 4.71	3.89 6.76
400	1.13 1.19	1.16 1.24	1.22 1.32	1.28 1.42	1.32 1.47	1.38 1.57	1.42 1.64	1.49 1.74	1.54 1.84	1.60 1.92	1.67 2.04	1.72 2.12	1.78 2.23	1.81 2.29	1.85 2.37	1.90 2.46	1.96 2.55	2.03 2.69	2.12 2.85	2.23 3.06	2.39 3.36	2.62 3.83	3.02 4.66	3.86 6.70
1000	1.08 1.11	1.13 1.19	1.19 1.28	1.26 1.38	1.30 1.44	1.36 1.54	1.41 1.61	1.47 1.71	1.53 1.81	1.58 1.89	1.65 2.01	1.70 2.09	1.76 2.20	1.80 2.26	1.84 2.34	1.89 2.43	1.95 2.53	2.02 2.66	2.10 2.82	2.22 3.04	2.38 3.34	2.61 3.80	3.00 4.62	3.85 6.66
∞	1.00 1.00	1.11 1.15	1.17 1.25	1.24 1.36	1.28 1.41	1.35 1.52	1.40 1.59	1.46 1.69	1.52 1.79	1.57 1.87	1.64 1.99	1.69 2.07	1.75 2.18	1.79 2.24	1.83 2.32	1.88 2.41	1.94 2.51	2.01 2.64	2.09 2.80	2.21 3.02	2.37 3.32	2.60 3.78	2.99 4.60	3.84 6.64

Answers

to Odd-Numbered Exercises

Numerical answers depend upon the extent of rounding off the computations and upon the order of operations; consequently, the student should not expect to agree precisely with all of the following answers. Answers of a non-numerical nature are included to give the student a rough idea of the kind of answer expected for such exercises.

Chapter 2

3. If 6 is chosen as the class interval, boundaries will be 81.5–87.5 and 171.5–177.5 and class marks will be 84.5 and 174.5.

7. Class boundaries are 0, 1, 2, 3, 4, 5, 6.

9. Skewed to the right, since students with less than a C average will drop out or be removed from school, and the mean is probably not higher than half way between a C and B average.

15. $x = \dfrac{u}{12} + 5$.

17. 175.3.

19. (a) 2.07, (b) .72.

21. 6.6.

23. 68 per cent and 95 per cent.

25. $\sigma \doteq 1$.

27. (a) The mean will be increased by 10 pounds, but the standard deviation will not be affected. (b) The mean and standard deviation will both be increased by 10%.

29. $\bar{x} = 0$, $s = 1.005$; hence $\bar{x} \pm s$ includes all the measurements. The usual interpretation is meaningless here.

31. (a)

x	39.5	41.5	43.5	45.5	47.5	49.5	51.5	53.5	55.5	57.5	59.5	61.5
f	2	0	3	14	14	25	21	10	5	2	2	2

(b) $\bar{x} = 50.0$, $s = 4.0$
(c) $\bar{x} = 50.0$
(d) 71 per cent, 94 per cent
(e) 3.02
(f) Median = 49.9, interquartile range = 4.7
(g) 57.5.

33. No mode since 38, 42, and 46 occur twice, median = 44, range = 16, mean deviation = 4.2.

35. (a) 2.33, (b) 7.18, (c) 2.32.

Chapter 3

1. To each of the 8 outcomes for 3 tosses attach a fourth letter, H or T, to obtain the following 16 possible outcomes: HHHH, HHHT, HHTH, HHTT, HTHH, HTHT, THHH, THHT, HTTH, HTTT, THTH, THTT, TTHH, TTHT, TTTH, TTTT.

3. $\frac{1}{16}$.

5. (a) $.B_2B_1$ $.WB_1$ (b) $.BB$ $.WB$
$.B_1B_2$ $.WB_2$ $.BW$
$.B_1W$ $.B_2W$

7. (a) $\frac{4}{10}$ $\frac{3}{10}$ $\frac{3}{10}$

   •   •   •

   e_1 e_2 e_3

9. (a) $\frac{1}{12}$, (b) $\frac{1}{12}$, (c) $\frac{1}{2}$.

11. (a) $\frac{17}{18}$, (b) $\frac{4}{9}$, (c) $\frac{4}{9}$, (d) $\frac{5}{6}$, (e) $\frac{4}{9}$.

13. Yes, unless there were a very gradual steady climb or fall in the market. The stock market might rise rapidly during a year by means of a few big jumps, yet the frequency of ups might be less than the frequency of downs.

15. (a) $\frac{1}{6}$, (b) $\frac{16}{81}$, (c) $\frac{5}{18}$.

17. (a) .00763, (b) .00006, (c) .98461, (d) .01539, (e) .02313.

19. (a) .59, (b) .33.

21. (a) $\frac{1}{32}$, (b) $\frac{1}{64}$, (c) $\frac{3}{32}$.

23. (a) $\frac{2}{9}$, (b) $\frac{5}{9}$, (c) $\frac{4}{9}$.

25. (a) $\frac{1}{10}$, (b) $\frac{2}{5}$, (c) $\frac{7}{10}$, (d) $\frac{9}{10}$, (e) 1, (f) $\frac{1}{2}$, (g) $\frac{5}{6}$, (h) $\frac{1}{2}$.

27. $\frac{253}{4998}$.

29. (a) .44, (b) .70, (c) .052, (d) $.00 \overset{11}{\cdots} 0157$.

Chapter 4

3. $P\{4\} = \frac{1}{9}$, $P\{5\} = \frac{2}{9}$, $P\{6\} = \frac{3}{9}$, $P\{7\} = \frac{2}{9}$, $P\{8\} = \frac{1}{9}$.

7. 16 possible outcomes: AAAA, AAAN, AANA, ANAA, NAAA, AANN, ANAN, NAAN, ANNA, NANA, NNAA, ANNN, NANN, NNAN, NNNA, NNNN; hence $P\{0\} = (\frac{5}{6})^4$, $P\{1\} = 4(\frac{1}{6})(\frac{5}{6})^3$, $P\{2\} = 6(\frac{1}{6})^2(\frac{5}{6})^2$, $P\{3\} = 4(\frac{1}{6})^3(\frac{5}{6})$, $P\{4\} = (\frac{1}{6})^4$.

9. $P\{0\} = \frac{64}{729}$, $P\{1\} = \frac{192}{729}$, $P\{2\} = \frac{240}{729}$, $P\{3\} = \frac{160}{729}$, $P\{4\} = \frac{60}{729}$, $P\{5\} = \frac{12}{729}$, $P\{6\} = \frac{1}{729}$.

11. $\mu = 2$, $\sigma = \frac{2}{3}\sqrt{3}$.

13. (a) .0918, (b) .5375.

15. 4 feet 11.4 inches; hence, 4 feet $11\frac{1}{2}$ inches.

17. .46 and .47.

19. (a) <.001, (b) .93.

21. .009.

23. Trials are not independent. If it rains one day the chances are increased that it will rain the following day because storms often last more than one day.

25. .06.

27. (a)

x	0	1
$P\{x\}$	.6	.4

, (b)

x	1	2	3	4	5
$P\{x\}$	.1	.2	.3	.3	.1

,

(c)

x	0	1	2
$P\{x\}$	.36	.48	.16

, (d)

x	0	1	2
$P\{x\}$	$\frac{5}{15}$	$\frac{8}{15}$	$\frac{2}{15}$

,

(e)

x	3	4	5	6	7	8	9
$P\{x\}$	$\frac{2}{45}$	$\frac{4}{45}$	$\frac{9}{45}$	$\frac{10}{45}$	$\frac{11}{45}$	$\frac{6}{45}$	$\frac{3}{45}$

, (f) parts (a) and (c),

(g) $\mu = .8$, $\sigma \doteq .7$, (h) $P\{x\} = \dfrac{8!}{x!\,(8-x)!}(.4)^x\,(.6)^{8-x}$, (i) .666, (j) .668, (k) .07.

Chapter 5

1. Registrar's card files and random numbers or, say, select twenty 10-o'clock classes at random and select five students at random from each class.

3. The letter A is probably weighted rather heavily with names of English extraction; therefore, if such individuals tend to have higher or lower incomes than the average, a sample from the A's only would not be satisfactory. If there is no such association, the sample would be satisfactory.

5. Individuals replying are usually kind-hearted or difficult-to-please customers. Most individuals will not bother to answer; therefore, the sample will reflect opinions of those with extreme views.

Chapter 5

7. It would be necessary to discover whether the 600 who did not reply had the same views as those who did reply before one could trust the data obtained from the 400.

9. Associate each of the 190 lawyers with the 3-digit random numbers from 000 to 189; also with those from 200 to 389, those from 400 to 589, those from 600 to 789, and those from 800 to 989.

11. If markets are classified into, say, three groups according to their size, then it would be necessary to select as many clerks from each of the three groups, proportional to the number of clerks in each of the three groups, as is needed to total 25.

13. Households differ in size with respect to adults; therefore, households with a large number of adults will not be adequately represented.

15. (a) .84, (b) .001, (c) .84, (d) .01, (e) .04.

17. It would be about twice as tall and half as wide as the $\bar{x}$ curve.

25. .0258.

27. (a) .86, (b) .00, (c) .86, (d) .003, (e) .04.

Chapter 6

1. (a) $P\{e < 4.8\} = .95$, (b) 4.8 would be replaced by 2.4; hence twice the accuracy.

3. (a) 144 (using $z_0 = 2$) or 139 (using $z_0 = 1.96$), (b) 576 (using $z_0 = 2$) or 554 (using $z_0 = 1.96$).

5. (a) 64 (using $z_0 = 2$) or 62 (using $z_0 = 1.96$), (b) 576 (using $z_0 = 2$) or 554 (using $z_0 = 1.96$).

7. (a) $135.3 < \mu < 144.7$, (b) $136.1 < \mu < 143.9$.

9. (a) $P\{e < 1.4\} \doteq .95$, (b) 100 ($z_0 = 2$), or 97 ($z_0 = 1.96$), (c) $40.6 < \mu < 43.4$.

11. $19.8 < \mu < 24.2$.

13. $27.9 < \mu < 33.2$.

17. $P\{e < .09\} \doteq .95$.

19. Approximately 12,650.

21. $.55 < p < .65$.

23. (a) $140.7 < \mu < 159.3$, (b) $141.6 < \mu < 158.4$.

25. (a) .14, $|\bar{x} - \mu| = |-.035 - 0| = .035$; hence compatible with .14, (b) 655, (c) $-.125 < \mu < .055$, which contains 0.

Chapter 7

1. Assuming an individual is innocent until proved guilty, the hypothesis to be tested is that the individual is innocent; hence the type I error is convicting an innocent individual and the type II error is letting a thief go free. Society considers a type I error more serious than a type II error.

3. $\alpha = \frac{1}{4}$, $\beta = \frac{3}{4}$.

5. $z = -1.33$; hence accept H_0.

7. $z = 3.67$; hence undoubtedly superior.

9. $\bar{x} = 71.6$, $s = 31.4$; hence limits are 30–114. Control appears to exist, but data are too few to make reliable conclusions.

11. $t = 2.30$, $t_0 = 2.20$; hence reject H_0.

15. $z = 1.71$; hence accept H_0.

17. $\alpha = .25$, $\beta = .51$.

21. $z = 1.17$; hence no.

23. Honest mathematically means $p = \frac{1}{2}$ exactly, whereas honest from a practical point of view means that p is approximately equal to $\frac{1}{2}$.

25. $p' = .0255$; hence limits are .0105 and .0405. If percentages are used, multiply these answers by 100. Out of control on days numbered 18, 22, and 38.

27. $z = 1.23$; hence no.

29. $z = 1.68$; hence reject $p_1 - p_2 \le .10$ in favor of $p_1 - p_2 > .10$. Use right tail critical region here and calculate $\sigma_{p_1'-p_2'}$ from the formula $\sqrt{\dfrac{p_1 q_1}{n_1} + \dfrac{p_2 q_2}{n_2}}$.

31. $(a)\, z = -.50$; hence accept H_0, $(b)\, z = -1.06$; hence accept H_0, $(c)\, s_1{}^2 = .141$, $s_2{}^2 = .316$, $z = -1.11$; hence accept H_0, $(d)\, z = -1.98$; hence reject H_0, $(e)\, z = -.59$; hence accept H_0, (f) boundaries are $\mu \pm 3\sigma_{\bar{x}} = 0 \pm \frac{3}{2}$. All values lie inside this control band. $(g)\, t = -1.11$; hence accept H_0. The z and t values are the same to this accuracy. $(h)\, \beta = .45$.

33. $t = .92$, $t_0 = 2.10$; hence accept H_0.

35.

p	0	.1	.3	.5	.7	.9	1.0
β	1	.99	.91	.75	.51	.19	0

37.

p	0	.5	.6	.7	1
β	1	.856	.685	.448	0

A weak test unless the alternative value of p is larger than .7. A larger sample is needed for a better test.

Chapter 8

1. $(c)\, r = .93$.

3. $(a)\, .9$, $(b)\, .3$, $(c)\, -.7$.

5. The number of accidents per year of drivers who have accidents decreases with age. The relationship here is undoubtedly a real one.

7. If x denotes tide height and y denotes traffic density, then both x and y would tend to be large around 8:00 A.M. and 6:00 P.M. and small around 2:00 P.M.

9. $r = -.16$.

13. $z = 1.71$; hence accept H_0.

15. $.12 < \rho < .73$.

17. $n = 97$. The value $\rho = 0$ leads to maximum inaccuracy; hence assume $\rho = 0$.

Chapter 9

1. Should pass through the points $(0, -1)$ and $(5, \frac{1}{2})$.

3. (a) 600 dollars, 1200 dollars, (b) formula undoubtedly derived for average families with regular incomes and therefore not applicable outside the range considered.

5. $y' = 2.25x + 175$.

7. $s_e = 1.74$.

9. Both are based on small samples, and therefore they may be poor estimates of the theoretical standard deviations of errors of prediction.

13. (b) $y' = 12.82 + 6.58x$, (d) $-4.4, 3.0, 2.7, 2.9, -12.7, -13.9, -3.9, -2.4$, 6.0, 14.5, -4.3, 12.4, (e) 121.39; wild extrapolation! (f) $s_e = 9.15$, (g) $y' = 3.67 + 6.58x$ and $y' = 21.97 + 6.58x$.

15. $.57 < \beta < 3.93$.

17. $t = -.33$, $t_0 = 2.23$; hence accept H_0.

19. (a) $y' = 5.18 + 1.50x_1 + .877x_2$, (b) $-.4, -2.1, -2.1, -7.3, 2.7, -.1$, 1.3, $-.4$, 1.6, 5.2, 1.7, $-.1$, (c) $s_e = 3.4$, (d) $y' = 9.43 + 1.64x_1$, (e) $s_e = 3.9$; hence the addition of x_2 helped some, but not a great deal.

Chapter 10

1. $\chi^2 = 26.6$, $\chi_0^2 = 16.9$; hence reject hypothesis of same conditions.

3. $\chi^2 = 35$, $\chi_0^2 = 7.8$; hence distribution differs.

5. $\chi^2 = 13.2$, $\chi_0^2 = 6.0$; hence reject independence.

7. $\chi^2 = 3.2$, $\chi_0^2 = 6.0$; hence accept hypothesis of same opinions.

9. $z = 2.2$; hence reject hypothesis. It can be shown that $z^2 = \chi^2$ value for this type of problem.

13. (a) $7.6 < \sigma < 14.6$, (b) $8.4 < \sigma < 12.4$.

15. (a) $8.6 < \sigma < 11.9$, (b) $8.9 \lessgtr \sigma < 11.5$.

Chapter 11

1. $z = -1.92$, $z_0 = -1.64$; hence reject H_0.

3. (a) $R = 64$. Critical region outside interval $(79, 131)$ corresponds to $\alpha = .052$; hence reject hypothesis of no difference, (b) $z = -3.1$; hence reject hypothesis.

5. $z = -.66$; hence accept H_0.

7. $t = 4.10$, $t_0 = 2.10$; hence reject H_0. The t test appears to reject H_0 more easily than the rank-sum test does, thus indicating that it may be a more delicate test for testing a shift in the mean when it applies.

9. $r = .90$, $r_0 = .41$; hence reject hypothesis that matching had no effect.

11. $r \geq .377$ from Table IX. For normal theory using the z transformation and Table VI, $r \geq .38$; hence critical values are nearly the same here.

15. $u = 12$, $n_1 = n_2 = 12$, critical values are 7 and 19; hence accept randomness.

Chapter 12

1. $F = 13.6$, $\nu_1 = 3$, $\nu_2 = 20$, $F_0 = 3.10$; hence reject hypothesis that catalysts have no effect.

3. $F_c = 18.4$, $\nu_1 = 3$, $\nu_2 = 12$, $F_0 = 3.49$; hence types differ. $F_r = 6.6$, $\nu_1 = 4$, $\nu_2 = 12$, $F_0 = 3.26$; hence workmen differ.

5. $F = 10.8$, $\nu_1 = 3$, $\nu_2 = 12$, $F_0 = 3.49$; hence reject the hypothesis of no plot differences.

7. (a) $n_j = r$ then; therefore the denominator becomes $c(r - 1)$, (b) letting s_j^2 be the variance of column j, it follows that

$$\sum_{i=1}^{n_j} (x_{ij} - \bar{x}._j)^2 = (n_j - 1)s_j^2 \quad \text{and} \quad \sum_{j=1}^{c} \sum_{i=1}^{n_j} (x_{ij} - \bar{x}._j)^2 = \sum_{j=1}^{c} (n_j - 1)s_j^2.$$

Thus $\sum_{j=1}^{c} (n_j - 1)s_j^2 \Big/ \sum_{j=1}^{c} (n_j - 1)$ is a weighted mean of the s_j^2 with weights

$(n_j - 1) \Big/ \sum_{j=1}^{c} (n_j - 1)$, that is, with weights proportional to degrees of freedom and summing to one.

9. $F = 1.02$, $\nu_1 = 2$, $\nu_2 = 19$, $F_0 = 3.52$; hence accept the hypothesis of no differences due to methods.

Chapter 13

1. $u = 26$, $n_1 = 28$, $n_2 = 29$, $z = -.8$ (using $\frac{1}{2}$ correction); hence accept randomness, which is the correct decision here in view of the manner in which the data were obtained.

3. $u = 13$, $n_1 = 29$, $n_2 = 28$, $z = -4.3$ (using correction); hence reject randomness.

5. For example, 1, 1, -1, -1, 1, 1, -1, -1, 1, 1, -1, -1. Here $u = 6$, $n_1 = 6$, $n_2 = 6$; hence from Table X about what would be expected under randomness.

7. .5, .5, 1.2, 1.4, 1.0, .8, .4, .2, $-.1$, .6, .8, .2, .4, .6, 1.2, 1.7, 2.3, 3.3, 3.2, 2.7, 2.2, 1.4, 1.7, 1.0, .7, .4, 1.0, 1.9, 1.5, 1.3, 1.1.

9. 1.1, .8, .9, 1.3, .8, .3, .3, .5, .3, .2, .6, .7, .6, 1.2, 2.0, 2.3, 2.7, 2.8, 2.6, 2.2, 1.9, 1.3, 1.0, .8, 1.1, 1.1, 1.1, 1.4, 1.6.

11. A 16-term moving average should do it.

13. 299, 297, 297, 302, 298, 294, 304, 300, 305, 310, 309, 305, 327, 329, 333, 334, 337, 341, 336, 338, 343, 333, 339, 348.

15. $r = .77$. A cycle length of 12 is indicated, but the conclusion is not nearly so positive as in problem 14.

21. (*a*) .968; hence a 3.2 per cent decrease. (*b*) 1.083; hence an 8.3 per cent increase. (*c*) 1.059; hence a 5.9 per cent increase. (*d*) 1.071; hence a 7.1 per cent increase.

23. Index numbers give only rates of increase; hence one cannot use them to compare rental costs in the two cities.

Index